Heinemann IGCSE®

Extended Mathematics

Colin Nye

Holt, Payne, Rayment, Robinson

CW00393312

www.pearsonglobalschools.com

Free online support
Useful weblinks
24 hour online ordering

ALWAYS LEARNING

PEARSON

Heinemann is an imprint of Pearson Education Limited, a company incorporated in England and Wales, having its registered office at Edinburgh Gate, Harlow, Essex, CM20 2JE. Registered company number: 872828

www.pearsonglobalschools.com

Heinemann is a registered trademark of Pearson Education Limited

Text © Pearson Education Limited 2009

First published 2009

20 19 18 17
IMP 10 9 8 7

British Library Cataloguing in Publication Data is available from the British Library on request.

ISBN 978 0 435966 86 7

Copyright notice
All rights reserved. No part of this publication may be reproduced in any form or by any means (including photocopying or storing it in any medium by electronic means and whether or not transiently or incidentally to some other use of this publication) without the written permission of the copyright owner, except in accordance with the provisions of the Copyright, Designs and Patents Act 1988 or under the terms of a licence issued by the Copyright Licensing Agency, Saffron House, 6–10 Kirby Street, London EC1N 8TS (www.cla.co.uk). Applications for the copyright owner's written permission should be addressed to the publisher.

IGCSE® is the registered trademark of
Cambridge International Examinations.

Designed by Tony Richardson
Typeset by HL Studios
Original illustrations © Pearson Education Limited 2009
Illustrated by HL Studios, Adrian Barclay and Mark Raffe
Illustration on p.380 with kind permission of BridgeClimb Sydney
Cover design by Creative Monkey
Printed by CPI UK

Acknowledgements
The author and publisher would like to thank the following individuals and organisations for permission to reproduce photographs:

p.1 Pearson Education Ltd. / Jules Selmes; p.7 Image Source Ltd; p.29 Pearson Education Ltd. / Jules Selmes; p.30 Photodisc / Photolink; p.35 Photodisc / Malcolm Fife; p.37 Photodisc / Steve Cole; p.39 Photodisc / Karl Weatherly; p.42 Photodisc / Photolink / Jack Star; p.44 Digital Stock; p.47 Photodisc / Cybermedia; p.50 Photodisc / Neil Beer; p.51 Photodisc / Photolink; p.54 Pearson Education Ltd. / Jules Selmes; p.57 Pearson Education Ltd. / Gareth Boden; p.85 Digital Stock; p.91 Phovoir / Imagestate; p.97 Photodisc / Karl Weatherly; p.118 Photodisc / John A. Rizzo; p.143 Photodisc; p.173 Photodisc / Steve Cole; p.186 Pearson Education Ltd. / Carlos Reyes-Manzo; p.189 Photodisc / Siede Preis Photography; p. 191 Photodisc / Steve Cole; p.277 KPT Power Photos; p.319 Photodisc / Getty Images.

Every effort has been made to contact copyright holders of material reproduced in this book. Any omissions will be rectified in subsequent printings if notice is given to the publishers.

Past paper questions are reproduced by permission of the University of Cambridge Local Examinations Syndicate.

Contents

11 Linear graphs

12 Ratio and proportion

Introduction

This book has many features that will help you during the course. These features are described below.

Colour coding

The chapters have colour-coded page numbers to help you find related chapters quickly.

18   Number

102   Algebra

264   Space and shape

142   Statistics and Probability

Hint boxes

Helpful comments and hints feature throughout the book and key words are explained.

A now has 10 elements
and B now has 9 elements.

Example boxes

The book contains worked examples with explanatory notes throughout.

 EXAMPLE 2

A secretary can type 60 words per minute, but makes an average of 3 errors in every 60 words. What percentage of the words contain errors?

$\frac{3}{60}$ words contain errors

so $\frac{3}{60} = \frac{3}{60} \times 100\% = 5\%.$

Exercises

Exercises give students plenty of practice and are structured to provide a clear progression path. Icons indicate when use of a calculator is not allowed.
The answers to these exercises are available on the Teacher's CD (ISBN 978 0 435966 93 5).

 **EXERCISE 3C**

1 Work these out.
   (a) Increase 30 by 5%   (b) Increase 58 by 12%
   (c) Decrease 3400 ml by 18%   (d) Decrease 480 by 32%
   (e) Increase \$135 by $7\frac{1}{2}$%   (f) Decrease 890 ml by 8.4%

2 Firefighters are given a 4% pay rise. If John earned \$420 per week, how much will he earn after the pay rise?
   How many were there this year?

Past paper exam questions

At the end of each chapter, examination questions from past Cambridge IGCSE Mathematics papers are included so that you can test yourself using real past papers. The answers to these questions are available on the Teacher's CD (ISBN 978 0 435966 93 5).

EXAMINATION QUESTIONS

1 (a) Dina bought a car from a salesman for \$8400.
      When Dina sells the car she makes a loss of $22\frac{1}{2}$%
      For how much did she sell the car?   [1]
  (b) The saleman made a profit of 40% when he sold the the car for \$8400.
      How much did he pay for the car?   [2]

   (CIE Paper 2, Jun 2000)

Chapter 1

Matrices

This chapter will show you how to

- ✔ display information
- ✔ find the order of a matrix
- ✔ find the sum and product of two matrices
- ✔ calculate the determinant
- ✔ find the inverse

1.1 Displaying information

A matrix stores information.

The diagram shows roads joining five towns A, B, C, D and E.

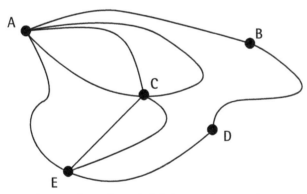

We can store the number of roads joining each town in a matrix. For example there are 3 roads joining A and C.

$$
\begin{array}{c}
 & & \text{To} \\
 & & \begin{array}{ccccc} A & R & C & D & E \end{array} \\
\text{From} & \begin{array}{c} A \\ B \\ C \\ D \\ E \end{array} & \begin{pmatrix} 0 & 1 & 3 & 0 & 1 \\ 1 & 0 & 0 & 1 & 0 \\ 3 & 0 & 0 & 0 & 2 \\ 0 & 1 & 0 & 0 & 1 \\ 1 & 0 & 2 & 1 & 0 \end{pmatrix}
\end{array}
$$

You can see in the matrix if there is a road between any two towns.

The information in a matrix will have large brackets round it.

Write down a road matrix for these towns.

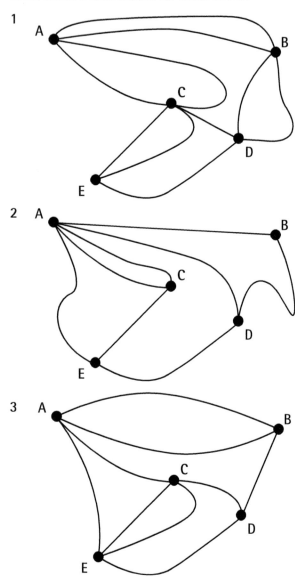

1

2

3

Sports results and league tables are another example of information stored in a matrix. Here are some football league tables.

Home games		P	W	D	L	Points
1.	Lorenzo	11	7	2	2	23
2.	Boca	11	7	2	2	23
3.	Victoria	11	7	2	2	23
4.	Lanus	10	6	2	2	20
5.	Newell	10	5	2	3	17
6.	Sarandi	10	5	2	3	17
7.	Estudiantes	10	4	2	4	14
8.	Gimnasia	10	4	6	0	18
9.	Sarsfield	10	3	3	4	12
10.	Colon	10	3	4	3	13

Away games		P	W	D	L	Points
1.	Lorenzo	10	6	1	3	19
2.	Boca	10	6	1	3	19
3.	Victoria	10	6	1	3	19
4.	Lanus	9	5	2	3	17
5.	Newell	9	3	5	1	14
6.	Sarandi	9	3	2	4	11
7.	Estudiantes	9	4	2	3	14
8.	Gimnasia	9	2	3	4	9
9.	Sarsfield	9	4	2	3	14
10.	Colon	9	2	4	3	10

All games		P	W	D	L	Points
1.	Lorenzo	21	13	3	5	42
2.	Boca	21	13	3	5	42
3.	Victoria	21	13	3	5	42
4.	Lanus	19	11	4	4	37
5.	Newell	19	8	7	4	31
6.	Sarandi	19	8	4	7	28
7.	Estudiantes	19	8	4	7	28
8.	Gimnasia	19	6	9	4	27
9.	Sarsfield	19	7	5	7	26
10.	Colon	19	5	8	6	23

You can see that the tables for Home and Away are not in points order.

They have to be in the same team order as the final matrix, then you can add them to get the final result.

11	7	2	2	23
11	7	2	2	23
11	7	2	2	23
10	6	2	2	20
10	5	2	3	17
10	5	2	3	17
10	4	2	4	14
10	4	6	0	18
10	3	3	4	12
10	3	4	3	13

+

10	6	1	3	19
10	6	1	3	19
10	6	1	3	19
9	5	2	3	17
9	3	5	1	14
9	3	2	4	11
9	4	2	3	14
9	2	3	0	9
9	4	2	3	14
9	2	4	3	10

=

21	13	3	5	42
21	13	3	5	42
21	13	3	5	42
19	11	4	4	37
19	8	7	4	31
19	8	4	7	28
19	8	4	7	28
19	6	9	4	27
19	7	5	7	26
19	5	8	6	23

To add two matrices together you add corresponding terms.

1.2 Order

To be able to add two matrices together they must be exactly the same size, known as the **order** of the matrix.

The order of a matrix is recorded as the number of rows by the number of columns.

The rows come first.

The tables in the sports example are 10×5 as they have 10 rows and 5 columns of data.

 EXAMPLE 1

Write down the order of the matrices.

$$A = \begin{pmatrix} 3 & 1 \\ 1 & 1 \\ 7 & 2 \end{pmatrix} \text{ and } B = (2 \ \ 3 \ \ -5)$$

The order of A is 3×2

The order of B is 1×3

A has 3 rows and 2 columns.

B has 1 row and 3 columns.

EXERCISE 1B

Write down the order of these matrices.

1 $\begin{pmatrix} 2 & 3 & 8 & 6 & 2 \end{pmatrix}$
2 $\begin{pmatrix} 9 & -5 \end{pmatrix}$

3 $\begin{pmatrix} 2 & 1 & 3 \\ 0 & 0 & 0 \end{pmatrix}$
4 $\begin{pmatrix} 9 & 0 & 6 & 4 \\ 1 & 1 & 1 & 1 \end{pmatrix}$

5 $\begin{pmatrix} 1 & 0 \\ 0 & 1 \end{pmatrix}$
6 $\begin{pmatrix} 1 & 0 & 0 \\ 0 & 1 & 0 \\ 0 & 0 & 1 \end{pmatrix}$

7 $\begin{pmatrix} 2 \\ -2 \\ 3 \end{pmatrix}$
8 $\begin{pmatrix} 1 \\ 3 \end{pmatrix}$

9 $\begin{pmatrix} 1 & 1 \\ 2 & 2 \\ 5 & 1 \end{pmatrix}$
10 $\begin{pmatrix} 2 & 4 & 6 & 9 & 1 & -4 \\ 0 & 0 & 0 & 0 & 0 & 9 \end{pmatrix}$

1.3 Addition and subtraction

 EXAMPLE 2

$A = \begin{pmatrix} 1 & 3 & 5 \\ 2 & 6 & 1 \\ 7 & 0 & -3 \\ 1 & 1 & 1 \end{pmatrix}$ $B = \begin{pmatrix} 2 & 2 & 2 \\ 1 & 6 & 1 \\ -1 & 2 & 0 \\ 3 & 3 & 3 \end{pmatrix}$

Find A + B.

Both these matrices are 4 × 3 so they can be added term by term.

$A + B = \begin{pmatrix} 1+2 & 3+2 & 5+2 \\ 2+1 & 6+6 & 1+1 \\ 7+-1 & 0+2 & -3+0 \\ 1+3 & 1+3 & 1+3 \end{pmatrix} = \begin{pmatrix} 3 & 5 & 7 \\ 3 & 12 & 2 \\ 6 & 2 & -3 \\ 4 & 4 & 4 \end{pmatrix}$

continued ▼

Subtraction works in exactly the same way except that you subtact corresponding terms.

$$A - B = \begin{pmatrix} 1-2 & 3-2 & 5-2 \\ 2-1 & 6-6 & 1-1 \\ 7--1 & 0-2 & -3-0 \\ 1-3 & 1-3 & 1-3 \end{pmatrix} = \begin{pmatrix} -1 & 1 & 3 \\ 1 & 0 & 0 \\ 8 & -2 & -3 \\ -2 & -2 & -2 \end{pmatrix}$$

EXERCISE 1C

Work out the following, where possible.

Check the order.

1
$$A = \begin{pmatrix} 1 & 3 \\ 2 & 6 \\ 7 & 0 \\ 1 & 1 \end{pmatrix} \quad B = \begin{pmatrix} 2 & 2 \\ 1 & 6 \\ -1 & 2 \\ 3 & 3 \end{pmatrix}$$

(a) A + B   (b) A − B   (c) A + A

2
$$A = \begin{pmatrix} 2 & 2 & 5 & 4 \\ 1 & 2 & 1 & 2 \\ 0 & 9 & 1 & 7 \end{pmatrix} \quad B = \begin{pmatrix} 0 & 1 & 0 & 1 \\ 4 & 5 & 6 & 7 \\ 0 & -2 & 1 & -2 \end{pmatrix}$$

(a) A + B   (b) A − B   (c) B + B + B

3   A = (1 3 1 7)   B = (7 6 5 4)

(a) A + B   (b) A − B   (c) A + B + A + B

4
$$A = \begin{pmatrix} 6 & 1 & -6 & 8 \\ 0 & 2 & -1 & 5 \end{pmatrix} \quad B = \begin{pmatrix} 2 & 1 & -1 \\ 0 & 9 & 8 \end{pmatrix} \quad C = \begin{pmatrix} 3 & 5 & 3 & 9 \\ 5 & 1 & -2 & 1 \end{pmatrix}$$

(a) A + C   (b) B + C   (c) A + B   (d) A + B + C
(e) A − B   (f) A − C   (g) B + B

1.4 Multiplying by a scalar

You will see that there is another way of looking at the question 4(g), Exercise 1C.

$$\begin{pmatrix} 2 & 1 & -1 \\ 0 & 9 & 8 \end{pmatrix} + \begin{pmatrix} 2 & 1 & -1 \\ 0 & 9 & 8 \end{pmatrix} = \begin{pmatrix} 4 & 2 & -2 \\ 0 & 18 & 16 \end{pmatrix} + \begin{pmatrix} 2 & 1 & -1 \\ 0 & 9 & 8 \end{pmatrix}$$

You can see that B + B = 2B, similarly B + B + B = 3B and so on.

Multiplying a matrix by a scalar is the same as multiplying every term by that scalar.

EXERCISE 1D

$$A = \begin{pmatrix} 3 & 2 \\ 1 & -4 \end{pmatrix} \quad B = \begin{pmatrix} 1 & 2 \\ 0 & 3 \end{pmatrix}$$

Work these out.

1. $2A$
2. $4B$
3. $5A$
4. $-6B$
5. $-2A$
6. $2A + B$
7. $3A - 2B$
8. $3A + 4B$

1.5 Multiplying matrices

Looking back to the sports league table, the first five football teams had these results.

		W	D	L	Points
1.	Lorenzo	13	3	5	42
2.	Boca	13	3	5	42
3.	Victoria	13	3	5	42
4.	Lanus	11	4	4	37
5.	Newell	8	7	4	31

The points score is worked out by having 3 points for a win, 1 point for a draw and 0 points for a loss.

There is a connection between

$$\begin{pmatrix} 13 & 3 & 5 \\ 13 & 3 & 5 \\ 13 & 3 & 5 \\ 11 & 4 & 4 \\ 8 & 7 & 4 \end{pmatrix} \text{ and } \begin{pmatrix} 3 \\ 1 \\ 0 \end{pmatrix} \text{ and } \begin{pmatrix} 42 \\ 42 \\ 42 \\ 37 \\ 31 \end{pmatrix}$$

It is

$$13 \times 3 \; + \; 3 \times 1 \; + \; 5 \times 0 \; = 42$$
$$13 \times 3 \; + \; 3 \times 1 \; + \; 5 \times 0 \; = 42$$
$$13 \times 3 \; + \; 3 \times 1 \; + \; 5 \times 0 \; = 42$$
$$11 \times 3 \; + \; 4 \times 1 \; + \; 4 \times 0 \; = 37$$
$$8 \times 3 \; + \; 7 \times 1 \; + \; 4 \times 0 \; = 31$$

Or else, as it is written in matrices

$$\begin{array}{ccc} 3 & 1 & 0 \\ \uparrow & \uparrow & \uparrow \end{array}$$

$$\begin{pmatrix} 13 & 3 & 5 \\ 13 & 3 & 5 \\ 13 & 3 & 5 \\ 11 & 4 & 4 \\ 8 & 7 & 4 \end{pmatrix} \begin{pmatrix} 3 \\ 1 \\ 0 \end{pmatrix} = \begin{pmatrix} 42 \\ 42 \\ 42 \\ 37 \\ 31 \end{pmatrix}$$

The red is to help you see how this works.

and we have matrix multiplication.

EXAMPLE 3

Work out

$$\begin{pmatrix} 2 & 5 & 7 \\ 3 & 4 & 6 \\ -2 & 4 & -1 \end{pmatrix} \begin{pmatrix} 1 \\ 2 \\ 3 \end{pmatrix}$$

We use the idea above.

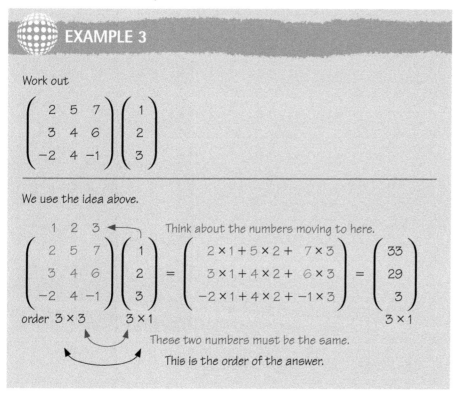

Take careful note of the order here because not all matrices can be multiplied together.

EXAMPLE 4

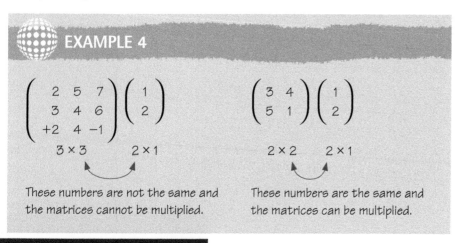

EXAMPLE 5

We can now multiply larger matrices with the method in Example 3.

$$\begin{pmatrix} 2 & 5 & 7 \\ 3 & 4 & 6 \\ -2 & 4 & -1 \end{pmatrix} \begin{pmatrix} 1 & 5 \\ 2 & 3 \\ 3 & 2 \end{pmatrix}$$

> Think of the second matrix in columns.

$$= \begin{pmatrix} 2 + 10 + 21 & 10 + 15 + 14 \\ 3 + 8 + 18 & 15 + 12 + 12 \\ -2 + 8 + -3 & -10 + 12 + -2 \end{pmatrix}$$

> Work with one column at a time as in Example 3.

$$= \begin{pmatrix} 33 & 39 \\ 29 & 39 \\ 3 & 0 \end{pmatrix}$$

EXAMPLE 6

It is important that you write the matrices in the correct order.

AB and **BA** are NOT the same thing.

$$A = \begin{pmatrix} 3 & 1 \\ 2 & 7 \end{pmatrix} \quad B = \begin{pmatrix} 5 & 8 \\ 4 & 1 \end{pmatrix}$$

$$AB = \begin{pmatrix} 3 & 1 \\ 2 & 7 \end{pmatrix} \begin{pmatrix} 5 & 8 \\ 4 & 1 \end{pmatrix} = \begin{pmatrix} 3 \times 5 + 1 \times 4 & 3 \times 8 + 1 \times 1 \\ 2 \times 5 + 7 \times 4 & 2 \times 8 + 7 \times 1 \end{pmatrix} = \begin{pmatrix} 19 & 25 \\ 38 & 23 \end{pmatrix}$$

$$BA = \begin{pmatrix} 5 & 8 \\ 4 & 1 \end{pmatrix} \begin{pmatrix} 3 & 1 \\ 2 & 7 \end{pmatrix} = \begin{pmatrix} 5 \times 3 + 8 \times 2 & 5 \times 1 + 8 \times 7 \\ 4 \times 3 + 1 \times 2 & 4 \times 1 + 1 \times 7 \end{pmatrix} = \begin{pmatrix} 31 & 61 \\ 14 & 11 \end{pmatrix}$$

$$AB \neq BA$$

1 Multiply the following matrices where possible.
Where it isn't possible, explain why.

$$A = \begin{pmatrix} 5 & 1 & 0 \\ 2 & 3 & 5 \\ 1 & 2 & 3 \end{pmatrix} \quad B = \begin{pmatrix} 2 \\ 1 \\ 7 \end{pmatrix} \quad C = \begin{pmatrix} 1 & 3 & 8 \end{pmatrix} \quad D = \begin{pmatrix} 1 & 8 \\ 2 & 3 \\ 5 & 4 \end{pmatrix} \quad E = \begin{pmatrix} 2 & 5 \end{pmatrix}$$

(a) **AB** (b) **AC** (c) **CD** (d) **CB**

(e) **DC** (f) **BA** (g) **DE** (h) **EB**

(i) **EB** (j) **BC**

2 Work this out.

$$\begin{pmatrix} 3 & 0 \\ 0 & 3 \end{pmatrix} \begin{pmatrix} 4 & 3 & 5 & 1 \\ 0 & 0 & 4 & 4 \end{pmatrix}$$

3 Multiply these.

$$\begin{pmatrix} 0 & 1 \\ 1 & 0 \end{pmatrix} \begin{pmatrix} 4 & 6 & 4 & 6 \\ 1 & 1 & 3 & 3 \end{pmatrix}$$

State the order of your answer.

4 Multiply these.

$$\begin{pmatrix} 0 & 1 \\ 1 & 0 \end{pmatrix} \begin{pmatrix} -1 & 0 \\ 0 & 1 \end{pmatrix}$$

Give the order of your answer.

5 Multiply these.

$$\begin{pmatrix} 2 & 0 \\ 0 & 1 \end{pmatrix} \begin{pmatrix} 8 \\ 3 \end{pmatrix}$$

1.6 Matrices of order 2 × 2

These are matrices that you will use later in transformations.

Identity matrix I

$$I = \begin{pmatrix} 1 & 0 \\ 0 & 1 \end{pmatrix}$$

The property of this matrix can be seen below.

$$\begin{pmatrix} 1 & 0 \\ 0 & 1 \end{pmatrix} \begin{pmatrix} 4 & 5 \\ 1 & 1 \end{pmatrix} = \begin{pmatrix} 4 & 5 \\ 1 & 1 \end{pmatrix} \quad \text{and} \quad \begin{pmatrix} 4 & 5 \\ 1 & 1 \end{pmatrix} \begin{pmatrix} 1 & 0 \\ 0 & 1 \end{pmatrix} = \begin{pmatrix} 4 & 5 \\ 1 & 1 \end{pmatrix}$$

$$IA = A \qquad\qquad AI = A$$

In general, $IA = AI = A$, for 2×2 matrices.

Zero matrix O

$$\mathbf{O} = \begin{pmatrix} 0 & 0 \\ 0 & 0 \end{pmatrix}$$

$$\begin{pmatrix} 0 & 0 \\ 0 & 0 \end{pmatrix} \begin{pmatrix} 4 & 5 \\ 1 & 1 \end{pmatrix} = \begin{pmatrix} 0 & 0 \\ 0 & 0 \end{pmatrix} \quad \text{and} \quad \begin{pmatrix} 4 & 5 \\ 1 & 1 \end{pmatrix} \begin{pmatrix} 0 & 0 \\ 0 & 0 \end{pmatrix} = \begin{pmatrix} 0 & 0 \\ 0 & 0 \end{pmatrix}$$

$$\mathbf{OA} = \mathbf{O} \qquad\qquad\qquad \mathbf{AO} = \mathbf{O}$$

In general, $\mathbf{OA} = \mathbf{AO} = \mathbf{O}$, for 2×2 matrices.

Determinant

For the matrix $\quad \mathbf{A} = \begin{pmatrix} a & b \\ c & d \end{pmatrix}$

The determinant is defined as $|\mathbf{A}| = ad - bc$.

EXAMPLE 7

$$A = \begin{pmatrix} 2 & 5 \\ 3 & 9 \end{pmatrix}$$

$$|A| = 2 \times 9 - 5 \times 3$$
$$= 18 - 15$$
$$= 3$$

Inverse matrix

We need to find a matrix $\mathbf{A}^{-1}$ so that $\mathbf{AA}^{-1} = \mathbf{I}$.

There are two ways of doing this.

Let $\mathbf{A} = \begin{pmatrix} 5 & 6 \\ 3 & 4 \end{pmatrix}$

 EXAMPLE 8

Method 1

Let $\mathbf{A}^{-1} = \begin{pmatrix} a & b \\ c & d \end{pmatrix}$

Then $\begin{pmatrix} 5 & 6 \\ 3 & 4 \end{pmatrix} \begin{pmatrix} a & b \\ c & d \end{pmatrix} = \begin{pmatrix} 1 & 0 \\ 0 & 1 \end{pmatrix}$

multiply out the matrices and we have

$$\begin{pmatrix} 5a + 6c & 5b + 6d \\ 3a + 4c & 3b + 4d \end{pmatrix} = \begin{pmatrix} 1 & 0 \\ 0 & 1 \end{pmatrix}$$

This will give two pairs of simultaneous equations and we can then find a, b, c and d.

Method 1 is very slow and one where it is easy to make mistakes. Method 2 is much quicker.

Method 2

$\mathbf{A} = \begin{pmatrix} 5 & 6 \\ 3 & 4 \end{pmatrix}$ $\qquad$ $\mathbf{M} = \begin{pmatrix} a & b \\ c & d \end{pmatrix}$

$|\mathbf{A}| = 20 - 18 = 2$ $\qquad$ $|\mathbf{M}| = ad - bc$

$\mathbf{A}^{-1} = \dfrac{1}{2} \begin{pmatrix} 4 & -6 \\ -3 & 5 \end{pmatrix}$ $\qquad$ $\mathbf{M}^{-1} = \dfrac{1}{ad - bc} \begin{pmatrix} d & -b \\ -c & a \end{pmatrix}$

$\mathbf{A}^{-1} = \begin{pmatrix} 2 & -3 \\ -1\frac{1}{2} & 2\frac{1}{2} \end{pmatrix}$

The numbers in red change places.

The numbers in green change sign.

Divide every term by the determinant.

You can also see from this method that there is no inverse when the determinant is zero.

You cannot divide by zero.

A matrix with no inverse is known as a singular matrix.

A matrix with an inverse is called non-singular.

EXAMPLE 9

Find the inverse of

$$B = \begin{pmatrix} 6 & -3 \\ 7 & 4 \end{pmatrix}$$

$|B| = 24 - -21 = 45$

$$B^{-1} = \frac{1}{45} \begin{pmatrix} 4 & 3 \\ -7 & 6 \end{pmatrix}$$

$$B^{-1} = \begin{pmatrix} \frac{4}{45} & \frac{1}{15} \\ \frac{-7}{45} & \frac{2}{15} \end{pmatrix}$$

> The answer could be left like this as all the terms do not simplify.

> But fractions should be simplified if you do divide.

 EXERCISE 1F

Find the inverse, where possible, of the following matrices.

1. $A = \begin{pmatrix} 2 & 5 \\ 4 & 11 \end{pmatrix}$

2. $B = \begin{pmatrix} 3 & 10 \\ 1 & 4 \end{pmatrix}$

3. $C = \begin{pmatrix} 1 & 2 \\ 0 & 2 \end{pmatrix}$

4. $D = \begin{pmatrix} 2 & 0 \\ 0 & 2 \end{pmatrix}$

5. $E = \begin{pmatrix} 3 & -1 \\ 1 & 1 \end{pmatrix}$

6. $F = \begin{pmatrix} 2 & 4 \\ -1 & \frac{1}{2} \end{pmatrix}$

7. $G = \begin{pmatrix} -2 & -2 \\ 1 & 2 \end{pmatrix}$

8. $H = \begin{pmatrix} -5 & -3 \\ -1 & -1 \end{pmatrix}$

9. $J = \begin{pmatrix} \frac{1}{2} & 1 \\ 1 & 2 \end{pmatrix}$

10. $K = \begin{pmatrix} 4 & 1 \\ 8 & 2 \end{pmatrix}$

Powers of a matrix

A 2 × 2 matrix can be squared, cubed, etc.

- A^2 means $A \times A$
- A^3 means $A \times A \times A$ but this will have to be worked out in two stages $(A \times A) \times A$

EXAMPLE 10

$$A = \begin{pmatrix} 1 & 2 \\ 3 & 4 \end{pmatrix}$$

$$A^2 = \begin{pmatrix} 1 & 2 \\ 3 & 4 \end{pmatrix}\begin{pmatrix} 1 & 2 \\ 3 & 4 \end{pmatrix} = \begin{pmatrix} 7 & 10 \\ 15 & 22 \end{pmatrix}$$

$$A^3 = \begin{pmatrix} 1 & 2 \\ 3 & 4 \end{pmatrix}\begin{pmatrix} 1 & 2 \\ 3 & 4 \end{pmatrix}\begin{pmatrix} 1 & 2 \\ 3 & 4 \end{pmatrix}$$

$$= \begin{pmatrix} 7 & 10 \\ 15 & 22 \end{pmatrix}\begin{pmatrix} 1 & 2 \\ 3 & 4 \end{pmatrix}$$

$$= \begin{pmatrix} 37 & 54 \\ 81 & 118 \end{pmatrix}$$

EXERCISE 1G

$$A = \begin{pmatrix} 3 & 1 \\ -2 & 5 \end{pmatrix} \qquad B = \begin{pmatrix} 1 & 2 \\ 2 & -1 \end{pmatrix}$$

Work these out.

1 $A + I$	2 $(A + I)^2$	3 A^2
4 $2A$	5 $A^2 + 2A + I$	6 A^4
7 AB	8 BA	9 $|A|$
10 A^{-1}	11 B^2	12 $(A + B)^2$
13 $A^2 + 2AB + B^2$	14 $|B|$	15 B^{-1}

EXAMINATION QUESTIONS

1 (a)
$$\begin{pmatrix} 3 & 0 & 0 \\ 9 & 5 & 0 \\ 4 & -3 & 2 \end{pmatrix} \begin{pmatrix} 1 \\ q \\ r \end{pmatrix} = \begin{pmatrix} p \\ -26 \\ 35 \end{pmatrix}$$

Find the values of p, q and r. [4]

(b)
$$\mathbf{M} = \begin{pmatrix} t & 6 \\ t & 5t \end{pmatrix} \text{ and } \mathbf{M}^{-1} = \begin{pmatrix} -5t & 6 \\ t & -t \end{pmatrix} \text{ where } \mathbf{M}^{-1} \text{ is the inverse of } \mathbf{M} \text{ and } t \neq 0.$$

Write down an equation in t and solve it. [4]

(c)
$$\begin{pmatrix} x & 2 \end{pmatrix} \begin{pmatrix} x \\ 5 \end{pmatrix} = kx \text{ is a matrix equation}$$

Find the value of k if $x^2 + 8x + 10 = 0$. [1]

(CIE Paper 4, Nov 2000)

2
$$\mathbf{A} = \begin{pmatrix} 2 & -3 \\ -2 & 5 \end{pmatrix} \qquad \mathbf{B} = \begin{pmatrix} 4 & 3x \\ 0 & -1 \end{pmatrix} \qquad \mathbf{C} = \begin{pmatrix} 10 & -15 \\ -2 & 3 \end{pmatrix}$$

(a) $\mathbf{A} + 2\mathbf{B} = \mathbf{C}$.
Write down an equation in x and solve it. [2]
(b) Explain why $\mathbf{C}$ does not have an inverse. [1]
(c) Find $\mathbf{A}^{-1}$, the inverse of $\mathbf{A}$. [2]

(CIE Paper 2, Jun 2002)

3
$$\mathbf{A} = \begin{pmatrix} 2 & -1 \\ 1 & 1 \end{pmatrix}$$

(a)
Find the 2×2 matrix $\mathbf{P}$ such that $\mathbf{A} + \mathbf{P} = \begin{pmatrix} 0 & 0 \\ 0 & 0 \end{pmatrix}$, [2]

(b)
Find the 2×2 matrix $\mathbf{Q}$ such that $\mathbf{AQ} = \begin{pmatrix} 1 & 0 \\ 0 & 1 \end{pmatrix}$, [3]

(CIE Paper 2, Nov 2002)

4 (a)
Multiply $\begin{pmatrix} 5 & 4 \\ -3 & -2 \end{pmatrix} \begin{pmatrix} 2 & 1 & -4 \\ 0 & 3 & 6 \end{pmatrix}$.

[2]

(b)
Find the inverse of $\begin{pmatrix} 5 & 4 \\ -3 & -2 \end{pmatrix}$.

[2]

(CIE Paper 2, Jun 2003)

5

$\mathbf{P} = \begin{pmatrix} 1 & 3 \\ 5 & 7 \end{pmatrix}$ $\mathbf{Q} = \begin{pmatrix} -1 & -2 \end{pmatrix}$ $\mathbf{R} = \begin{pmatrix} 1 & 2 & 3 \end{pmatrix}$ $\mathbf{S} = \begin{pmatrix} -1 \\ 2 \\ 3 \end{pmatrix}$

Only some of the following matrix operations are possible with matrices **P**, **Q**, **R** and **S** above.

PQ, **QP**, **P + Q**, **PR**, **RS**.

Write down and calculate each matrix operation that is possible.

[6]

(CIE Paper 4, Nov 2003)

6

$\mathbf{A} = \begin{pmatrix} 5 & -8 \end{pmatrix}$ $\mathbf{B} = \begin{pmatrix} 2 & 6 \\ 5 & -4 \end{pmatrix}$ $\mathbf{C} = \begin{pmatrix} 4 & 6 \\ 5 & -2 \end{pmatrix}$ $\mathbf{D} = \begin{pmatrix} 4 \\ -2 \end{pmatrix}$

(a) Which one of the following matrix calculations is **not** possible? [2]
    (i) **AB**   (ii) **AD**   (iii) **BA**   (iv) **DA**

(b) Calculate **BC**. [2]

(c) Use your answer to (b) to write down **B**$^{-1}$, the inverse of **B**. [1]

(CIE Paper 2, Jun 2004)

7

$\mathbf{C} = \begin{pmatrix} 5 & -2 \\ 1 & 4 \end{pmatrix}$ $\mathbf{D} = \begin{pmatrix} 4 & 2 \\ -1 & 5 \end{pmatrix}$

(a) Write as a single matrix. [2]
    (i) **C − 3D**,   (ii) **CD**. [2]

(b) Find **C**$^{-1}$. [2]

(CIE Paper 2, Nov 2004)

Chapter 2

Sets

This chapter will show you how to
- ✔ use set language and notation
- ✔ use Venn diagrams
- ✔ solve problems

2.1 Set language

A **set** is a collection of elements which can be described in some way.

For example   *A* is a set of six capital cities.

A = {Beijing, Jakarta, Kuala Lumpur, Oslo, Paris, Wellington}

The special brackets {..., ..., ...} are used around the list to show the set. Commas are used to separate the elements.

When sets are written down, a **Universal set** ℰ is usually stated. This is a set from which other sets can be selected.

In our example the universal set could be... capital cities I have visited.

In set notation this would be written as

ℰ = {Amsterdam, Beijing, Brussels, Gabarone, Jakarta, Pretoria, Kuala Lumpur, London, Oslo, Paris, Seoul, Wellington}

A = {Beijing, Jakarta, Kuala Lumpur, Oslo, Paris, Wellington}

In a Venn diagram this would be shown as

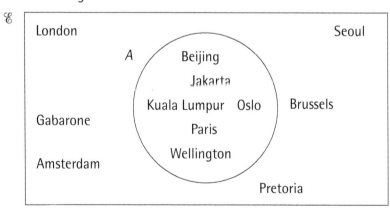

The diagram can be any shape but circles and rectangles are the most common.

2.2 Venn diagrams

A' The **complement of** *A*

A' is often pronounced '*A* dash'.

All those not in *A* but in ℰ, are shown in the shaded area.

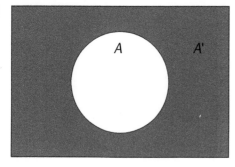

A ∩ *B* The **intersection** of *A* and *B*

This is the region where *A* and *B* intersect.

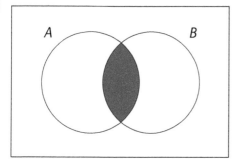

A ∩ *B*

A ∪ *B* The **union** of *A* and *B*

This is the whole region inside *A* and *B*.

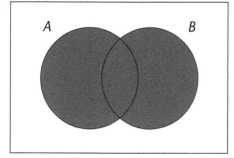

A ∪ *B*

Typical examination questions will ask you to shade various parts of a Venn diagram.

EXAMPLE 1

Shade the following regions

(a) $A \cap B'$ **(b)** $(A \cap B)'$ **(c)** $A \cup B'$

(d) $A \cap (B \cap C)$ **(e)** $A \cup (B \cap C)$ **(f)** $A' \cap (B \cup C)$

(a) $A \cap B'$ is the overlap between A and everywhere outside B.

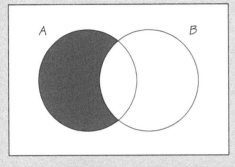

(b) $(A \cap B)'$ is everywhere outside the intersection of A and B.

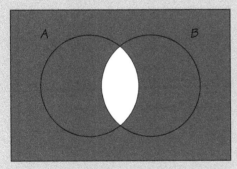

(c) $A \cup B'$ is the set A plus everywhere outside of B.

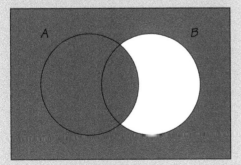

continued ▼

The next three parts have 3 sets involved and the usual diagram for this is as shown below.

(d) $A \cap (B \cap C)$ is the overlap of all three sets.

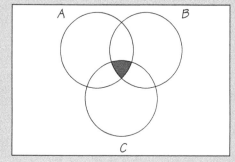

(e) $A \cup (B \cap C)$ is the set A plus the overlap of B and C.

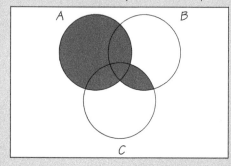

(f) $A' \cap (B \cup C)$

With more complicated expressions like this you can build them up step by step.

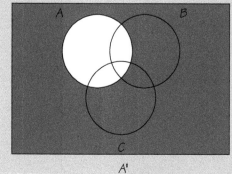

A'

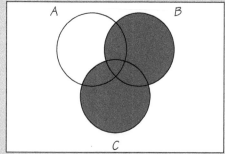

$B \cup C$

continued ▼

The final diagram is the overlap of the previous two.

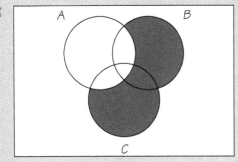

EXERCISE 2A

Copy the diagram and shade the required region for each part.

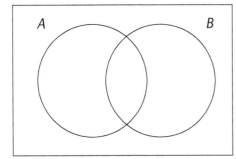

1 $A' \cap B$	**2** $A' \cup B$	**3** $A' \cap B'$
4 $(A \cup B)'$	**5** $(A' \cap B)'$	**6** $(A \cup B')'$
7 $(A \cap B) \cup (A \cap B')$	**8** $(A' \cap B') \cup (A \cap B')$	

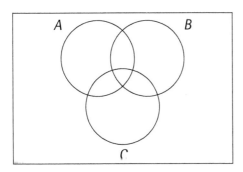

9 $A \cap (B \cap C')$	**10** $(A \cup C) \cap B$	**11** $(A \cup B) \cap C$
12 $A \cup B \cup C$	**13** $A \cap C \cap B'$	**14** $(A \cup C) \cap B'$
15 $A \cap C$	**16** $A \cap B'$	

You may also be asked to do this exercise in reverse and write down the set description of a diagram.

EXAMPLE 2

Write down the set notation for this region.

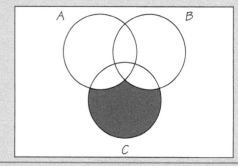

The region shaded is in C and outside of A ∪ B.

This is C ∩ (A ∪ B)'.

EXERCISE 2B

Write the set notation for the following regions.

1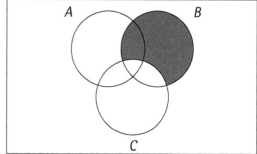

2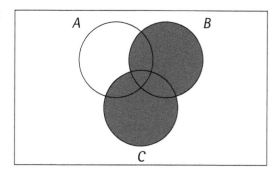

3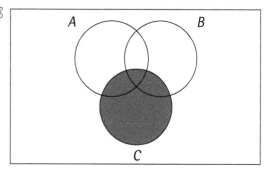

4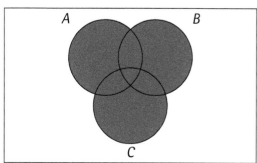

5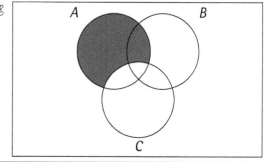

2.3 Listing sets

Returning to our first example.

$\mathscr{E}$ = {Amsterdam, Beijing, Brussels, Gabarone, Jakarta, Pretoria, Kuala Lumpur, London, Oslo, Paris, Seoul, Wellington}

A = {Beijing, Jakarta, Kuala Lumpur, Oslo, Paris, Wellington}
B = {Oslo, Paris, Seoul}

A' The **complement** of A is all those not in A but in $\mathscr{E}$.

A' = {Amsterdam, Brussels, Gabarone, Johannesburg, London, Seoul}

$A \cap B$ The **intersection** of A and B is the common elements of A and B.

$A \cap B$ = {Oslo, Paris}

$A \cup B$ The **union** of A and B is one of each of A and B.

$A \cup B$ = {Beijing, Jakarta, Kuala Lumpur, Oslo, Paris, Seoul, Wellington}

We also have a new set, B, where B = {Oslo, Paris, Seoul}.

2.4 Other notation

$n(A)$ = 6	The **number of elements** in set A is 6.
Oslo $\in A$	Oslo is an **element** of set A.
Seoul $\notin A$	Seoul is **not an element** of set A.
$\varnothing$	The **empty** set or a set with no elements or { }. For example, capital cities I have visited beginning with the letter Z.
$C \subset A$	C is a **proper subset** of A. All of C is inside A but some elements in A are not in C. A = {Beijing, Jakarta, Kuala Lumpur, Oslo, Paris, Wellington} C = {Beijing, Oslo, Paris}

$D \subseteq A$	D is a **subset** of A. This means that every element of D is an element of A.
$E \not\subseteq A$	E is **not a subset** of A.
$F \not\subset A$	F is **not a proper subset** of A.

There is also a formal set language which is sometimes used.

Here are two examples.

$A = \{x : x \text{ is even}\}$	This translates to A is the set of numbers x such that x is an even number.
$B = \{(x,y) : y = 2x + 3\}$	This translates to B is the set of points such that they lie on the line $y = 2x + 3$.

EXAMPLE 3

$\mathscr{E} = \{1, 2, 3, 4, 5, 6, 7, 8, 9, 10\}$

$A = \{1, 3, 5, 7, 9\}$ $B = \{2, 4, 6, 8\}$ $C = \{2, 3, 5, 7\}$

List the elements of the following sets.

(a) $A \cap B$ (b) $A \cup B$ (c) A'

(d) B' (e) $A \cap C$ (f) $B \cap C$

(g) $B \cup C$ (h) $(B \cap C)'$ (i) $A' \cap (B \cup C)$

Straightforward ones are (a) to (f).

(a) $\{\}$ no common elements in A and B

(b) $\{1, 2, 3, 4, 5, 6, 7, 8, 9\}$ one of each of A and B

(c) $\{2, 4, 6, 8, 10\}$ not in A but in $\mathscr{E}$

(d) $\{1, 3, 5, 7, 9, 10\}$ not in B but in $\mathscr{E}$

(e) $\{3, 5, 7\}$ common to A and C

(f) $\{2\}$ common to B and C

continued ▼

The remaining three parts need extra lines of working.

(g) $C' = \{1, 4, 6, 8, 9, 10\}$ first find C'

     $B \cup C' = \{1, 2, 4, 6, 8, 9, 10]$ one of each of B and C'

(h) $B \cap C = \{2\}$ first find $B \cap C$

     $(B \cap C)' = \{1, 3, 4, 5, 6, 7, 8, 9, 10\}$ not in $B \cap C$

(i) $A' = \{2, 4, 6, 8, 10\}$ first find A'

     $B \cup C = \{2, 3, 4, 5, 6, 7, 8\}$ then find $B \cup C$

     $A' \cap (B \cup C) = [2, 4, 6, 8]$ common to A' and $B \cup C$

EXERCISE 2C

1   $\mathscr{E} = \{1, 2, 3, 4, 5, 6, 7, 8, 9, 10\}$

   $X = \{2, 4, 6, 8\}$ $Y = \{1, 3, 5, 7\}$ $Z = \{3, 6, 9\}$

List the elements of the following sets.

(a) $X \cap Y$ (b) $X \cup Z$ (c) $X' \cap Y$

(d) $(Y \cap Z)'$ (e) $X \cap Y'$ (f) $Y \cup Z'$

2   $\mathscr{E} = \{a, b, c, d\}$

   (a) Write down all the subsets of $\mathscr{E}$ with three elements.

   (b) Write down n($\mathscr{E}$).

3   $\mathscr{E} = \{1, 2, 3, 4, 5, 6, 7, 8, 9, 10, 11, 12, 13, 14, 15, 16\}$

   $T = \{1, 3, 6, 10, 15\}$ $S = \{1, 4, 9, 16)$ $P = \{2, 3, 5, 7, 11, 13\}$

List the elements of the following sets.

(a) $S \cap T$ (b) $P \cap T$ (c) $S \cup T$

(d) P' (e) $P' \cup T$ (f) $(P \cup T)'$

(g) $\emptyset$ (h) $P \cup S \cup T$ (i) $(P \cup S \cup T)'$

Work these out.

(j) n(T)   (k) n($\emptyset$)   (l) n($P \cup T$)

You may be asked to put listed sets on a Venn diagram. Start by identifying the intersections, then draw the diagram and fill in the elements.

 **EXAMPLE 4**

Draw a Venn diagram to illustrate the sets $\mathscr{E}, T, S$ and P.

$\mathscr{E} = \{1, 2, 3, 4, 5, 6, 7, 8, 9, 10, 11, 12, 13, 14, 15, 16\}$

$T = \{1, 3, 6, 10, 15\}$ $S = \{1, 4, 9, 16\}$ $P = \{2, 3, 5, 7, 11, 13\}$

Identify all the intersections

$S \cap T = \{1\}$ $S \cap P = \emptyset$ $P \cap T = \{3\}$ and $P \cap S \cap T = \emptyset$

We can see that

- S and T do intersect
- P and S don't intersect
- P and T do intersect
- We don't have all 3 circles intersecting.

This means the diagram looks like this

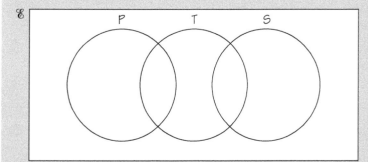

We can now enter the numbers starting with the intersections, then complete T, P and S. Don't forget to fill up the set $\mathscr{E}$.

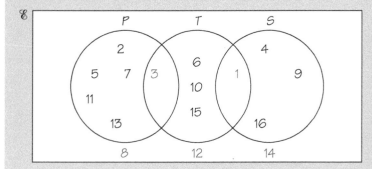

Don't forget P, T, S etc.

EXERCISE 2D

1 $\mathscr{E} = \{1, 2, 3, 4, 5, 6, 7, 8, 9, 10\}$

$P = \{2, 3, 5, 7\}$ $O = \{1, 3, 5, 7, 9\}$ and $S = \{1, 4, 8\}$

Draw a Venn diagram to illustrate these sets.

2 $\mathscr{E} = \{1, 2, 3, 4, 5, 6, 7, 8, 9, 10, 11, 12, 13, 14, 15\}$

$F = \{4, 8, 12, 16\}$ $T = \{3, 6, 9, 12, 15\}$ $P = \{2, 3, 5, 7, 11, 13\}$

Draw a Venn diagram to illustrate these sets.

3 $\mathscr{E} = \{a, b, c, e, h, i, m, o, s, t, u\}$

$V = \{a, e, i, o, u\}$ $M = \{a, h, m, s, t\}$ $L = \{m, o, s, t\}$

Draw a Venn diagram to illustrate these sets.

4 $\mathscr{E} = \{1, 2, 3, 4, 5, 6, 7\}$

$A = \{1, 2, 3, 4\}$ $B = \{1, 2, 3\}$ $C = \{1, 2\}$

Draw a Venn diagram to illustrate these sets.

5 $\mathscr{E} = \{\text{quadrilaterals}\}$

$S = \{\text{squares}\}$ $P = \{\text{parallelograms}\}$ $K = \{\text{kites}\}$

Draw a Venn diagram to illustrate these sets.

2.5 Problem solving

EXAMPLE 5

A and B are sets such that $n(A) = 10$, $n(B) = 9$ and $n(A \cap B) = 5$. Find $n(A \cup B)$.

You will need a Venn diagram to solve this problem.

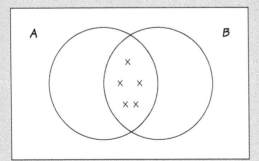

Start with the intersection if possible, $n(A \cap B) = 5$

continued ▼

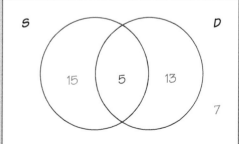

A

B

$\mathscr{E}$

We can see that n(A ∪ B) = 14.

> A now has 10 elements
> and B now has 9 elements.

1 *A* and *B* are sets such that n(A) = 7, n(B) = 12 and n(A ∩ B) = 5. Find n(A ∪ B).

2 *A* and *B* are sets such that n(A) = 9, n(B) = 6 and n(A ∩ B) = 4. Find n(A ∪ B).

3 *A* and *B* are sets such that n(A) = 10, n(B) = 10 and n(A ∩ B) = 5. Find n(A ∪ B).

4 *A* and *B* are sets such that n(A) = 65, n(B) = 40 and n(A ∩ B) = 8. Find n(A ∪ B).

5 *A* and *B* are sets such that n(A ∩ B) = 5, n(B) = 13 and n(A ∪ B) = 20. Find n(A).

6 *A* and *B* are sets such that n(A) = 10, n(B) = 6 and n(A ∪ B) = 12. Find n(A ∩ B).

Sometimes the problem will be in words.

EXAMPLE 6

In a lunch time survey of 40 students it was found that 20 had sandwiches, 18 had a drink, 5 had a sandwich and a drink and the rest had nothing. How many had nothing?

$\mathscr{E}$

S

D

15   5   13

7

continued ▼

We can start with the 5 for those who had both.

Next we can find the 15 from 20 − 5.

Followed by the 13 from 18 − 5.

We now have a total inside the circles of 33.

This means we can now calculate the 7 from 40 − 33.

So 7 students had nothing to eat or drink.

$n(S) = 20$

$n(D) = 18$

$n(\mathscr{E}) = 40$

EXERCISE 2F

1 30 students were asked when they watched TV on one day.
25 watched TV in the evening,
8 watched TV in the morning and 5 watched TV at both times.

How many students did not watch TV on that day?

2 In another class of 30 students, 1 student did not watch TV,
4 watched TV in the morning and in the evening while 23 only
watched TV in the evening.

How many students watched TV in the morning?

3 An aircraft with 120 passengers flying to Australia stops on the way
in Dubai and Hong Kong. 30 of the passengers have been to both
countries before, 46 have been to Dubai before and 70 have been
to Hong Kong before.

(a) How many passengers have visited neither country before?

(b) What is the probability that a passenger chosen at random has
visited Dubai but not Hong Kong?

4 In a class of 20 students, everyone is studying Mathematics or
Physics.
18 students are studying Mathematics.
8 students are studying Physics.

How many students are studying Mathematics and Physics?

5 In a survey of 30 people, 26 have a cell phone and 18 have
a computer. Four of the group do not have a cell phone or a
computer.

How many of the group have a cell phone and a computer?

6 1000 passengers are on board a ship. The ship stops at Acapulco, Barbados and Curaçao.

15 passengers have visited all three countries before.

30 passengers have visited Acapulco and Barbados before.

105 passengers have visited Acapulco and Curaçao before.

15 people have visited Barbados and Curaçao before.

In total, 215 have visited Acapulco, 325 have visited Barbados and 525 have visited Curaçao before.

(a) How many have visited only Acapulco before?

(b) How many have visited Barbados or Curaçao before?

(c) How many have not visited any of these places before?

7 At a school end of year party there are 3 drinks to choose from, Apple juice, banana shake or cola.

110 students attended the party and 74 had apple juice, 93 had banana shake, and 87 had cola.

64 students had apple juice and banana shake.

71 had banana shake and cola.

60 had apple juice and cola.

50 had all three drinks

How many students had

(a) just banana shake,

(b) none of the drinks,

(c) apple juice and banana shake but not cola,

(d) at least two different drinks?

EXAMINATION QUESTIONS

1 ℰ

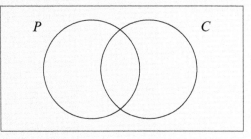

There are 22 students in a class.
15 of these students study Physics (*P*) and 17 study Chemistry (*C*).
3 study neither Physics nor Chemistry.
(a) By using a copy of the Venn diagram, or otherwise, find the number of students
who study both Physics and Chemistry. [2]
(b) On a copy of the Venn diagram shade the region $P' \cap C$. [1]

(CIE Paper 2, Nov 2000)

2 12 friends take a holiday together in Jordan and Saudi Arabia.
9 have already been to Jordan and 4 have already been to Saudi Arabia.
The probability that one of the 12, chosen at random, has already been to both countries is $\frac{1}{4}$.
(a) Write down the number of friends who have been to both countries. [1]
(b) Copy the Venn diagram below.

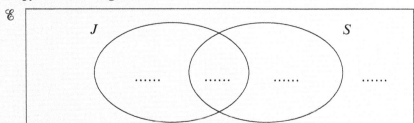

$J = \{$those who have already been to Jordan$\}$
$S = \{$those who have already been to Saudi Arabia$\}$
Write the number of friends in each part of your Venn diagram. [4]
(c) Write down the value of $n(J \cup S)$. [1]

(CIE Paper 4, Jun 2001)

3 One of 36 tourists on holiday in Namibia and South Africa is chosen at random.

The probability that he has been to South Africa before is $\frac{1}{2}$.

The probability that he has been to Namibia before is $\frac{4}{9}$.

The probability that he has been to neither country before is $\frac{1}{3}$.

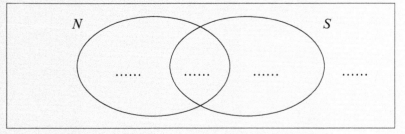

The set N represents those who have been to Namibia before.

The set S represents those who have been to South Africa before.

Copy the diagram, calculate and fill in the number of tourists in each part
of the Venn diagram above. [4]

(CIE Paper 2, Nov 2001)

4

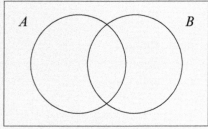

Diagram 1

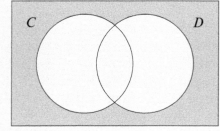

Diagram 2

(a) Copy Diagram 1 and shade the area which represents $A \cup B'$. [1]

(b) Describe in set notation the shaded area in Diagram 2. [1]

(CIE Paper 2, Jun 2002)

---

5 Three sets A, B and K are such that $A \subset K$, $B \subset K$ and $A \cap B = \varnothing$.

Draw a Venn diagram to show this information. [2]

(CIE Paper 2, Nov 2002)

6 Copy the diagram and write each of these four numbers in the correct place in the Venn diagram.

$$2.6, \quad \frac{4}{17}, \quad \sqrt{12}, \quad \sqrt{\frac{112}{7}}$$

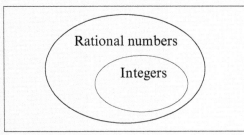

[4]

(CIE Paper 2, Jun 2003)

7 $\mathscr{E} = \{-2\frac{1}{2}, -1, \sqrt{2}, 3.5, \sqrt{30}, \sqrt{36}\}$
$X = \{\text{integers}\}$
$Y = \{\text{irrational numbers}\}$
List the members of
(a) X, [1]
(b) Y. [1]

(CIE Paper 2, Nov 2003)

8 There are 30 students in a class.
20 study Physics, 15 study Chemistry and 3 study neither Physics nor Chemistry.

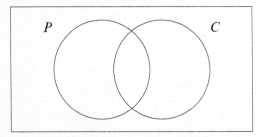

(a) **Copy and complete** the Venn diagram to show this information. [2]
(b) Find the number of students who study both Physics **and** Chemistry. [1]
(c) A student is chosen at random. Find the probability that the student studies Physics but not Chemistry. [2]

(CIE Paper 4, Jun 2004)

9 $\mathcal{E} = \{40, 41, 42, 43, 44, 45, 46, 47, 48, 49\}$
$A = \{\text{prime numbers}\}$
$B = \{\text{odd numbers}\}$
(a) Copy the Venn diagram and place the 10 numbers in the correct places.

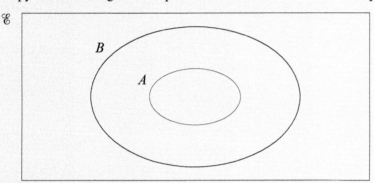

[2]

(b) State the value of n$(B \cap A')$. [1]

(CIE Paper 2, Nov 2004)

---

10 n$(\mathcal{E}) = 21$, n$(A \cup B) = 19$, n$(A \cap B') = 8$ and n$(A) = 12$
Copy and complete the Venn diagram to show this information.

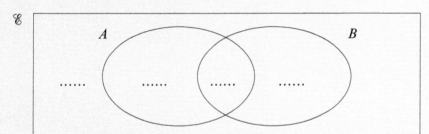

[3]

(CIE Paper 2, Jun 2005)

Chapter 3

Percentages

This chapter will show you how to

✔ solve percentage problems
✔ solve compound percentage problems

3.1 Using percentages to compare amounts

You can use percentages to compare quantities, such as working out which of two or more amounts is the greater, or which of two or more offers is the 'best buy'.

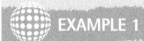 **EXAMPLE 1**

Village A has a population of 1540 of which $\frac{3}{20}$ are under 16 years of age. Village B has a population of 1250 of which 18% are under 16 years of age. Which village has the greater number of people under 16 years of age?

Village A
Number of people under 16 $= \frac{3}{20}$ of 1540

$$= \frac{3}{20} \times 1540$$

$$= \frac{3 \times 1540}{20}$$

$$= 231$$

Village B
Number of people under 16 $= 18\%$ of 1250

$$= \frac{18}{100} \times 1250$$

$$= \frac{18 \times 1250}{100}$$

$$= 225$$

So Village A has the greater number of people under 16.

To compare, use decimals, fractions or percentages to work out the amounts.

1   Which one is the best offer?
    Explain your answer.

2   Which weekend break is cheaper?

Original price **$75**
NOW 32% off

Original price **$125**
NOW 60% off

3   A special offer on breakfast cereal was shown on two different
    boxes originally priced at $1.72 for 144 g.
    One stated '25% extra free' the other said '$\frac{1}{4}$ off the price'.
    Is this the same offer or is one a better buy?

3.2 Writing one quantity as a percentage of another

To write one quantity as a percentage of another

Write the first quantity as a fraction of the second quantity. Then
multiply by 100 to convert to a percentage.

For example, 18 as a percentage of 45 $= \frac{18}{45} \times 100\% = 40\%$.

When you sit a test, your mark is often written as a fraction.

For example, if you score 17 out of 25 it would be written as $\frac{17}{25}$.

You convert this to a percentage by multiplying by 100.

So $\frac{17}{25} = \frac{17}{25} \times 100\% = 68\%$

Check
$\frac{17}{25} = 17 \div 25$
$= 0.68$
$= 68\%$

EXAMPLE 2

A secretary can type 60 words per minute, but makes an average of
3 errors in every 60 words. What percentage of the words contain errors?

$\frac{3}{60}$ words contain errors

so $\frac{3}{60} = \frac{3}{60} \times 100\% = 5\%$.

EXERCISE 3B

1 Ramat gets the following scores in his tests.
Write them as percentages.

Subject	English	Maths	French	History	Geography
Score	22	40	17	34	43
Total marks	40	75	30	65	80

2 In my class there are 4 left-handed people. If there are 28 people in the class, what percentage are left-handed?

3 In a game there are 14 blue blocks, 20 green and 12 red. Write the number of red blocks as a percentage of the number of blocks.

4 A model is 8 cm long. The width of a wheel is 25 mm. Write the width of the wheel as a percentage of the length of the model.

> Take care to make all the units the same.

5 The following table shows the number of people in a drama club.

	Male	Female
Adult	17	15
Child	12	18

(a) What percentage of the club are male?

(b) What percentage of the club are girls?

(c) Write the number of adults as a percentage of the number of people in the club.

> Give your answers to the nearest whole percentage.

6 A trainee secretary makes an average of 10 errors in every 80 words. What percentage of the words contain errors?

7 A factory produces 500 medical instruments in a day but on average 15 of these are faulty. What percentage is faulty?

3.3 Adding and subtracting a percentage of a quantity

You will often be asked to increase (or decrease) a quantity by a given percentage.

1 Add the % increase to 100%
(Subtract the % decrease from 100%)

2 Convert this % to a decimal.

3 Multiply the original amount by this decimal.

EXAMPLE 3

Liz earns $150 per week.
Next week she is due to receive a pay rise of 6%.
What will be her new weekly pay?

Increase = 6%
New %   = 100% + 6%
        = 106%
        = 1.06

Liz's new weekly pay
        = 1.06 × $150
        = $159

Divide by 100 to convert a % to a decimal.

 EXAMPLE 4

Toby reduces his weight by 8% from 95 kg.
What is his new weight?

Decrease = 8%
New %   = 100% − 8%
        = 92%
        = 0.92

Toby's new weight
        = 0.92 × 95 kg
        = 87.4 kg

Divide by 100 to convert a % to a decimal.

 EXERCISE 3C

1 Work these out.
  (a) Increase 30 by 5%   (b) Increase 58 by 12%
  (c) Decrease 3400 ml by 18%   (d) Decrease 480 by 32%
  (e) Increase $135 by $7\frac{1}{2}$%   (f) Decrease 890 ml by 8.4%

2 Firefighters are given a 4% pay rise. If John earned $420 per week, how much will he earn after the pay rise?

3 There has been a 6% decrease in the number of reported thefts in Walton this past year. There were 350 reported thefts last year.
  How many were there this year?

4 I pay $28 for my train ticket and Peter pays $17.60.
  How much will we have to pay after the $7\frac{1}{2}$% increase?

All fares to increase by 7½%

5 A new car costs $8450. After two years the value of the car will have decreased by 43%. How much will the car be worth ?

6 Sales of a magazine, costing $1.95, decreased by 11% this week. They sold 4300 copies last week.

How much money have they lost on their sales this week?

7 Juanita started her new job earning $12 000 per year, increasing by 3% after 3 months. Melinda started on $11 500 per year, increasing by 5% after 3 months.

Who has the greater salary after 3 months?

8 Ali weighed 84 kg. He lost $4\frac{1}{2}$% of his body weight when he started running but then put 2% of his new weight back on.

(a) How much was Ali's lowest weight?

(b) How much does Ali weigh now?

9 In 2000 the number of pairs of breeding sparrows was estimated as 200 000. This decreased by 38% in 2001. In 2002 there was a slight recovery with an increase of 4%.

How many breeding pairs were estimated at the end of 2002?

10 Sean, Yvan and Lana each invested $250. Sean's money increased in value by $6\frac{3}{4}$%. Yvan's money decreased by $2\frac{1}{2}$% and Lana's money increased by $4\frac{1}{4}$%.

How much does each have now?

General Sales Tax (GST)

GST is added to many items that you buy and to bills for services. This is an example of percentage increase.

The rate of GST is $17\frac{1}{2}$%, which means that you will pay an extra $17\frac{1}{2}$% on top of the cost of the item you buy.

The rate of GST varies from country to country.

 EXAMPLE 5

A digital camera is advertised for sale at $240 (excluding GST). How much will you have to pay?

'Excluding' means that GST must be added on to the advertised price.

Increase $= 17\frac{1}{2}$%
New % $= 100\% + 17\frac{1}{2}$%
$= 117\frac{1}{2}$%
$= 1.175$

$117\frac{1}{2} \div 100 = 117.5 \div 100$
$= 1.175$
This is your multiplier to work out the % increase.

Cost of digital camera
$= 1.175 \times \$240$
$= \$282$

The GST makes quite a difference to the price!

1 Work out **(a)** the GST and **(b)** the total cost of each item.
   (i) a DVD player at $130 (ex. GST)
   (ii) a phone at $39.99 (ex. GST)

Take the rate of GST to be $17\frac{1}{2}\%$. Give your answers to the nearest cent.

2 What is the total cost of a TV sold for $126 + GST?

3 Which car is the more expensive?

4 A meal for four costs $73.58 plus GST. If the four people decide to share the bill equally, how much will each pay?

5 The cost of a scooter is $375 + GST. Jas decides to pay by credit. He pays an initial deposit of 15% and then 12 monthly payments of $35. How much more does Jas pay by buying on credit?

6 Which method is cheaper? Find how much can be saved using the cheaper method.

$199 + GST

BUY NOW!

or

22% Deposit
Plus
12 monthly payments
of $19.75

3.4 Percentage change

You will need to write one quantity as a percentage of another when you are asked to work out **percentage change**.

Percentage change $= \dfrac{\text{change}}{\text{original amount}} \times 100\%$.

Always work out the change first. Don't forget that it is the *original* amount that goes on the bottom of the fraction.

 EXAMPLE 6

The original cost of a DVD player is $225. In a sale it is reduced to $180. What is the percentage decrease in the price?

These examples are typical of the questions you can expect on your IGCSE exam papers.

Decrease in price $\quad = \$225 - \$180$
$\quad\quad\quad\quad\quad\quad\quad = \$45$

Percentage decrease $\quad = \dfrac{\text{decrease}}{\text{original amount}} \times 100\%$
$\quad\quad\quad\quad\quad\quad\quad\quad = \dfrac{45}{225} \times 100\%$
$\quad\quad\quad\quad\quad\quad\quad\quad = 20\%$

EXAMPLE 7

The average attendance at a team's home games last season was 55 000. This year the average attendance is 58 575. What percentage increase is this?

Increase $= 58\,575 - 55\,000$

$= 3575$ — First find the increase.

Percentage increase $= \dfrac{\text{increase}}{\text{original amount}} \times 100\%$

$= \dfrac{3575}{55\,000} \times 100\%$ — Then divide by the original amount.

$= 6.5\%$ — Write the answer as a percentage.

EXERCISE 3E

1 What is the percentage decrease in the price of the coat (originally $95)?

2 Jamie was given a pay rise. He used to earn $12 000 and now earns $12 400. What was the percentage increase in his pay?

3 The number of car thefts in Brigton rose from 483 in 2002 to 504 in 2003. What percentage increase is this?

4 The number of students taking a particular subject at A level has dropped from 4015 to 3984.

   (a) What is the percentage reduction?

   (b) If there is the same percentage reduction the following year, how many students will take the A level then?

5 The cost of a holiday has risen from $556 to $604.50.

   (a) What is the percentage increase?

   (b) Owing to a fuel crisis, the holiday company puts a 15% surcharge on the new cost of the holiday.
     What is the total percentage increase of the holiday now?

Percentage profit and loss

When you are dealing with money problems you will often meet the terms **profit** and **loss**, depending on whether you make money or lose money on the sale of an item.

You also need to know the terms **cost price**, the amount you pay for an item, and **selling price**, the amount you sell it for.

The formula for percentage change now becomes

Percentage profit (loss) $= \dfrac{\text{profit (loss)}}{\text{cost price}} \times 100\%$.

The cost price is the *original* price of the item and goes on the bottom of the fraction.

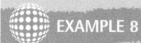 **EXAMPLE 8**

A car salesman buys a car for $2500 then sells it for $3200. What is his percentage profit?

Profit $= \$3200 - \$2500$
        $= \$700$

Percentage profit $= \dfrac{\text{profit}}{\text{cost price}} \times 100\%$

        $= \dfrac{700}{2500} \times 100\% = 28\%$

 EXAMPLE 9

Derwin bought a new motorbike for $5450 but traded it in for another a year later. He got a trade-in value of $4578. What percentage loss is this?

Loss $= \$5450 - \$4578$
        $= \$872$

Percentage loss $\quad= \dfrac{\text{loss}}{\text{cost price}} \times 100\%$

        $= \dfrac{872}{5450} \times 100\% = 16\%$

 EXERCISE 3F

1   Ahmed sold a CD player for $30. He had bought it for $35. What was his percentage loss?

2   Sarah restores skateboards. She bought one for $5 and sold it for $18.25. What was her percentage profit?

3   For each of the following, find the percentage profit or loss.

Cost price	$50	$34	$6	$73.50	$125	$3500
Selling price	$65	$24	$7.50	$69.50	$84	$3635

4   A sack of pet food costs $15.50. If you buy two sacks the shop only charges $13.25 per sack. What is the percentage discount per sack when you buy two sacks?

> Discount is an amount taken off the price. It is worked out in the same way as a profit or loss.

5   Amy has a ticket for a rock concert. It cost her $32.50 and she wants to sell it for $45. What will be her percentage profit?

6 A DVD was sold for $14.99. It cost the shop $9 to buy.
   What was the percentage profit?

7 The house price index was quoted as 106.2 in February 2006,
   compared with a base index of 100 in February 2005.
   (a) What was the percentage increase?
   (b) If a house cost $190,000 in February 2006, what was its likely
       value 12 months earlier?

3.5 Reverse percentages

In some problems you are told the amount *after* a percentage increase
or decrease and you have to work out the *original* amount.

Remember that the *original* amount in any calculation is always taken
to be *100%* and the final amount will be a given percentage above
or below 100%, depending on whether there has been an increase or
a decrease.

If it is a percentage increase,
... add the % change to 100% then convert this % to a decimal.

If it is a percentage decrease,
... subtract the % change from 100% then convert this % to a
decimal.

Set up your answer with this information and you will see that a
simple division is all you need to do.

EXAMPLE 10

Calculate the original amount.

Original amount	% change	Final amount
$?	10% increase	$66

Original (100%) + 10% = 110%

110% as a decimal = 1.10

Original amount × 1.10 = Final amount
Original amount × 1.10 = $66

$$\text{Original amount} = \frac{\$66}{1.10}$$
$$= \$60$$

The original amount has been
increased by 10%.

Always multiply the original
amount by the decimal.

The answer to questions of this type
is always found by doing a division.

Do **not** make the mistake of
working out the given percentage
of the *final* amount and then
subtracting.

EXAMPLE 11

Sarah bought a new washing machine from a store offering all items at 20% off. If she paid $344, what was the original price of the washing machine?

$100\% - 20\% = 80\%$
80% as a decimal $= 0.80$
Original price $\times 0.80 =$ Sale price
Original price $\times 0.80 = \$344$
$$\text{Original price} = \frac{\$344}{0.80}$$
$$= \$430$$

The original price has been reduced by 20%.

Check 20% of $430
$= 0.20 \times \$430 = \$86$
$\$430 - \$86 = \$344$

EXERCISE 3G

1 A computer is reduced by 12% in a sale. It now costs $334.40. What was the original price of the computer?

2 After a pay rise of 4%, Kim earned $14 560. What did she earn before the pay rise?

3 A mobile phone was priced at $135 including GST. What would be the price before GST was added?

Assume GST $= 17.5\%$

4 A spring is stretched by 32% to a length of 22 cm. What length was it before it was stretched?

5 A seal pup increases its body weight by $4\frac{1}{2}$ % in one day. It now weighs 6.27 kg. What did it weigh yesterday?

6 A shop advertises 'We will pay your GST'. How much would I pay for a bike priced at $87.50 inclusive of GST?

7 The total number of pupils in school this year is 1034. This is a $5\frac{1}{2}$ % increase on last year.

   (a) How many pupils were there last year?

   (b) Next year they expect an increase in pupils of 3%. How many pupils will there be then?

8 The value of a car depreciates by 17% in its first year.

   (a) If it is worth $12 035 after one year, what was its original price?

   (b) The original price included GST. How much was the car excluding GST?

Depreciates means that its value goes down.

9 After paying a 12% deposit on a house, I needed a loan for $76 120. The agent charged me $2\frac{1}{4}$ % of the *full* cost of the house for a survey of the property. How much did I have to pay for the survey?

10 During heating, a metal rod expands by $1\frac{1}{4}$ %.

(a) If the rod measures 40.5 cm when hot, what was its length originally?

(b) After 10 minutes, it remains 0.5% longer than its original length. What is the length of the rod at this time?

3.6 Repeated percentage change

Examples of repeated percentage change include **compound interest** and population changes.

When you **invest** money the interest you earn is calculated using compound interest.

In compound interest

- the rate of interest is fixed
- the amount of interest you receive each year is not the same
- the interest is calculated on the sum of money you invested in the first place *plus* any interest you have already received.

> The amount you pay back on a loan is also calculated using compound interest.

 EXAMPLE 12

Venetia puts $800 into an account paying 5% p.a. compound interest. How much does she have in her account after two years?

At the start of year 1 she has $800

Interest at the end of year 1 = 5% of $800   = 0.05 × $800
       = $40

At the end of year 1 she has $800 + $40   = $840
Interest at the end of year 2 = 5% of $840   = 0.05 × $840
       = $42

At the end of year 2 she has $840 + $42   = $882

Venetia has $882 in her account after 2 years.

> p.a. stands for 'per annum' meaning 'each year'.

> Notice the decimal version of 5% (0.05). It can be easier to use than $\frac{5}{100}$.

> Notice how you use the sum of money at the end of one year to calculate the interest earned at the end of the next year.

There is another way to calculate the amount of money you will have if you invest it at compound interest.

1 Add the rate of interest to 100%.

2 Convert this % to a decimal.

3 Multiply the original amount of money by this decimal as many times as the number of years given in the question.

> This method is quick and easy to use.

> You *must* remember to add the rate of interest to 100% before you convert to the decimal you will use as a multiplier.

> Notice that this method gives you the final amount of money, not the interest.

In Example 16, Venetia invested $800 at a rate of interest of 5% p.a. for two years.

Step 1   100% + 5% = 105%

Step 2   105% = 1.05

Step 3 $800 × 1.05 × 1.05 = $800 × (1.05)² = $882

These ideas can also be used to solve problems which do not involve money, but any quantity that is increasing or decreasing.

 EXAMPLE 13

There are 5000 whales of a certain species, but scientists think that their numbers are reducing by 8% each year.
Estimate how many of these whales there will be in three years.

___

Numbers are reducing by 8% each year.
So 100% − 8% = 92% and 92% = 0.92 as a decimal
Number of whales in 3 years' time

$$= 5000 × 0.92 × 0.92 × 0.92$$
$$= 5000 × (0.92)^3$$
$$= 3893.44$$

Estimated number of whales   = 3890

In Example 13 the number of whales reduces by 8% of the number *at the start of each year.*

Each % calculation is done on a *different* number so you must use the same methods as for compound interest problems.

The whales are *reducing* in number so you must *subtract* the % from 100%.

Using the power button on your calculator speeds up the calculation.

Give answers to 3 s.f.

 EXAMPLE 14

Lee invests $500 in a bank. The rate of interest is fixed at 3.6% compound interest. How much money will he have if he leaves it in the bank for 10 years?

___

Rate of interest = 3.6%
100% + 3.6% = 103.6% = 1.036
After 10 years Tony will have $500 × (1.036)¹⁰
$$= $712.1435717...$$
$$= $712.14$$

The money will increase so add 3.6% to 100%.

Using the power button is much quicker than doing
$500 × 1.036 × 1.036 × 1.036 × 1.036 × ...
(10 times altogether).

 EXERCISE 3H

1 Amita invests $135 for two years at a rate of 4% p.a. compound interest.
How much will she have at the end of the two years?

2 A new car cost $12 000. Each year the value of the car depreciates by $8\frac{1}{2}$%. What will the car be worth at the end of three years?

3 The population of doves is increasing in parts of a country. One estimate is that a population of 2000 pairs is increasing at a rate of $6\frac{1}{2}\%$ each year. How many pairs of doves will there be at the end of five years?

4 Sami has a choice of ways to invest the $250 legacy left by her grandfather. She can invest it at $4\frac{1}{4}\%$ p.a. for 5 years or she can invest it for 2 years at 5% p.a. followed by 3 years at $3\frac{1}{2}\%$ p.a. Which one is best?

5 The seal population in Scotland is estimated to decline at the rate of 16% each year. In 2001, 3000 seals were counted. How many years will it take for the population to fall below 1000?

6 A company rents a car at $260 per month. In the rental agreement, the price is reduced by $2\frac{1}{2}\%$ each month after the first 6 months.

  (a) Work out the difference between the amount paid in the 6th and 7th months.

  (b) How much will the car cost in total in the first 9 months?

  (c) Work out the total amount paid up to the end of the second year.

7 Juanita earns $21 000 a year. This increases by 6% each year. How long will it take her to earn over $25 000 per year?

8 Mamet earns $14 250 per year. His contract says this will increase each year in line with the annual rate of inflation. An estimate for the annual rate of inflation is $3\frac{1}{2}\%$.

  (a) Find his salary at the end of three years.

  (b) Find his monthly pay at the end of five years.

  (c) If the rate of inflation is $5\frac{1}{4}\%$ instead of $3\frac{1}{2}\%$, how much more is his monthly pay at the end of five years?

Compare the monthly pay for the two rates of inflation.

9 How long will it take each of the following investments to reach $1 000 000?

  (a) $200 000 invested at a rate of 15%

  (b) $150 000 invested at a rate of 19%

1 (a) Dina bought a car from a salesman for $8400.
        When Dina sells the car she makes a loss of $22\frac{1}{2}\%$
        For how much did she sell the car?   [1]
   (b) The saleman made a profit of 40% when he sold the the car for $8400.
        How much did he pay for the car?   [2]

(CIE Paper 2, Jun 2000)

2 (a) Maria paid $1320 tax in 1999. She paid 10% less tax in 2000.
        Calculate the tax Maria paid in 2000.   [1]
   (b) $1320 was 10% **more** than she paid in 1998.
        Calculate the tax Maria paid in 1998.   [2]

(CIE Paper 2, Jun 2001)

3 Elena invests $P for 9 months at 4% Simple Interest per year. She receives $39 interest.
   Calculate the value of P.   [2]

(CIE Paper 2, Nov 2001)

4 Chris saves $3500 this year. This is 40% more than he saved last year.
   Calculate how much he saved last year.   [3]

(CIE Paper 4, Jun 2002)

5 The temperature decreased from 25°C to 22°C.
   Calculate the percentage decrease.   [2]

(CIE Paper 2, Jun 2002)

6 (a) The winning distance in the javelin competition was 80 metres.
        Otto's throw was 95% of the winning distance.
        Calculate the distance of Otto's throw.   [2]
   (b) Pamela won the long jump competition with a jump of 6.16 metres.
        This was 10% further than Mona's jump.
        How far did Mona jump?   [2]

(CIE Paper 4, Nov 2002)

7 Nyali paid $62 for a bicycle. She sold it later for $46.
   What was her percentage loss?   [2]

   (CIE Paper 2, Nov 2002)

8 (a) On Wednesday, the cost of a $16 ticket was reduced by 15%.
        Calculate this new reduced cost.   [2]
   (b) A $10 ticket costs 25% more than it did last year.
        Calculate the cost last year.   [2]

   (CIE Paper 4, Jun 2003)

9 In 1950, the population of Switzerland was 4 714 000.
   In 2000, the population was 7 087 000.
   Work out the percentage increase from 1950 to 2000.   [2]

   (CIE Paper 2, Jun 2003)

10 (a) Fatima buys a city-bike which has a price of $120.
        She pays 60% of this price and then $10 per month for 6 months.
         (i) How much does Fatima pay altogether?   [2]
        (ii) Work out your answer to part (i) as a percentage of the original price of $120. [2]
   (b) Mohammed pays $159.10 for a mountain-bike in a sale.
        The original price had been reduced by 14%.
        Calculate the original price of the mountain-bike.   [2]

   (CIE Paper 4, Jun 2004)

11 Sara has $3000 to invest for 2 years.
   She invests the money in a bank which pays Simple Interest at the rate of 7.5% per year.
   Calculate how much interest she will receive at the end of the two years.   [2]

   (CIE Paper 2, Jun 2004)

12 A house was built in 1985 and cost $62 000.
   It was sold in 2003 for $310 000.
   (a) Work out the 1985 price as a percentage of the 2003 price.   [2]
   (b) Calculate the percentage increase in the price from 1985 to 2003.   [2]

   (CIE Paper 2, Jun 2005)

Chapter 4

Approximations

This chapter will show you how to
- ✔ round numbers
- ✔ estimate answers to calculations by using approximations
- ✔ understand limits of accuracy

4.1 Rounding

Why is it necessary to use a rounded or approximate answer rather than an exact answer?

'The land area of a country is 94 251 square kilometres.'
How can the land area of a country be measured so accurately?
Do you really need to know the exact area?
You could say
'The land area of a country is about 90 000 square kilometres.'

You can give the land area to a lesser **degree of accuracy** by rounding to the nearest 1000 or 100 or 10. The answers are 94 000, 94 300 and 94 250 respectively, but it is unlikely you would want it to be any more accurate than 94 000.

Remember that when a number falls *exactly* halfway between two limits you always round *upwards*.
So 1465 (exactly halfway between 1460 and 1470) rounds up to 1470, to the nearest 10.

Rounding to a given number of decimal places

You are often asked to give an answer to a number of decimal places.

The final answer must have only as many decimal places as the question asks for, no more and no less.

Follow these simple rules.

1   Count the number of places you want, to the right of the decimal point.

2   Look at the next digit.
    If it is 5 or more, you need to round up the digit in the previous decimal place.
    If it is 4 or less you leave the previous decimal digit as it is.

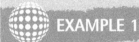 **EXAMPLE 1**

Write 8.14973 to **(a)** 1 d.p. **(b)** 2 d.p. **(c)** 3 d.p.

(a) 8.1 4973 = 8.1 (1 d.p.) — The *next* digit is 4 so the 1 is *unchanged*.

(b) 8.14 973 = 8.15 (2 d.p.) — The *next* digit is 9 so the 4 must be *rounded up* to 5.

(c) 8.149 73 = 8.150 (3 d.p.) — The *next* digit is 7 so the 9 must be *rounded up*.
Since this would make it 10, the 4 needs to change to 5.

You need to keep the 0 in **(c)** because you must have 3 d.p.
The answers of 8.15 in **(b)** and 8.150 in **(c)** are not the same since 8.15 is to an accuracy of 2 d.p. and 8.150 is to an accuracy of 3 d.p.

 EXERCISE 4A

1 Round the following to 1 decimal place (1 d.p.).
   (a) 5.83   **(b)** 7.39   **(c)** 2.15   **(d)** 5.681
   (e) 4.332   **(f)** 15.829   **(g)** 11.264   **(h)** 17.155
   (i) 145.077   **(j)** 521.999

2 Round to 2 decimal places.
   (a) 3.259   **(b)** 6.542   **(c)** 0.877   **(d)** 0.031
   (e) 11.055   **(f)** 4.007   **(g)** 3.899   **(h)** 2.3093
   (i) 0.0009   **(j)** 5.1299

3 Round to 3 d.p.
   (a) 1.2546   **(b)** 5.2934   **(c)** 4.1265
   (d) 0.0007   **(e)** 0.000 08

4 Round 15.1529 to
   (a) 1 decimal place   **(b)** 2 d.p.
   (c) 3 d.p.   **(d)** the nearest whole number.

5 In a race the time for the winner was given as 15.629 seconds.
   Write this to **(a)** the nearest second **(b)** 1 d.p. **(c)** 2 d.p.
   The time for the second place was 15.634 seconds.
   (d) Round this as you did for **(a)**, **(b)**, and **(c)** above.
       What do you notice?

Rounding to a given number of significant figures

Significant figures are 'important' figures and the most significant figure in a number is the one with the greatest place value.

Follow these simple rules.

1 Start from the most significant figure and count the number of figures that you want.

2 Look at the next digit.
If it is 5 or more you need to round up the previous digit.
If it is 4 or less you leave the previous digit as it is.

3 Put in any zeros needed to locate the decimal point and indicate place value.

> The most significant figure is the *first non-zero* figure reading from the left.

> This is *very* important.

 EXAMPLE 2

Round 26 818 to

(a) 1 significant figure (1 s.f.)   (b) 2 s.f.

(a) 26 818 = 30 000   (1 s.f.)

(b) 26 818 = 27 000   (2 s.f.)

> The *next* digit is 6 so the 2 must be *rounded up* to 3.
> You *must* include zeros to locate the decimal point and indicate the place value of the 3.

> The *next* digit is 8 so the 6 must be *rounded up* to 7.

 EXAMPLE 3

Write 0.007 038 6 to

(a) 1 s.f.   (b) 2 s.f.

(a) 0.007 038 6 = 0.007

(b) 0.007 038 6 = 0.0070

> The most significant figure is the *first non-zero* figure reading from the left, 7.
> The *next* digit is 0 so the 7 is *unchanged*.

> The *next* digit is 3 so the 0 is *unchanged*.
> You *must* keep the 0 after the 7 because it is the second significant figure.

In both of these examples, the zeros after the decimal point but before the 7 locate the decimal point and indicate the place value of the 7.

 EXERCISE 4B

1 Round these to 1 significant figure.
(a) 2862   (b) 19 473   (c) 257 394
(d) 84 693   (e) 4.86

2　Round to 2 s.f.

(a) 6842　　　　　　(b) 32 841　　　　(c) 153 945

(d) 267 149　　　　(e) 5.32

3　Round the following to 1 s.f.

(a) 0.037　　　　　(b) 0.042　　　　　(c) 0.0059

(d) 0.0035　　　　 (e) 0.509

4　Round to 2 s.f.

(a) 0.574　　　　　(b) 0.000 382　　　(c) 0.001 92

(d) 0.203　　　　　(e) 0.001 99

5　The population of a town is given as 293 465.
　　What is this rounded to

(a) 1 s.f.　　　　　(b) 2 s.f?

6　The length of a boat is given as 43.562 m.
　　What is this rounded to

(a) 2.s.f　　　　　(b) 3.s.f?

4.2　Approximations and error

Estimating using approximations

When you do a calculation using your calculator, do you always believe the answer? What if you press a wrong button? Would you realise what you had done?

You can check your answer using **approximations**.

To **estimate** an approximate answer

1　Round all of the numbers in the calculation to 1 significant figure.

2　Do the calculation using these approximations.

> This is a skill you will need. Some examination questions ask you to show how to get estimates to calculations by using approximations.

EXAMPLE 4

Use approximations to estimate the answers to these calculations.

(a) 6.89×3.375

(b) $38.45 \div 7.56$

(c) $\dfrac{181.03 \times 0.48}{8.641}$

(d) $\dfrac{6.85^2}{2.19 \times 11.7}$

(a) $6.89 \times 3.375 \approx 7 \times 3 = 21$

(b) $38.45 \div 7.56 \approx 40 \div 8 = 5$

(c) $\dfrac{181.03 \times 0.48}{8.641} \approx \dfrac{200 \times 0.5}{9} = \dfrac{100}{9} \approx 11$

(d) $\dfrac{6.85^2}{2.19 \times 11.7} \approx \dfrac{7^2}{2 \times 10} = \dfrac{49}{20} \approx 2.5$

The approximate answers in Example 4 are close to the answers of the original calculations.

(a) $6.89 \times 3.375 = 23.25375$ \qquad Approximate answer = 21

(b) $38.45 \div 7.56 = 5.0859...$ \qquad Approximate answer = 5

(c) $\dfrac{181.03 \times 0.48}{8.641} = 10.0560...$ \qquad Approximate answer = 11

(d) $\dfrac{6.85^2}{2.19 \times 11.7} = 1.8312...$ \qquad Approximate answer = 2.5

 EXERCISE 4C

1 Use approximations to estimate the answers to these problems.

(a) 7.63×8.36 \qquad\qquad (b) $15.28 \div 4.85$

(c) $(3.62 + 7.17) \times 8.57$ \qquad (d) $\dfrac{4\,287 \times 4862}{37 \times 53}$

(e) $\dfrac{8.63 \times 4.95}{(2.7)^2}$ \qquad\qquad (f) $\dfrac{7.53 - 2.86}{1.35 + 1.44}$

2 Calculate the actual answers in question 1 and check to see if your approximations were reasonable.

3 A company bought 2815 kg of cloves to crush and package. The cloves cost $17.85 per kg. Estimate the total cost.

4 A fruit stall sells a box of 460 pears for $38 in total. Estimate how much each pear cost.

5 The cost of a school trip per pupil is $4.85 for tickets, $2.15 for transport, plus $1.12 for meals. If there are 224 pupils going on the trip, estimate the total cost.

6 My car, on average, does 8.5 kilometres to the litre over a distance of 348 kilometres. Work out approximately

(a) how many litres of petrol were used

(b) total cost if petrol cost 89c per litre.

7 A wall will need 127 bricks for each row and will be 17 bricks high. A brick has a mass of 3.4kg.

(a) Estimate the number of bricks needed.

(b) What is the approximate total mass of the bricks?

Accuracy of measurement

Continuous measure can take any values. The accuracy of the measure depends on the measuring instrument.

For example, if you measure your height as 174 cm, it may not be exactly 174 cm. It is likely to be 174 cm *to the nearest centimetre*. This means that the true height lies between 173.5 cm and 174.5 cm. You can write this as   173.5 cm $\leqslant$ height $<$ 174.5 cm

In the same way, if your mass is 68 kg to the nearest kilogram, it will be nearer to 68 kg than to either 67 kg or 69 kg.
The true mass is   67.5 kg $\leqslant$ mass $<$ 68.5 kg

> Notice that the $\leqslant$ sign is used for the minimum value but the $<$ sign is used for the maximum value. You will see the reason for this at the end of this section.

> Any measurement given *to the nearest whole unit* may be inaccurate by up to *one half unit in either direction.*
>
> The minimum value is known as the **lower bound.**
>
> The maximum value is known as the **upper bound.**

 EXAMPLE 5

A tube of toothpaste is 10 cm long, to the nearest half centimetre. What are the upper and lower bounds for the length?

Upper bound = 10.25 cm
Lower bound = 9.75 cm

 EXERCISE 4D

1   Give the range of possible values for these measurements.

   (a) 4 cm (to the nearest cm)   (b) 45 kg (to the nearest kg)
   (c) 173 g (to the nearest g)   (d) 340 mm (to the nearest mm)
   (e) 3.6 m (to 1 d.p.)   (f) 12.3 *l* (to 1 d.p.)
   (g) 122.5 g (to 1 d.p.)   (h) 0.6 cm (to 1 d.p.)
   (i) 7.24 km (to 2 d.p.)   (j) 9.67 min (to 2 d.p.)
   (k) 4.92 g (to 2 d.p.)   (l) 7.02 m*l* (to 2 d.p.)

2   Give the possible range of values of these.

   (a) 7 m   (b) 7.0 m   (c) 7.00 m   (d) 7.000 m
   (e) Explain why the answers are not all the same.

 **EXAMPLE 6**

A rectangle has sides of 8 cm and 5 cm, each measured to the nearest centimetre.
Find the upper and lower bound for the area.

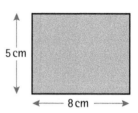

5 cm

8 cm

---

8 cm means a length in the range 7.5 cm ⩽ length < 8.5 cm

5 cm means a width in the range 4.5 cm ⩽ width < 5.5 cm

The rectangle could be as small as 7.5 cm by 4.5 cm

So the minimum area = 7.5 × 4.5 cm²

                  = 33.75 cm²

Lower bound of the area of the rectangle = 33.75 cm²

The area must be less than 8.5 × 5.5 = 46.75 cm²

Upper bound of the area of the rectangle = 46.75 cm²

Note that the rectangle cannot be 46.75 cm² in area. Any value up to, but not including, this is possible.

The lower bound of the area and the upper bound of the area are *not* an equal distance from the nominal area 8 × 5 = 40 cm².
The lower bound is 6.25 cm² less but the upper bound is 6.75 cm² more.

This idea can be extended to values which are given to *any* degree of accuracy, not just to the nearest whole number.

 **EXAMPLE 7**

$v = u + at$ is a formula used to calculate the final velocity (v) of an object when you know its initial velocity (u), its acceleration (a) and the time (t) over which the acceleration takes place.

If $u = 4.6$ m/s, $a = 1.8$ m/s² and $t = 7.5$ s, all correct to 1 d.p., calculate the maximum value of the final velocity.

Acceleration is measured in m/s² (metres per second per second).

4.6 m/s must lie between 4.55 m/s and 4.65 m/s

1.8 m/s² must lie between 1.75 m/s² and 1.85 m/s²

7.5 s must lie between 7.45 s and 7.55 s

So   max v = 4.65 + (1.85 × 7.55)

              = 4.65 + 13.9675

              = 18.6175

              = 18.6 (to 1 d.p.)

Note that if a number is given correct to 1 d.p. (to the nearest 0.1) it must lie 0.05 either side of its nominal value.
For example, 4.6 will be 4.6 ± 0.05 = 4.55 to 4.65.

The maximum value of the product $a \times t$ occurs when both a and t take their maximum value.

Example 7 shows you how to handle a product of terms.

The maximum value is obtained when each of the terms in the product takes its maximum value.

The minimum value would be found when each term takes its minimum value.

 **EXAMPLE 8**

You want to cut 53 cm from a piece of wood 120 cm long, both measurements given to the nearest cm.
What is the maximum length of the remaining piece?

120 cm lies between 119.5 cm and 120.5 cm.
53 cm lies between 52.5 cm and 53.5 cm.

(120.5 cm − 52.5 cm) will give the maximum answer.

So the maximum length of the remaining piece
= 120.5 − 52.5 cm
= 68 cm

Maximum − Minimum

You can see that
119.5 − 53.5 would give the *least* possible length of the remaining piece
ie. Minimum − Maximum.

For division, you use one upper bound and one lower bound to obtain the maximum and minimum answers, in the same way.

These results are summarised as

Consider two quantities A and B.

Maximum $(A + B) = \max A + \max B$
Minimum $(A + B) = \min A + \min B$

Maximum $(A \times B) = \max A \times \max B$
Minimum $(A \times B) = \min A \times \min B$

Maximum $(A − B) = \max A − \min B$
Minimum $(A − B) = \min A − \max B$

Maximum $(A \div B) = \max A \div \min B$
Minimum $(A \div B) = \min A \div \max B$

Note that for *addition* and *multiplication* ...
MAX = max and max
MIN = min and min

... but for *subtraction* and *division* ...
MAX = max and min
MIN = min and max

When questions involve a combination of these operations you must take care to perform the appropriate calculation at each stage.

 **EXAMPLE 9**

This formula works out the value of the acceleration, a, for an object which increases its velocity from u to v in travelling a distance s.

$$a = \frac{v^2 - u^2}{2s}$$

If $v = 12.4$ m/s and $u = 3.8$ m/s (both correct to 1 d.p.) and $s = 14$ m (correct to the nearest metre), calculate the minimum value of a. (The units of a will be m/s².)

It is a formula similar to the one used in Example 7.

continued ▼

The lower and upper bounds of each of the quantities are

$$12.35 \leqslant v < 12.45$$
$$3.75 \leqslant u < 3.85$$
$$13.5 \leqslant s < 14.5$$

$a = (v^2 - u^2) \div (2s)$ which is a division

So   min $a = \min(v^2 - u^2) \div \max(2s)$

But $(v^2 - u^2)$ is a subtraction

So $\min(v^2 - u^2) = \min v^2 - \max u^2$
$$= (\min v)^2 - (\max u)^2$$

Final calculation is

$$\min a = \frac{(\min v)^2 - (\max u)^2}{\max (2s)}$$
$$= \frac{12.35^2 - 3.85^2}{2 \times 14.5}$$
$$= \frac{137.7}{29}$$
$$= 4.74827... \text{ m/s}^2$$

Do not attempt to do the calculation without first breaking it down into smaller steps.

You can then see what are the appropriate values to use for each bit of the numerator and for the denominator.

The final answer has been left in its exact form as seen on your calculator display.

 EXERCISE 4E

1   If $a = 3.2$ cm, $b = 6.7$ cm and $c = 4.3$ cm, all correct to the nearest millimetre, find the least possible value for each of these calculations.

   (a) $a + b + c$ (b) $b \times a$ (c) $b - c$ (d) $c \div a$

2   A rectangle is measured as 3.6 cm by 7.2 cm correct to 1 d.p.
   (a) Find the upper and lower bound for each measurement.
   (b) Find the smallest possible area of the rectangle.

3   Sami runs a race in 24 minutes and Peter runs it in 21 minutes, both measured to the nearest minute. What is the greatest possible difference in their times?

4   The lawn shown is measured to the nearest metre. What is the difference between the greatest and the smallest possible areas?

5   Sally wins a 100 m race in 15.2 seconds to the nearest tenth of a second. The length of the track is measured to the nearest metre.
   (a) What is the possible range of times that Sally ran?
   (b) What is the possible range of lengths for the race?
   (c) What is the fastest possible speed of her run?

6   A cube has a volume of 72 cm^3, to the nearest cm^3.
   Find the range of possible values for the length of the side.

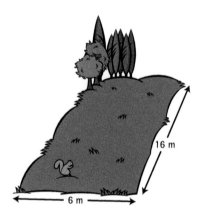

16 m

6 m

7 A rectangular block with a mass of 0.784 kg correct to 3 d.p. measures 6.4 cm by 3.7 cm by 2.8 cm to 1 d.p.

   (a) Find the greatest and least possible volume of the block.

   (b) Find the range of possible mass for the block.

   (c) Find the greatest possible density of the material.

8 A car travelled for 32.4 kilometres at an average speed of 34.8 km/h. Find the least amount of time in minutes for the journey.

The upper bound

Why is the $\leqslant$ sign used for the lower bound but the $<$ sign used for the upper bound?

Look at the value for u given in Example 9, $u = 3.8$.
You wrote $3.75 \leqslant u < 3.85$

The convention used in mathematics is that when a number ends in '5' it is rounded upwards.
If you were asked to write 3.85 correct to 1 d.p. you would write 3.9.
If you were asked to write 3.84999... correct to 1 d.p. the correct response is to write 3.8.

This is a recurring decimal where the nines go on forever.

So, although 3.85 rounds up to 3.9 it is also the upper bound of 3.8 (it seems to be connected to both!)
This is why the $<$ sign is always used for the upper bound.

1   The height of Mont Blanc is 4810 m, correct to the nearest 10 m.
    What is the least possible height?   [1]

    (CIE Paper 2, Jun 2000)

2

    The equal sides of the isosceles triangle are each 7.7 cm, correct to the nearest millimetre.
    The perimeter is 21.7 cm, also correct to the nearest millimetre.
    Calculate the smallest possible length of the third side of the triangle.
    Show your working.   [2]

    (CIE Paper 2, Nov 2000)

3   The capacity of a jug is 3.5 litres correct to the nearest 0.1 litres.
    The capacity of a glass is 0.25 litres correct to the nearest 0.01 litres.
    (a) (i)   What is the minimum capacity of the jug?   [1]
        (ii) What is the maximum capacity of the glass?   [1]
    (b) Calculate the greatest number of glasses which you can be sure to fill from a full jug. [1]

    (CIE Paper 2, Jun 2001)

4   Elena has eight rods each of length 10 cm, correct to the nearest centimetre.
    She places them in the shape of a rectangle, three rods long and one wide.

    (a) Write down the minimum length of the rectangle.   [1]
    (b) Calculate the minimum area of the rectangle.   [1]

    (CIE Paper 2, Jun 2002)

5   The length of a road is 380 m, correct to the nearest 10 m.
Maria runs along this road at an average speed of 3.9 m/s.
This speed is correct to 1 decimal place.
Calculate the greatest possible time taken by Maria.   [3]

(CIE Paper 2, Nov 2002)

---

6   A rectangular field is 18 metres long and 12 metres wide.
Both measurements are correct to the nearest metre.
Work out exactly the smallest possible area of the field.   [2]

(CIE Paper 2, Jun 2003)

---

7   The population, P, of a small island was 6380, correct to the nearest 10.
Copy and complete the statement about the limits of P.

$$\ldots\ldots\ldots\ldots\ldots \leqslant P < \ldots\ldots\ldots\ldots\ldots$$ [2]

(CIE Paper 2, Jun 2004)

---

8   A square has sides of length d metres.
This length is 120 metres, correct to the nearest 10 metres.
(a) Copy and complete the statement

$$\ldots\ldots\ldots\ldots\ldots \leqslant d < \ldots\ldots\ldots\ldots\ldots$$ [1]

(b) Calculate the difference between the largest and the smallest possible
areas of the square.   [2]

(CIE Paper 2, Nov 2004)

---

9   To raise money for charity, Jalaj walks 22 km, correct to the nearest kilometre,
every day for 5 days.
(a) Copy and complete the statement for the distance, d km, he walks in one day.

$$\ldots\ldots\ldots\ldots\ldots \leqslant d < \ldots\ldots\ldots\ldots\ldots$$ [2]

(b) He raises $1.60 for every kilometre that he walks.
Calculate the least amount of money that he raises at the end of the 5 days.   [1]

(CIE Paper 2, Jun 2005)

Chapter 5

Area and volume

This chapter will show you how to
- ✔ calculate the circumference and area of a circle
- ✔ find the arc length and area of a sector
- ✔ draw planes of symmetry
- ✔ calculate the surface area and volume of prisms, pyramids, cones and spheres

5.1 Circumference of a circle

The diameter (*d*) of the circle is twice the radius (*r*).

Circumference = $2\pi r$

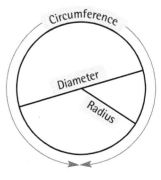

 **EXAMPLE 1**

Find the circumference of a circle of radius 2.6 cm.

$C = 2\pi r$

circumference $= 2 \times \pi \times 2.6$
$= 16.3$ cm

Use $\pi = 3.142$ or the value from your calculator.
Give your answer to 3 s.f.

 **EXAMPLE 2**

The end of a pipe is a circle of diameter 9.2 mm.
Calculate the circumference of the end of the pipe.

diameter $= 19.2$ mm
radius $= 9.6$ mm
circumference $= 2 \times \pi \times 9.6$
$= 3.77$ mm

 **EXAMPLE 3**

The distance around the edge of a circular pond is 10.5 m.
Calculate the radius of the pond.

None of the diagrams in this chapter are to scale.

$$C = 2\pi r$$
$$10.5 = 2\pi \times r$$
$$\frac{10.5}{2\pi} = r$$
$$r = 1.67 \text{ m (3 s.f.)}$$

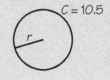

$C = 10.5$

 EXERCISE 5A

In all the following questions take π = 3.142 or use the π button on your calculator.

1 Find the circumference of the circle when the **diameter** is
   (a) 2 cm   (b) 5 cm   (c) 12 cm   (d) 18.4 cm (e) $8\frac{1}{2}$ cm

2 Find circumference of the circle when the **radius** is
   (a) 6 cm   (b) 15 cm   (c) 24 cm   (d) 9.5 cm   (e) $4\frac{1}{2}$ cm

3 The diameter of a coin is 20 mm. Calculate its circumference.

4 The diameter of a CD is 12 cm. Calculate its circumference.

5 The centre circle of a football pitch has a diameter of 6 m.
   Calculate the length of the white line which forms the circle.

6 A circular flower bed of diameter 4 m has a plastic strip around the edge of it. How long is this plastic strip?

7 A circular patch of grass has a radius of 7 m.
   Calculate the circumference.

8 The length of the minute hand of a clock is 2.5 m.
   Calculate the distance travelled by the tip of the hand in one hour.

9 A barrel of radius 26 cm has a metal band fixed around its top edge. How long is this strip of metal?

10 A tin of soup has a label around it.
   The radius of the can is 4 cm. How long is the label?

11 The circumference of the Earth is 40 000 km.
   Calculate the diameter of the Earth.

12 The distance around a circle of stones is 274.4 m.
   Calculate the diameter of the circle of stones.

13 A waterwheel has a circumference of 69 m.
   Calculate the radius of the waterwheel.

14 A tyre has a circumference of 70 cm. What is the radius of the wheel it fits?

5.2 Area of a circle

Area = πr^2

 EXAMPLE 4

Find the area of a circle of diameter 6.8 cm

---

diameter = 6.8 cm

radius = 3.4 cm

Area = πr^2

Area = $\pi \times 3.4^2$

= 36.3 cm²

> Make sure you square first and then multiply by π.

 EXAMPLE 5

A circular rug has an area of 2.4 m².
Calculate the diameter of the rug.

Area = πr^2

2.4 = πr^2

$\dfrac{2.4}{\pi} = r^2$

r^2 = 0.76394...

r = 0.87403...

diameter = 1.75 m (3 sf)

> Keep at least 4 figures in the working. Round off at the end.

 EXERCISE 5B

1 Calculate the areas of these circles.

(a)

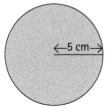

←5 cm→

(b)

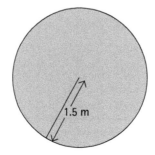

1.5 m

(c)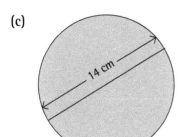

(d)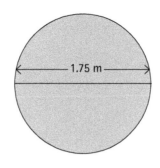

2 A circular table has a radius of 0.5 m. Calculate the area of the table.

3 A circular pond has a diameter of 4.8 m. Calculate the area of the pond.

4 The base of a vase is a circle with diameter 12 cm. Calculate the area of the base of the vase.

5 Find the shaded area in each of these.

(a)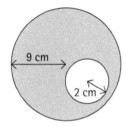

(b)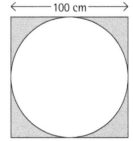

6 A circle has area 180 cm².
Calculate the radius of the circle.

7 A circular plate has area 500 cm².
Calculate the diameter of the plate.

8 A circular garden has an area of 250 m².
(a) Calculate the radius of the garden.
(b) Calculate the circumference of the garden.

9 The area of the cross-section of a water wheel is 45 m². Calculate the circumference of the water wheel. Give your answer to the nearest metre.

10 In the diagram, the area of circle B is twice the area of circle A. Work out the radius of circle B.

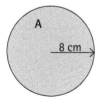

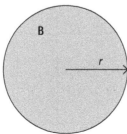

EXAMPLE 6

A garden is in the shape of a rectangle with two semicircles, one on the length of the rectangle and one on the width, as shown in the diagram.

Calculate the area of the garden, giving your answer to the nearest square metre.

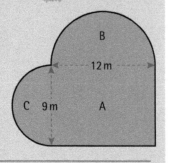

Area of semicircle
$= \frac{1}{2}$ area of circle.
Diameter of B = 12 m, so radius = 6 m.
Diameter of C = 9 m, so radius = 4.5 m.

Area of rectangle $A = 12 \times 9$
$= 108 \text{ m}^2$

Area of semicircle $B = \frac{1}{2} \times \pi \times 6^2$
$= 56.548...$

Area of semicircle $C = \frac{1}{2} \times \pi \times 4.5^2$
$= 31.808...$

Total area $= 108 + 56.548... + 31.808...$
$= 196.35...$
$= 196 \text{ m}^2$ (nearest square metre)

If you rounded each of the three answers to the nearest whole number and then added them your answer would be
$108 + 57 + 32 = 197 \text{ m}^2$
(which is incorrect).
You should round at the *end* of the calculation.

EXERCISE 5C

Find the area of each of these shapes

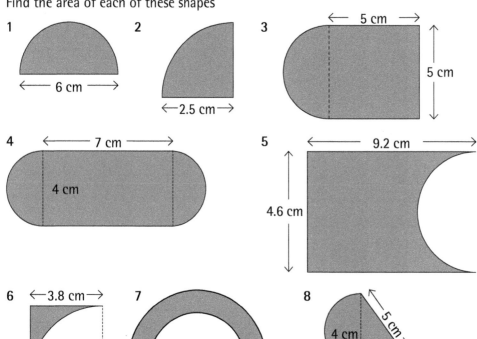

1   6 cm

2   2.5 cm

3   5 cm   5 cm

4   7 cm   4 cm

5   9.2 cm   4.6 cm

6   3.8 cm

7   5 cm   1.5 cm   1.5 cm

8   4 cm   5 cm   3 cm

9 The following shape is made up of a semicircle with a diameter of 10 cm, and a quarter circle with a radius of 3 cm.

Find (a) the area
    (b) the perimeter.

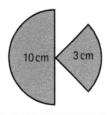

Sectors and arcs

A **sector** is part of a circle formed by drawing two radii. The distance along the circumference between the points where the radii meet the circumference is the **arc** length.

The diagram shows two sectors. The smaller one is called the **minor sector** and the larger one the **major sector**.

The length of the arc of the smaller sector is called the **minor arc** and the length of the larger one is called the **major arc**.

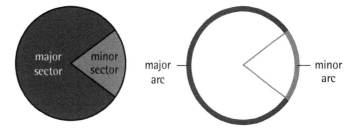

A sector is a fraction of the whole circle. The arc length and the sector area both depend on the size of the angle at the centre of the circle.

If the angle at the centre of the circle is θ, the arc length and the sector area are calculated as follows

$$\text{Arc length} = \frac{\theta}{360} \times \text{circumference} = \frac{\theta}{360} \times 2\pi r$$

$$\text{Sector area} = \frac{\theta}{360} \times \text{area of whole circle} = \frac{\theta}{360} \times \pi r^2$$

EXAMPLE 7

Find the arc length and area of a sector of a circle of radius 6 cm if the angle of the sector is 75°.

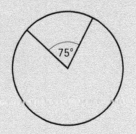

$$\text{Arc length} = \frac{75}{360} \times 2 \times \pi \times 6$$
$$= 7.85 \text{ cm (3 s.f.)}$$
$$\text{Sector area} = \frac{75}{360} \times \pi \times 6^2$$
$$= 23.5619\ldots$$
$$= 23.6 \text{ cm}^2 \text{ (3 s.f.)}$$

EXAMPLE 8

The length of the minor arc of a circle is 3π cm and the length of the major arc is 15π cm.

Find **(a)** the radius of the circle
      (b) the angle of the minor sector
      (c) the area of the minor sector, giving your answer in terms of π.

(a) The total circumference

$$= 3\pi + 15\pi = 18\pi$$

So $18\pi = 2 \times \pi \times r$

$$r = 9 \text{ cm}$$

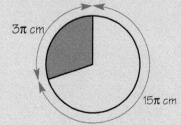

(b) Angle at centre $= \dfrac{\text{length of minor arc}}{\text{total circumference}} \times 360°$

$$= \frac{3\pi}{18\pi} \times 360°$$

$$= \frac{1}{6} \times 360° = 60°$$

(c) Area of minor sector $= \dfrac{1}{6} \times \pi \times 9^2$

$$= \frac{81}{6}\pi = 13.5\pi \text{ cm}^2$$

The question could have simply asked for the area of the minor sector, with none of the structure seen here.

You would then have to find an appropriate method.

EXERCISE 5D

1 Find the arc length of the following sectors.

(a)

6 cm

40°

(b)

8 cm

45°

(c)

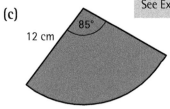

12 cm

85°

See Example 7.

2 Find the perimeter of the following sectors.

(a)

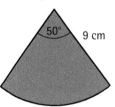

2 cm

30°

(b)

50° 9 cm

(c)

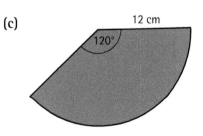

12 cm

120°

3 Calculate the perimeter of the following shapes.

(a) (b)

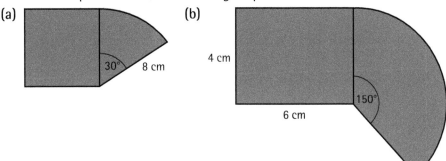

4 Find the area of the following sectors.

(a) (b) (c)

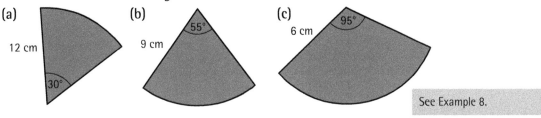

See Example 8.

5 Find the shaded area.

(a) (b)

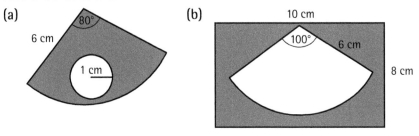

5.3 Three-dimensional shapes

Planes of symmetry

You can draw 3-D objects on squared paper.

Here are three diagrams of a cuboid. In each one you can see a **plane of symmetry** (shaded red).

A plane of symmetry divides a 3-D object into two equal halves, where one half is the mirror image of the other.

It is the 3-D equivalent of a line of symmetry.

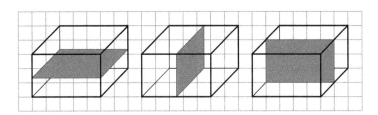

EXAMPLE 9

Copy this 3-D object on squared paper.
Show all its planes of symmetry.
Draw a separate diagram for each plane
of symmetry.

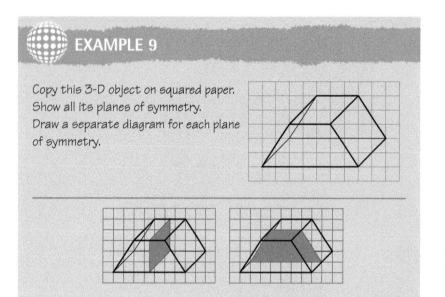

This object has two planes of
symmetry. If you made a horizontal
cut, the top 'half' would be smaller
than the bottom 'half', so the cut
would *not* be a plane of symmetry.

EXERCISE 5E

Copy these 3-D objects on squared paper.

Show all their planes of symmetry.

Draw a separate diagram for each plane of symmetry.

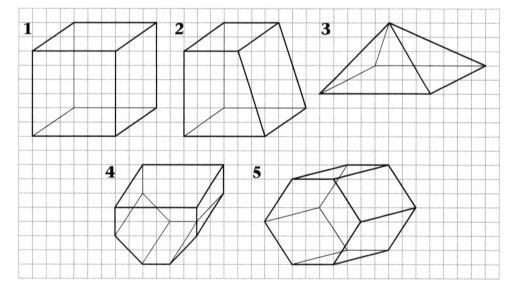

5.4 Volume

Prisms

A prism is a 3-D shape with a uniform **cross-section**.

The cross-sectional area is the area of the end of the shape which runs throughout its length.

In these examples of prisms, the area of the cross-section is shaded.

To find the volume of a prism, multiply the cross-sectional area by the length of the prism.

Volume = area of cross-section × length

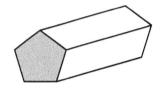

Cuboids

A cuboid is an example of a prism.
Volume = area of cross-section × length
= $wh \times l$
= whl

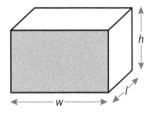

Cubes

A cube is a special case of a cuboid.
All its sides are the same length, x.
Volume of cube = x^3.

EXAMPLE 10

Find the volume of this prism.
All lengths are given in cm.

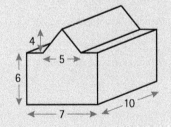

The area of the end of the prism must be found first. Split it up into a rectangle and a triangle, as shown.

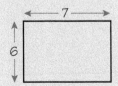

Area of rectangle = $7 \times 6 = 42$
Area of triangle = $\frac{1}{2} \times 5 \times 4 = 10$
Area of cross-section = $42 + 10 = 52$
Volume of prism = $52 \text{ cm}^2 \times 10 \text{ cm} = 520 \text{ cm}^3$

Find the volume of the following prisms.

1

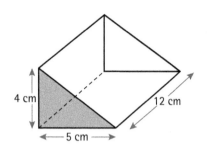

2

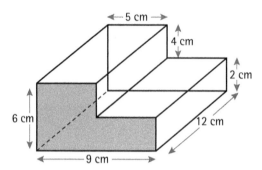

3

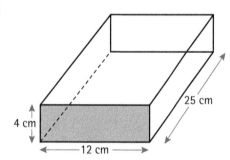

4   Find the volume of the following prisms. All measurements are in centimetres.

(a)

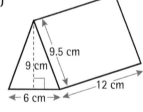

(b)

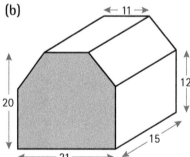

5   The skip shown is to be used to remove a rectangular mound of soil 6 m by 4 m by 2 m. How many times will it have to be emptied to remove all the soil from the site?

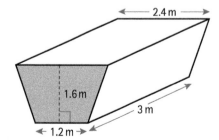

Cylinders

A cylinder is a prism whose cross-section is a circle.

Volume of a cylinder = area of cross-section × height

$$V = \pi r^2 h$$

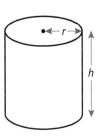

 EXAMPLE 11

A thin cylindrical tube is 2 metres long and has a diameter of 4.6 cm.
Calculate its volume.

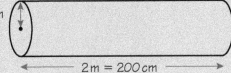

r = 2.3 cm

2 m = 200 cm

Always sketch a diagram to help you answer the question.

Diameter = 4.6 cm   so   Radius = 2.3 cm

Volume = $\pi r^2 h$
= $\pi \times (2.3)^2 \times 200$
= 3323.805 ... cm³
= 3320 cm³

Beware! You have mixed units and they need to be the same. It is best to work in centimetres here.

Use the π button on the calculator.

 EXAMPLE 12

A cylindrical container holds 8.5 litres of liquid when full.
The height of the container is 24 cm.
Calculate the radius of the base.

8.5 litres = 8.5 × 1000 cm³
= 8500 cm³

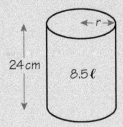

Volume = $\pi r^2 h$
8500 = $\pi \times r^2 \times 24$
$\dfrac{8500}{\pi \times 24} = r^2$
112.73... = r^2
$\sqrt{112.73...} = r$
Radius = 10.6 cm (3 s.f.)

24 cm   8.5 ℓ

You must convert litres into cm³ since the height is given in cm.

1 Find the volume of the following cylinders.

(a)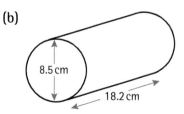

4 cm
2 cm

(b)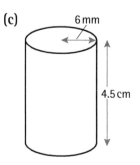

8.5 cm
18.2 cm

Take care with units.

(c) 6 mm

4.5 cm

2 The tube shown has an outside diameter of 27.6 cm, an inside diameter of 19.6 cm and is 45 cm long.

(a) Find its volume.

(b) It is made out of metal where 1 cm³ has a mass of 8.4 g. What is its mass?

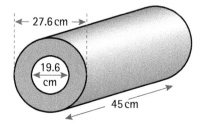

27.6 cm
19.6 cm
45 cm

Pyramids and cones

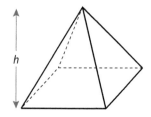

h

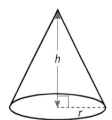

h
r

The volume of a cone or a pyramid is given by the formula

$$\text{Volume} = \tfrac{1}{3} \times \text{area of base} \times \textbf{perpendicular height}$$

So for a cone of base radius r and perpendicular height h,

$$\text{Volume} = \tfrac{1}{3}\pi r^2 h$$

EXAMPLE 13

Calculate the volume of this pyramid which has a square base of side 10 cm and a perpendicular height of 15 cm.

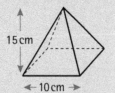

15 cm

10 cm

Volume = $\frac{1}{3}$ × area of base × perpendicular height
$= \frac{1}{3}$ × 10 × 10 × 15
= 10 × 10 × 5
= 500 cm³

 EXAMPLE 14

A cone has a volume of 200 cm³.
The radius of the base is 4 cm.
Calculate the perpendicular height of the cone.

Volume = $\frac{1}{3}\pi r^2 h$
$200 = \frac{1}{3}\pi \times 4^2 \times h$
$\dfrac{200 \times 3}{\pi \times 4^2} = h$

Height of cone = 11.9 cm (3 s.f.)

 EXERCISE 5H

1 Find the volume of the following objects.

(a)
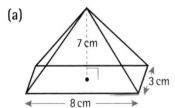
7 cm
3 cm
8 cm

(b)
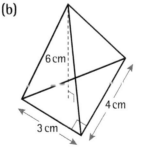
6 cm
3 cm
4 cm

(c)
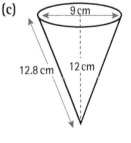
9 cm
12.8 cm
12 cm

2 A square-based pyramid has a perpendicular height of 7 cm and a volume of 84 cm³. What is the length of a side of the base?

Spheres

The volume of a sphere of radius r is given by the formula

$$\text{Volume} = \tfrac{4}{3}\pi r^3$$

 EXAMPLE 15

A sphere has a radius of 9 cm. Calculate its volume.

$$
\begin{aligned}
\text{Volume} &= \tfrac{4}{3}\pi\, r^3 \\
&= \tfrac{4}{3} \times \pi \times 9^3 \quad cm^3 \\
&= \tfrac{4}{3} \times \pi \times 729 \quad cm^3 \\
&= 3050 \ cm^3 \ (3 \ s.f.)
\end{aligned}
$$

 EXERCISE 5I

1 Find the volume of spheres with
   (a) radius 12 cm   (b) diameter 45.2 cm.

2 A hemisphere of clay with a radius of 16 cm is remodelled into a cylindrical pipe.

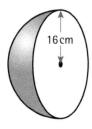

16 cm

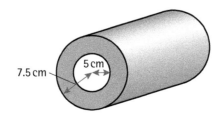

7.5 cm

5 cm

If the outer radius of the pipe is 7.5 cm and the inner radius is 5 cm, how long is the pipe if all the clay is used?

5.5 Surface area

Prisms

The surface area of a prism is found by adding the areas of all its faces.

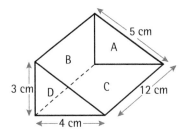

Area of triangle A $= \frac{1}{2} \times 3 \times 4 = 6$ cm²
Area of rectangle B $= 3 \times 12 = 36$ cm²
Area of rectangle C $= 4 \times 12 = 48$ cm²
Area of sloping face $= 5 \times 12 = 60$ cm²
Area of triangle D $= \frac{1}{2} \times 3 \times 4 = 6$ cm²

Total surface area $= 156$ cm²

EXERCISE 5J

Find the surface area of the following prisms.

1
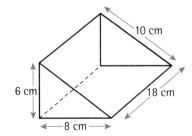

2
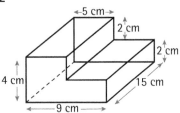

3
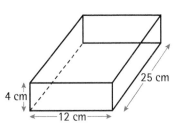

4
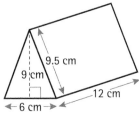

5
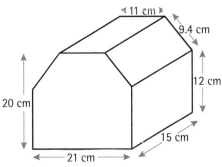

6
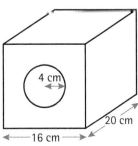

Cylinders

The **curved surface area** = circumference of base × height

$$csa = 2\pi rh$$

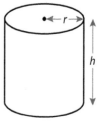

The **total surface area** of a solid cylinder is the curved surface area plus the two ends.

total surface area $= 2\pi rh + 2\pi r^2$

EXAMPLE 16

A solid cylinder is 2 metres long and has a radius of 2.3 cm. Calculate its total surface area.

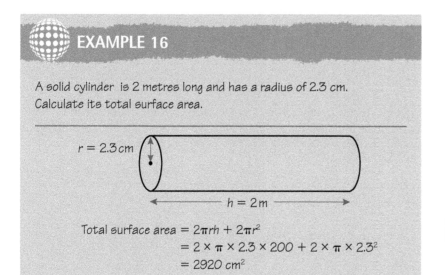

$r = 2.3$ cm

$h = 2$ m

Total surface area $= 2\pi rh + 2\pi r^2$
$= 2 \times \pi \times 2.3 \times 200 + 2 \times \pi \times 2.3^2$
$= 2920$ cm^2

units   2 m = 200 cm

EXERCISE 5K

Find the total surface area of the following cylinders.

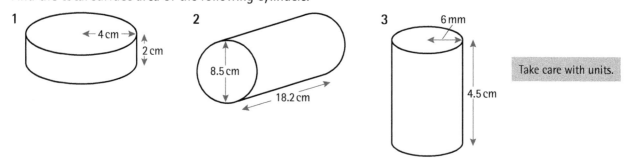

1   4 cm   2 cm

2   8.5 cm   18.2 cm

3   6 mm   4.5 cm

Take care with units.

Pyramids

The surface area of a pyramid with a base which is a square, a rectangle, a triangle or any polygon is found by adding together the areas of all the faces.

Cones

The surface area of a cone is slightly different since the cone is made up of a flat, circular base and a curved surface.

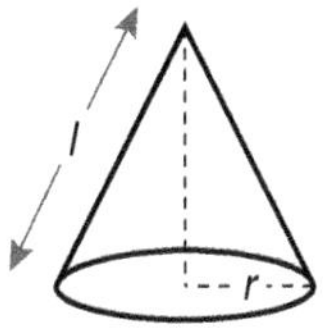

The area of the curved surface of the cone is given by the formula

Curved surface area $= \pi \times$ radius of base $\times$ **slant height**
$= \pi r l$

where r is the radius of the base of the cone and l is the slant height of the cone.

So, the **total** surface area of a cone

$= $ area of base $+$ curved surface area
$= \pi r^2 + \pi r l$
$= \pi r(r + l)$

There is more about cones in Chapter 17.

It is quicker to use this factorised version.

Spheres

The surface area of a sphere of radius r is given by the formula

$$S = 4\pi r^2$$

EXAMPLE 17

A sphere has a radius of 9 cm. Calculate its surface area.

Surface area $= 4\pi r^2$
$= 4 \times \pi \times 9^2$
$= 1020\ \text{cm}^2$

EXERCISE 5L

1 Calculate the surface area of a sphere of radius 3.4 m.

2 A sphere has surface area 548 m^2. Find the radius, giving your answer correct to 3 s.f.

1   On television a weather forecaster used a cloud symbol shown in the diagram.
    Its perimeter consists of a straight line *AE*, two semicircular arcs *APB* and *DQE* and the
    major arc *BRD* of a circle centre *C*.
    AE = 7.5 cm, *AB* = *DE* = 3 cm and *BC* = *CD* = 2.8 cm.
    Angle *BAE* = angle *DEA* = 70° and *X* is the midpoint of *BD*.
    [For π, use either your calculator value or 3.142.]

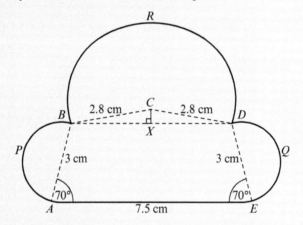

NOT TO SCALE

(a) (i)   Use the trapezium *ABDE* to show that *BX* = 2.724 cm.   [4]
    (ii) Calculate the angle *BCX*.   [2]
(b) Calculate
    (i)   the area of triangle *BCD*,   [3]
    (ii) the area of the trapezium *ABDE*,   [4]
    (iii) the area of the major sector *BCD*,   [3]
    (iv) the total area of the cloud symbol.   [3]

(CIE Paper 4, Nov 2000)

---

2   (a) Calculate the area of a sector of a circle which has an angle of 40° and a radius of 6 cm. [2]
    (b) A brooch is in the shape of a sector of a circle with 4 small identical circular holes.

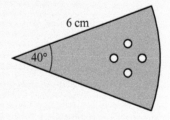

NOT TO SCALE

    The radius of each hole is 0.3 cm. Calculate
    (i)   the area of **one** hole,   [1]
    (ii) the area of the brooch, which is shaded in the diagram above.   [1]

(CIE Paper 2, Jun 2001)

3

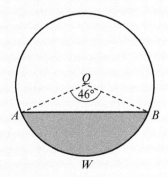

NOT TO SCALE

The diagram shows the circular cross-section of a horizontal pipe.
The shaded area shows water lying in the pipe.
The circle, centre O, has a radius 63.7 cm and angle $AOB = 46°$.
(a) Calculate the arc length AWB.   [3]
(b) Calculate the length of the straight line AB.   [3]
(c) Calculate the length of the perpendicular from O to AB.   [2]
(d) Write down the greatest depth of water in the pipe.
Give your answer correct to the nearest millimetre.   [2]

(CIE Paper 4, Nov 2001)

4 **(a)** A sector of a circle, radius 6 cm, has an angle of 20°.

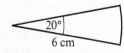

NOT TO SCALE

Calculate (i)   the area of the sector,   [2]
(ii) the arc length of the sector.   [2]

(b)

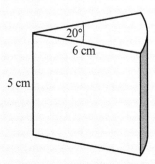

NOT TO SCALE

A whole cheese is a cylinder, radius 6 cm and height 5 cm.
The diagram shows a slice of this cheese with sector angle 20°.
Calculate
(i) the volume of the slice of cheese,   [2]
(ii) the **total** surface area of the slice of cheese.   [4]

(CIE Paper 4, Jun 2002)

5

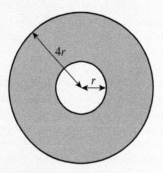

NOT TO SCALE

Two circles have radii r cm and $4r$ cm.

Find, in terms of π and r,

(a) the area of the circle radius $4r$ cm, [1]

(b) the area of the shaded ring, [1]

(c) the total length of the inner and outer edges of the shaded ring. [2]

(CIE Paper 2, Jun 2002)

6

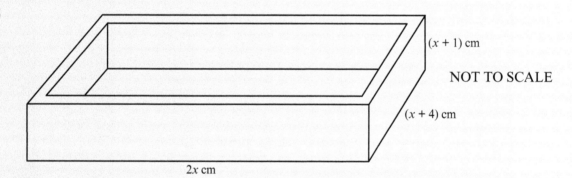

$(x + 1)$ cm

NOT TO SCALE

$(x + 4)$ cm

$2x$ cm

A rectangular-based **open** box has **external** dimensions of $2x$ cm, $(x + 4)$ cm and $(x + 1)$ cm.

(a) (i) Write down the volume of a cuboid with these dimensions. [1]

    (ii) Expand and simplify your answer. [1]

(b) The box is made from wood 1 cm thick.

    (i) Write down the **internal** dimensions of the box in terms of x. [3]

    (ii) Find the volume of the inside of the box and show that the volume of
    the wood is $8x^2 + 12x$ cubic centimetres. [3]

(CIE Paper 4, Jun 2003)

7

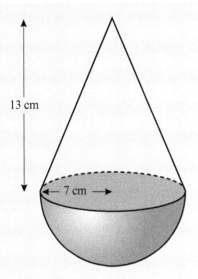

13 cm

7 cm

NOT TO SCALE

The diagram shows a solid made up of a hemisphere and a cone.
The base radius of the cone and the radius of the hemisphere are each 7 cm.
The height of the cone is 13 cm.

(a) (i) Calculate the total volume of the solid.
[The volume of a hemisphere of radius r is given by $V = \frac{2}{3}\pi r^3$.]
[The volume of a cone of radius r and height h is given by $V = \frac{1}{3}\pi r^2 h$.]   [2]
   (ii) The solid is made of wood and 1 cm^3 of this wood has a mass of 0.94 g.
Calculate the mass of the solid, in kilograms, correct to 1 decimal place.   [3]
(b) Calculate the curved surface area of the cone.
[The curved surface area of a cone of radius r and sloping edge l is given by $\pi r l$]   [3]
(c) The cost of covering all the solid with gold plate is $411.58.
Calculate the cost of this gold plate per square centimetre.
[The curved surface area of a **hemisphere** is given by $A = 2\pi r^2$.]   [5]

(CIE Paper 4, Jun 2004)

Chapter 6

Collecting and presenting data

This chapter will show you how to

✔ identify different types of data
✔ construct frequency tables for discrete and grouped data
✔ design and use two-way tables for discrete and grouped data
✔ draw bar charts and line graphs
✔ construct frequency diagrams

6.1 Types of data

Primary data is information you collect directly yourself, for example from questionnaires.

Secondary data is information that you get from existing records, for example newspapers, magazines, the internet.

Qualitative data contains descriptive words, for example a colour (red, green), or an activity (climbing, sailing), or a location (London, Paris). It is sometimes called categorical data.

Quantitative data contains numbers, such as temperatures, masses, areas, lengths, time, number of TVs or cars.

There are two types of quantitative data.

1   **Discrete data** can only have exact values.

Discrete data is 'countable'.
Discrete data examples

● Scores on a dice   4, 2, 6 •————————— '8' is not possible.
● Goals scored in a match   0, 2, 3 •————————— You can't score $2\frac{1}{2}$ goals!

2 **Continuous data** can take any value in a particular range.

Continuous data examples
- Mass   72 kg, 15.3 g
- Temperature   −4°C, 25°C, 100°C
- Length   800 m, 300 000 km, 2.6 mm

2.6 mm is measured to the nearest tenth of a millimetre.

Continuous data cannot be measured exactly. The accuracy depends on the measuring instrument, for example, ruler or thermometer, and the values are often approximate.

EXERCISE 6A

1 State whether each of the following sets of data are quantitative or qualitative.

    (a) Height   (b) Age

    (c) Eye colour   (d) Place of birth

    (e) Distance between home and school

    (f) Time spent travelling to work

2 State which of the following sets of data are discrete and which are continuous.

    (a) Cost   (b) Population   (c) Time

    (d) Weight   (e) Area   (f) IQ score

3 State whether each source will give primary or secondary data.

    (a) Collecting data from a traffic survey

    (b) Downloading data from the internet

    (c) Using data from a population survey

    (d) Using data found in a newspaper

    (e) Giving people a questionnaire

6.2 Data collection

You will need to know
- how to record and count data using tally marks
- what the frequency represents

When you have a large amount of data, start by organising it in a table. Use a **tally chart** to record each piece of data. Find the **frequency** (how often something occurs) by adding together the tally marks.

The complete table showing the tally marks and the frequency is called a **frequency table** in some textbooks or **frequency distribution**.

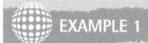

EXAMPLE 1

Here is the list of vowels in the first four sentences of a book.
Construct a frequency table for this data.

i, a, o, e, a, i, i, e, i, i, o, a, i, a, a, e, a, a, i, e
e, a, i, o, e, i, i, o, a, i, a, a, i, e, o, i, a, i, a, a
i, i, i, i, e, a, e, u, o, o, e, i, a, u, i, e, e, o, o, e
e, u, e, e, a, a, i, a, u, i, e, a, u, i, e

Vowel	Tally	Frequency
a	⦀⦀ ⦀⦀ ⦀⦀ ⦀⦀	20
e	⦀⦀ ⦀⦀ ⦀⦀ |||	18
i	⦀⦀ ⦀⦀ ⦀⦀ ⦀⦀ |||	23
o	⦀⦀ ||||	9
u	⦀⦀	5

The letters a, e, i, o and u are vowels.

To see how often each vowel occurs, put the results into a tally chart like this.

Group the tally marks into sets of five by drawing the fifth line through the previous four.

Seven looks like ⦀⦀ || rather than |||||||.

Class intervals

When you are dealing with continuous data that is widely spread, you can group the results together in regular intervals called classes or **class intervals**.

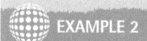

EXAMPLE 2

The heights of 31 pupils in a Year 10 class were measured to the nearest centimetre.

161, 153, 168, 171, 143, 161, 165, 156, 147, 158
161, 160, 180, 173, 149, 155, 164, 167, 173, 159
151, 163, 162, 174, 166, 157, 170, 161, 156, 181
168

Put these heights into a tally chart using class intervals of 140–149 cm, 150–159 cm, etc.

Height (cm)	Tally	Frequency
140–149	|||	3
150–159	⦀⦀ |||	8
160–169	⦀⦀ ⦀⦀ |||	13
170–179	⦀⦀	5
180–189	||	2
	Total	31

When data is grouped like this in a class interval, you need to remember that information about the individual heights is lost.

Check the total in the frequency column is the same as the original number of values in the actual data list.

Class intervals are groupings of quantitative data. When you group data, you should use between five and ten class intervals.

Class intervals are usually of equal widths.

You can also write class intervals using the symbols $<$ for 'less than' and $\leqslant$ for 'less than or equal to'. For example, the data from Example 2 could be shown as in the table below.

Height h (cm)	Tally	Frequency
$140 \leqslant h < 150$	|||	3
$150 \leqslant h < 160$	$\cancel{||||}$ |||	8
$160 \leqslant h < 170$	$\cancel{||||}$ $\cancel{||||}$ |||	13
$170 \leqslant h < 180$	$\cancel{||||}$	5
$180 \leqslant h < 190$	||	2
	Total	31

Let h be the symbol for the height in cm.

The first class interval $140 \leqslant h < 150$ includes any height greater than or equal to 140 cm but less than 150 cm. It does not include 150 cm.

Data-capture sheets

A pre-prepared table like the one shown in Example 2 is called a **data-capture sheet**. These are useful for collecting and ordering data before choosing how to present your results.

 **EXERCISE 6B**

1 The list below shows the marks gained by 29 pupils in a test.

```
22  27  18  23  25  19  17  20
23  20  18  22  20  19  24  21
16  19  18  22  14  19  18  21
20  19  25  25  21
```

Copy and complete the frequency table below.

Mark	Tally	Frequency
1–10		
11–20		
21–30		
	Total	29

2 The masses of twenty students in the sixth form were recorded.

```
46 kg  55 kg  53 kg  75 kg  62 kg
59 kg  84 kg  63 kg  68 kg  74 kg
78 kg  60 kg  57 kg  61 kg  48 kg
81 kg  73 kg  67 kg  64 kg  77 kg
```

Copy and complete the frequency table below using five equal class intervals.

Mass m (kg)	Tally	Frequency
$40 \leqslant m < 50$		
$80 \leqslant m < 90$		
	Total	20

3 During a school cross-country run the following times were recorded (rounded to the nearest minute).

```
15   18   23   27   17   21   24   19   20   28
33   26   24   19   23   28   25   19   17   31
38   24   28   21   24   26   26   19   18   27
17   26   21   23   26   19   18   26   24   27
26   16   24   28   29   19   18   33   23   29
```

Construct a grouped frequency table showing the tally marks and frequencies and using class intervals 10–14, 15–19, 20–24, 25–29, 30–34, 35–40.

4 These amounts of money were collected for a charity.

```
$86   $89   $51   $61   $11   $56   $82   $87   $4    $89
$43   $93   $31   $20   $61   $3          $65   $3    $56   $84
$38   $80   $42   $64   $66   $22   $3    $34
```

Construct a frequency table using five equal class intervals beginning with $0 \leqslant m < 20$, where m means the amount of money collected in dollars.

5 Construct a data-capture sheet for throwing a six-sided fair dice. The sheet should include headings for tally marks and frequency.

6 A traffic survey is being conducted on the colours of cars passing a road junction. Construct a data-capture sheet to record this data.

6.3 Two-way tables

Two-way tables are similar to frequency tables but show two or more types of information at the same time.

Bus timetables, league tables, school performance tables and holiday brochure prices are often two-way tables.

EXAMPLE 3

In a survey of 32 pupils, 6 girls walked to school, 10 boys went by bus, and 4 boys cycled. Of the remaining 11 girls, only 1 cycled to school. No-one travelled by any other method.

(a) Draw a two-way table to show this information.

(b) Complete the table and find
   (i) how many girls went by bus?
   (ii) how many pupils walked to school?

(a)

	Walked	Cycled	Bus	Total
Boys		4	10	
Girls	6	1		17
Total				32

6 girls walked and there were 11 remaining
6 + 11 = 17

The total number of boys is
32 − 17 = 15.

(b)

	Walked	Cycled	Bus	Total
Boys	1	4	10	15
Girls	6	1	10	17
Total	7	5	20	32

The number of boys that walked is
15 − (4 + 10) = 1.

The number of girls who came to school by bus is
17 − (6 + 1) = 10.

(i) 10 girls went by bus.
(ii) 7 pupils walked to school.

Check the totals are correct
7 + 5 + 20 = 32.

The total number who walked, cycled and came by bus can now be completed.

 EXAMPLE 4

The following two-way table shows the heights of pupils in five Year 11 classes.

Height h (cm)	Frequency				
	11A	11B	11C	11D	11E
$140 \leqslant h < 150$	3	6	4	5	4
$150 \leqslant h < 160$	6	5	7	5	6
$160 \leqslant h < 170$	10	9	11	8	12
$170 \leqslant h < 180$	7	6	4	9	5
$180 \leqslant h < 190$	4	5	4	3	5

This is an example of a two-way table using continuous data for the height column.

The intervals can be either $140 < x \leqslant 150$ or $140 \leqslant x < 150$. Either of these may be used in the examination.
You must check to see which one is being used.
In the first one 150 is included in the interval but 140 is not.
In the second one 140 is included in the interval but 150 is not.

(a) How many pupils are taller than or equal to 180 cm?

(b) How many pupils are in class 11C?

(c) How many pupils took part in the survey?

(d) What percentage of pupils are taller than or equal to 160 cm but less than 180 cm? (Give your answer to the nearest whole number.)

continued ▼

Height h (cm)	Frequency					
	11A	11B	11C	11D	11E	Total
$140 \leqslant h < 150$	3	6	4	5	4	22
$150 \leqslant h < 160$	6	5	7	5	6	29
$160 \leqslant h < 170$	10	9	11	8	12	50
$170 \leqslant h < 180$	7	6	4	9	5	31
$180 \leqslant h < 190$	4	5	4	3	5	21
Totals	30	31	30	30	32	153

Find the totals across and down by adding more columns and rows to the table. The final total in the bottom right-hand corner should be the same by adding the final row and final column.

(a) 21 pupils taller than or equal to 180 cm.

(b) 30 pupils in 11C.

(c) 153 pupils took part.

(d) $\dfrac{(50 + 31)}{153} \times 100 = 53\%$.

 EXAMPLE 5

The table below shows part of a holiday brochure giving the cost of a fly–drive holiday. The prices shown are per person in dollars.

Group	Number of days						Extra night
	2	3	4	5	6	7	
5/6 adults sharing	170	178	185	190	193	196	25
4 adults sharing	173	184	190	197	199	205	25
3 adults sharing	179	192	202	213	220	227	25
2 adults sharing	179	192	202	213	220	227	25
Child	148	148	148	148	148	148	25

(a) Find the cost of a 3-day holiday for 4 adults and 3 children.

(b) What is the cost of a fly–drive holiday for 2 adults and 2 children for 10 days?

(a) A 3-day holiday for 4 adults costs 4 × $184 = $736
   For 3 children costs 3 × $148 = $444
   Total cost of the holiday = $736 + $444 = $1180

(b) 2 adults for 10 days = (2 × $227) + (2 × 3 × $25) = $604
   2 children for 10 days = (2 × $148) + (2 × 3 × $25) = $446
   Total cost of holiday = $604 + $446 = $1050

Use the figures in the '3 days' column. Read the rows for 4 adults and 1 child and don't forget to multiply by 3.

Work out the cost for 7 days then add on 3 extra nights. Read the rows for 2 adults and 1 child. Multiply the cost for 1 child by 2.

EXERCISE 6C

1 In a school survey of 50 boys and 50 girls, 41 boys were right-handed and only 6 girls were left-handed. Copy the two-way table below and complete it to show this information. Use the table to work out an estimate of the percentage of pupils in the school who are left-handed.

	Left-handed	Right-handed	Total
Girls	6		
Boys			
Total			

2 In the 2001 population survey, the male population of Poynton (Central) was 3522 and the number of females in Poynton (West and East) was 3898. The population of Poynton (Central) was 6792 and the total population of Poynton was 13 433.
Construct a two-way table to show this information.
Complete the table.
What is the total percentage of females in Poynton?
(Give your answer to the nearest whole number.)

3 The following table gives the English results for a school.

		Level					
		3	4	5	6	7	8
English	Boys	11	28	34	31	15	1
	Girls	4	20	36	43	22	5

(a) Copy the table and extend it to find the totals in each row and each column.

(b) How many pupils took the test?

(c) What percentage of boys achieved a level 5 or higher?
Give your answer to 1 d.p.

(d) What percentage of girls achieved a level 7?
Give your answer to 1 d.p.

4 The table shows the distances (in km) between some French cities.

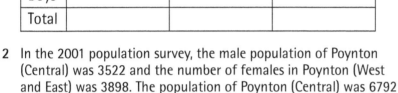

Bordeaux
870	Calais					
658	855	Grenoble				
649	1067	282	Marseille			
804	1222	334	188	Nice		
579	292	565	776	931	Paris	
244	996	536	405	560	706	Toulouse

The distance between Calais and Paris is 292km.

Find

(a) the distance between Bordeaux and Marseille

(b) the distance between Toulouse and Grenoble

(c) the total distance travelled from Paris to Calais to Bordeaux and back to Paris.

5 Using the two-way table in Example 5 on page 90, find the cost of

(a) a 5-day holiday for 3 adults and 4 children

(b) an 8-day holiday for 6 adults and no children.

6 In a local fun-run event the following results were recorded by all the competitors. Times are given to the nearest minute.

Age a (years)	Time t (minutes)			
	$0 \leqslant t < 10$	$10 \leqslant t < 20$	$20 \leqslant t < 30$	$30 \leqslant t < 40$
$5 \leqslant a < 10$	0	1	12	36
$10 \leqslant a < 15$	2	46	59	27
$15 \leqslant a < 20$	7	65	37	13

This is an example of a two-way table using continuous data for both the columns and the rows.

(a) How many runners finished in under 20 minutes?

(b) How many runners were aged 15 years or over?

(c) How many runners took part in the fun-run altogether?

(d) What percentage of runners completed the course in under 10 minutes? Give your answer to the nearest whole number.

6.4 Frequency diagrams

For grouped, continuous data you will need to draw a frequency diagram similar to a bar chart, but with no gaps between the bars and a scale on both axes.

EXAMPLE 6

Draw a frequency diagram to show the heights of 31 sunflowers.

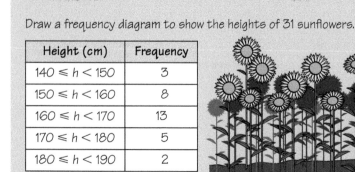

Height (cm)	Frequency
$140 \leqslant h < 150$	3
$150 \leqslant h < 160$	8
$160 \leqslant h < 170$	13
$170 \leqslant h < 180$	5
$180 \leqslant h < 190$	2

continued ▼

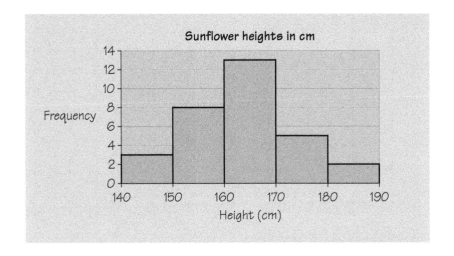

For continuous data there are no gaps between the bars.

The width of each bar is the same as the class interval.

The horizontal axis must have a continuous scale.

EXERCISE 6D

1 The following frequency table shows the results of a school survey into the most popular flavoured drinks.

   (a) Draw a bar chart to display this data.

   (b) How many students took part in this survey?

Flavour	Frequency
Cola	12
Lemon	16
Orange	33
Mango	13
Lime	26

2 The number of newspapers sold in a small shop in one day is shown in the table.

   (a) How many newspapers did the shop sell that day?

   (b) Draw a bar chart to show this data.

   (c) What percentage of the newspapers sold were the Daily Times?

Newspaper	Frequency
Daily Planet	17
Daily Times	35
Daily Echo	26
Daily Herald	47
Daily News	75

3 A carpenter sorts a box of mixed nails into nails of different lengths (l)

   (a) How many nails were in the box?

   (b) What percentage of the nails were of length $2 < l \leqslant 3$?

   (c) Draw a frequency diagram to show this data.

Length l (cm)	Frequency
$0 < l \leqslant 1$	18
$1 < l \leqslant 2$	47
$2 < l \leqslant 3$	12
$3 < l \leqslant 4$	21
$4 < l \leqslant 5$	22

4 The table shows the results of a survey on the width of students' hand-spans, w (in cm).

Hand span (cm)	Frequency
$15 < w \leqslant 17$	4
$17 < w \leqslant 19$	6
$19 < w \leqslant 21$	12
$21 < w \leqslant 23$	7
$23 < w \leqslant 25$	3

Draw a frequency diagram to show this information.

5 Draw a frequency diagram to show the following information.

Length, x (cm)	Frequency
$0 < x \leqslant 5$	6
$5 < x \leqslant 10$	11
$10 < x \leqslant 15$	8
$15 < x \leqslant 20$	5

6 The table gives the age range of the members of a local sports centre.

Draw a frequency diagram to show the spread of ages.

Age	Frequency
$0 \leqslant$ age < 10	23
$10 \leqslant$ age < 20	45
$20 \leqslant$ age < 30	56
$30 \leqslant$ age < 40	36
$40 \leqslant$ age < 50	49
$50 \leqslant$ age < 60	32
$60 \leqslant$ age < 70	16

6.5 Histograms

Data that is grouped and continuous can be displayed as a **histogram**.

- As the data is continuous there are no gaps between the bars.

- The bars can be different widths (to represent different **class intervals**).

- The *areas* of the bars are proportional to the frequencies they represent.

- The vertical axis shows the **frequency density**.

- The horizontal axis must be a continuous scale.

The frequency density is given by

$$\text{frequency density} = \frac{\text{frequency}}{\text{class interval}}.$$

> The class interval is the difference between the two ends points of the data. The class interval is also called the class width.

The shape of a histogram gives a measure of how the data is distributed or spread.

EXAMPLE 7

Construct a histogram for this data on the heights of students in a survey.

Height (cm)	Frequency
$155 \leqslant h < 160$	2
$160 \leqslant h < 165$	6
$165 \leqslant h < 170$	14
$170 \leqslant h < 175$	19
$175 \leqslant h < 180$	8
$180 \leqslant h < 185$	1

The class interval for $155 \leqslant h < 160$ is $160 - 155 = 5$.

Height (cm)	Frequency	Frequency density
$155 \leqslant h < 160$	2	$2 \div 5 = 0.4$
$160 \leqslant h < 165$	6	$6 \div 5 = 1.2$
$165 \leqslant h < 170$	14	$14 \div 5 = 2.8$
$170 \leqslant h < 175$	19	$19 \div 5 = 3.8$
$175 \leqslant h < 180$	8	$8 \div 5 = 1.6$
$180 \leqslant h < 185$	1	$1 \div 5 = 0.2$

Extend the table by including a column for calculating frequency density.

The class intervals are all 5.

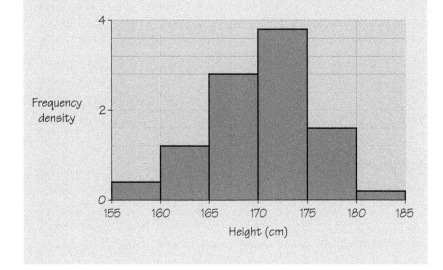

The data is continuous, so there are no gaps between the bars.

Since the class intervals are all equal, the heights, as well as the areas, of the bars are proportional to the frequency.

EXAMPLE 8

The masses of tomatoes in a mixed bag are given in the following frequency table.

Draw a histogram for this data.

Mass m (grams)	Frequency
10 ≤ m < 20	10
20 ≤ m < 25	15
25 ≤ m < 30	12
30 ≤ m < 40	42
40 ≤ m < 60	50
60 ≤ m < 90	27

Mass m (grams)	Frequency	Class interval (grams)	Frequency density
10 ≤ m < 20	10	10	10/10 = 1.0
20 ≤ m < 25	15	5	15/5 = 3.0
25 ≤ m < 30	12	5	12/5 = 2.4
30 ≤ m < 40	42	10	42/10 = 4.2
40 ≤ m < 60	50	20	50/20 = 2.5
60 ≤ m < 90	27	30	27/30 = 0.9

In this example, the class intervals are *not* equal. Extend the table to include the class interval. This helps reduce errors in calculating the frequency density.

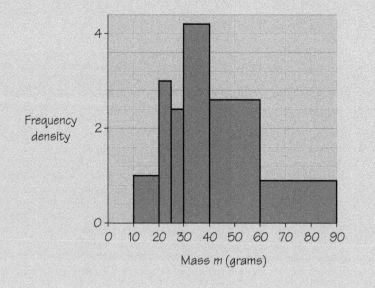

In this example, the **area** of each rectangle represents the frequency.

EXERCISE 6E

1   The frequency table below shows the salary structure for a small company. Use this information to draw a histogram.

Salary, s ($)	Frequency
5000 ⩽ s < 10 000	2
10 000 ⩽ s < 18 000	4
18 000 ⩽ s < 24 000	2
24 000 ⩽ s < 35 000	6
35 000 ⩽ s < 50 000	1

2   In a fishing competition the total catches for each angler were recorded as shown in the frequency table below.

Catch (kg)	Frequency
0 to less than 0.5	2
0.5 to less than 0.9	6
0.9 to less than 1.5	4
1.5 to less than 2.2	1
2.2 to less than 2.9	4
2.9 to less than 3.8	2
3.8 to less than 5.4	1

Draw a histogram to display this data.

3   The age structure for members of a local leisure centre is shown below.

Age, a (years)	Frequency
0 ⩽ a < 5	4
5 ⩽ a < 11	18
11 ⩽ a < 16	36
16 ⩽ a < 19	24
19 ⩽ a < 22	41
22 ⩽ a < 35	49
35 ⩽ a < 50	32
50 ⩽ a < 65	14
65 ⩽ a < 90	3

Draw a histogram to represent the age structure of the centre.

4 The following histogram shows the amount of sponsor money
collected from a class of 32 students.

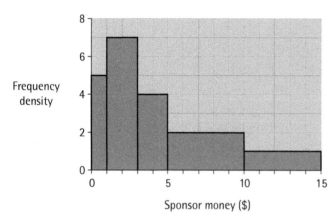

Sponsor money ($)

Construct a frequency table for this data to show how many
students are involved in each class interval.

EXAMINATION QUESTIONS

1 500 eggs were sorted by mass into five different sizes.

	Mass (m grams)	Frequency
Small	$35 \leqslant m < 40$	20
Medium	$40 \leqslant m < 50$	60
Standard	$50 \leqslant m < 60$	200
Large	$60 \leqslant m < 75$	180
Extra large	$75 \leqslant m < 80$	40

Draw an accurate histogram to represent this information.
Use a scale of 2 cm to represent 5 grams on the horizontal axis and
an area scale of 1 square centimetre to represent 5 eggs. [6]

(CIE Paper 4, Jun 2000)

2

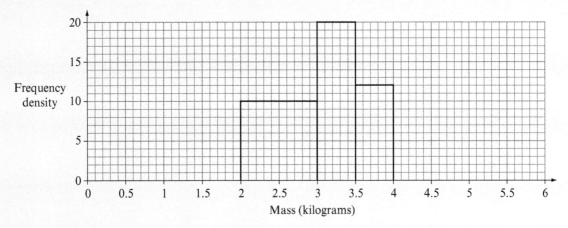

The mass of each baby born in a hospital during one week is recorded.
The results for babies whose mass is between 2 kg and 4 kg are shown in the histogram.
(a) Complete the frequency table below.

Mass (m) in kilograms	Frequency
$2 < m \leqslant 3$	10
$3 < m \leqslant 3.5$	
$3.5 < m \leqslant 4$	

[2]

(b) 8 babies were born with a mass m kilograms such that $4 < m \leqslant 6$.
Copy and complete the histogram above to show this information. [1]

(CIE Paper 2, Nov 2000)

3

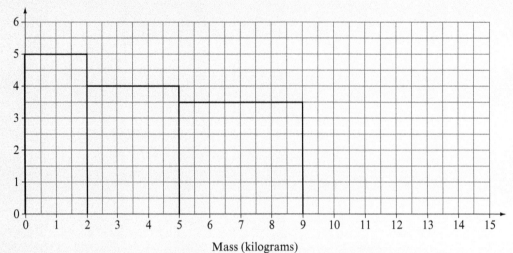

Mass (kilograms)

Mass (x kg)	$0 < m \leqslant 2$	$2 < m \leqslant 5$	$5 < m \leqslant 9$	$9 < m \leqslant 15$
Frequency	10			12

The mass, x kilograms, of each small child in a hospital was recorded.
(a) Use the histogram to help you fill in the two missing frequencies in the table. [2]
(b) Copy the graph and draw the rectangle for the $9 < m \leqslant 15$ group on the histogram. [1]

(CIE Paper 2, Nov 2001)

---

4 The grouped frequency table shows the amount (A) spent on travel by a number of students.

Cost of travel (A)	$0 < A \leqslant 10$	$10 < A \leqslant 20$	$20 < A \leqslant 40$
Frequency	15	m	n

A student drew a histogram to represent this data.
The area of the rectangle representing the $0 < A \leqslant 10$ group was equal to the sum of the areas of the other two rectangles.
Explain why $m + n = 15$. [1]

(CIE Paper 4, Jun 2002)

---

5 120 passengers on an aircraft had their baggage weighed.
The results are shown in the table.

Mass of baggage (M kg)	$0 < M \leqslant 10$	$10 < M \leqslant 15$	$15 < M \leqslant 20$	$20 < M \leqslant 25$	$25 < M \leqslant 40$
Number of passengers	12	32	28	24	24

Using a scale of 2 cm to represent 5 kg, draw a horizontal axis for $0 < M \leqslant 40$.
Using an area scale of 1 cm² to represent 1 passenger, draw a histogram for this data. [7]

(CIE Paper 4, Nov 2003)

Chapter 7

Expanding brackets and factorising

This chapter will show you how to

✔ expand and simplify expressions with brackets
✔ solve equations and inequalities involving brackets
✔ factorise by removing a common factor
✔ expand two brackets

7.1 Expanding brackets

You will need to know how to

● multiply positive and negative numbers
● add and subtract negative numbers
● collect like terms

When multiplying algebraic terms remember that

$$x \times 3 = 3 \times x = 3x$$
$$y \times y = y^2$$
$$gh = g \times h$$

More complicated multiplications can also be simplified.

 **EXAMPLE 1**

Simplify $3f \times 4g$.

$$
\begin{aligned}
3f \times 4g &= 3 \times f \times 4 \times g \\
&= 3 \times 4 \times f \times g \\
&= 12 \times fg \\
&= 12fg
\end{aligned}
$$

> To multiply algebraic terms, multiply the numbers then multiply the letters.

Multiplying a bracket

You can work out 6×34 by thinking of 34 as $30 + 4$.

$$
\begin{aligned}
6 \times 34 &= 6 \times (30 + 4) \\
&= 6 \times 30 + 6 \times 4 \\
&= 180 + 24 \\
&= 204
\end{aligned}
$$

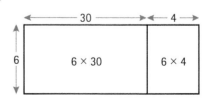

Brackets are often used in algebra.

$6(x + 4)$ means $6 \times (x + 4)$

As in the 6×34 example, you have to multiply each term inside the brackets by 6.

$$6(x + 4) = 6 \times x + 6 \times 4$$
$$= 6x + 24$$

It is like working out the area of a rectangle that has length $x + 4$ and width 6

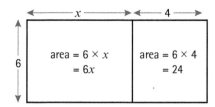

Total area $= 6(x + 4)$
$$= 6 \times x + 6 \times 4$$
$$= 6x + 24$$

You find the total area by adding the area of the two smaller rectangles.

When you do this it is called **expanding the brackets**.

It is also known as **removing the brackets** or **multiplying out the brackets**.

When you remove the brackets you must multiply each term inside the brackets by the term outside the bracket.

EXAMPLE 2

Simplify these by multiplying out the brackets.

(a) $5(a + 6)$ **(b)** $2(x - 8)$ **(c)** $3(2c - d)$

(a) $5(a + 6)$ $= 5 \times a + 5 \times 6$
$$= 5a + 30$$

You must multiply each term inside the bracket by the term outside the bracket.

(b) $2(x - 8)$ $= 2 \times x - 2 \times 8$
$$= 2x - 16$$

$3 \times 2c = 3 \times 2 \times c = 6 \times c = 6c$

(c) $3(2c - d)$ $= 3 \times 2c - 3 \times d$
$$= 6c - 3d$$

EXERCISE 7A

1 Simplify these expressions.
   (a) $2 \times 5k$
   (b) $3 \times 6b$
   (c) $4a \times 5$
   (d) $3a \times 2b$
   (e) $4c \times 3d$
   (f) $x \times 5y$

2 Expand the brackets to find the value of these expressions.
   Check your answers by working out the brackets first.
   (a) $2(50 + 7)$
   (b) $5(40 + 6)$
   (c) $6(70 + 3)$
   (d) $3(40 - 2)$
   (e) $7(50 - 4)$
   (f) $8(40 - 3)$

> Remember, you must multiply each term inside the brackets by the term outside the bracket.
>
> A common mistake is to forget to multiply the second term.

3 Remove the brackets from these.
   (a) $5(p + 6)$
   (b) $3(x + y)$
   (c) $4(u + v + w)$
   (d) $2(y - 8)$
   (e) $7(9 - z)$
   (f) $8(a - b + 6)$

4 Expand the brackets in these expressions.
   (a) $3(2c + 6)$
   (b) $5(4t + 3)$
   (c) $2(5p + q)$
   (d) $3(2a - b)$
   (e) $6(3c - 2d)$
   (f) $7(2x + y - 3)$
   (g) $6(3a - 4b + c)$
   (h) $2(x^2 + 3x + 2)$
   (i) $4(y^2 - 3y - 10)$

> Remember
> $3 \times 2c = 3 \times 2 \times c = 6c$

5 Write down the 6 pairs of cards which show equivalent expressions.

$4(x + 2y)$	$4x + 2y$	$2(4x + y)$	$4(2x - y)$
A	B	C	D

$8x - 8y$	$4x + 8y$	$8(x - y)$	$2x - 8y$
E	F	G	H

$8x + 2y$	$2(x - 4y)$	$2(2x + y)$	$8x - 4y$
I	J	K	L

You can use the same method for expressions that have an *algebraic* term instead of a *number* term outside the bracket.

EXAMPLE 3

Expand the brackets in these expressions.
(a) $a(a + 4)$
(b) $x(2x - y)$
(c) $3t(t^2 + 1)$

(a) $a(a + 4) = a \times a + a \times 4$
$= a^2 + 4a$

(b) $x(2x - y) = x \times 2x - x \times y$
$= 2x^2 - xy$

(c) $3t(t^2 + 1) = 3t \times t^2 + 3t \times 1$
$= 3t^3 + 3t$

> Remember $a \times a = a^2$

> $x \times 2x = x \times 2 \times x = 2 \times x \times x$
> $= 2x^2$
> Remember $x \times y = xy$

> $3t \times t^2 = 3 \times t \times t \times t = 3t^3$

Expand the brackets in these expressions.

1 $b(b + 4)$

2 $a(5 + a)$

3 $k(k - 6)$

4 $m(9 - m)$

5 $a(2a + 3)$

6 $g(4g + 1)$

7 $p(2p + q)$

8 $t(t + 5w)$

9 $m(m + 3n)$

10 $x(2x - y)$

11 $r(4r - t)$

12 $a(a - 4b)$

13 $2t(t + 5)$

14 $3x(x - 8)$

15 $5k(k + l)$

16 $3a(2a + 4)$

17 $2g(4g + h)$

18 $5p(3p - 2q)$

19 $3x(2y + 5z)$

20 $r(r^2 + 1)$

21 $a(a^2 + 3)$

22 $t(t^2 - 7)$

23 $2p(p^2 + 3q)$

24 $4x(x^2 + x)$

> **Remember**
> $3x \times 4x = 4 \times 3 \times x \times x$
> $\qquad = 12x^2$

Adding and subtracting expressions with brackets

Adding

To add expressions with brackets, expand the brackets first, then collect **like terms** to simplify your answer.

> Collecting like terms means adding all the terms in x, all the terms in y and so on.

 EXAMPLE 4

Expand then simplify these expressions.

(a) $3(a + 4) + 2a + 10$

(b) $3(2x + 5) + 2(x - 4)$

(a) $3(a + 4) + 2a + 10 \quad = 3a + 12 + 2a + 10$
$= 3a + 2a + 12 + 10$
$= 5a + 22$

(b) $3(2x + 5) + 2(x - 4) = 6x + 15 + 2x - 8$
$= 6x + 2x + 15 - 8$
$= 8x + 7$

> Expand the brackets first. Then collect like terms.

> Expand both sets of brackets first.

Subtracting

If you have an expression like $-3(2x - 5)$, multiply both terms in the brackets by -3.

$$-3 \times 2x = -6x \quad \text{and} \quad -3 \times -5 = 15$$

So $-3(2x - 5) = -3 \times 2x + -3 \times -5$
$= -6x + 15$

> **Multiplying**
>
> | + | × | + | = | + |
> | + | × | − | = | − |
> | − | × | + | = | − |
> | − | × | − | = | + |

 **EXAMPLE 5**

Expand these expressions.
(a) $-2(3t + 4)$ (b) $-3(4x - 1)$

$-2 \times 3 = -6$ $-2 \times 4 = -8$

(a) $-2(3t + 4)$ $= -2 \times 3t + -2 \times 4$
$= -6t + -8$
$= -6t - 8$

(b) $-3(4x - 1)$ $= -3 \times 4x + -3 \times -1$
$= -12x + 3$

$-3 \times 4 = -12$ $-3 \times -1 = +3$

 EXAMPLE 6

Expand then simplify these expressions.
(a) $3(2t + 1) - 2(2t + 4)$ (b) $8(x + 1) - 3(2x - 5)$

(a) $3(2t + 1) - 2(2t + 4)$ $= 6t + 3 - 4t - 8$
$= 6t - 4t + 3 - 8$
$= 2t - 5$

Remember to multiply both terms in the second bracket by -2.

(b) $8(x + 1) - 3(2x - 5)$ $= 8x + 8 - 6x + 15$
$= 8x - 6x + 8 + 15$
$= 2x + 23$

Expand the brackets first.
Remember that $-3 \times -5 = +15$.
Then collect like terms.

 EXERCISE 7C

Expand these expressions.
1 $-2(2k + 4)$ 2 $-3(2x + 6)$ 3 $-5(3n - 1)$
4 $-4(3t + 5)$ 5 $-3(4p - 1)$ 6 $-2(3x - 7)$

Expand then simplify these expressions.
7 $3(y + 4) + 2y + 10$ 8 $2(k + 6) + 3k + 9$
9 $4(a + 3) - 2a + 6$ 10 $3(t - 2) + 4t - 10$
11 $3(2y + 3) + 2(y + 5)$ 12 $4(x + 7) + 3(x + 4)$
13 $3(2x + 5) + 2(x - 4)$ 14 $2(4n + 5) + 5(n - 3)$
15 $3(x - 5) + 2(x - 3)$ 16 $4(2x - 1) + 2(3x - 2)$
17 $3(2b + 1) - 2(2b + 4)$ 18 $4(2m + 3) - 2(2m + 5)$
19 $2(5t + 3) - 2(3t + 1)$ 20 $5(2k + 2) - 4(2k + 6)$
21 $8(a + 1) - 3(2a - 5)$ 22 $2(4p + 1) - 4(p - 3)$
23 $5(2g - 4) - 2(4g - 6)$ 24 $2(w - 4) - 3(2w - 1)$
25 $x(x + 3) + 4(x + 2)$ 26 $x(2x + 1) - 3(x - 4)$

7.2 Solving equations involving brackets

Equations sometimes involve brackets.

When dealing with equations involving brackets, you usually expand the brackets first.

 EXAMPLE 7

Solve $4(c + 3) = 20$.

Method A

$$4(c + 3) = 20$$
$$4c + 12 = 20$$
$$4c + 12 - 12 = 20 - 12$$
$$4c = 8$$
$$\frac{4c}{4} = \frac{8}{4}$$
$$c = 2$$

Expand the bracket by multiplying both terms inside the bracket by the term outside the bracket.

You must subtract 12 from both sides before dividing both sides by 4.

Method B

$$4(c + 3) = 20$$
$$c + 3 = \frac{20}{4}$$
$$c + 3 = 5$$
$$c = 5 - 3$$
$$c = 2$$

Since 4 divides exactly into 20 you can divide both sides by 4 first.

 EXAMPLE 8

Solve $2(3p - 4) = 7$.

$$2(3p - 4) = 7$$
$$6p - 8 = 7$$
$$6p - 8 + 8 = 7 + 8$$
$$6p = 15$$
$$\frac{6p}{6} = \frac{15}{6}$$
$$p = 2.5$$

Expand the bracket.

You must add 8 to both sides before dividing both sides by 6.

EXERCISE 7D

1   Solve these equations.
   (a) $4(g + 6) = 32$ (b) $7(k + 1) = 21$ (c) $5(s + 10) = 65$
   (d) $2(n - 4) = 6$ (e) $3(f - 2) = 24$ (f) $6(v - 3) = 42$
   (g) $4(m - 3) = 14$ (h) $2(w + 7) = 19$

2   Solve these equations.
   (a) $4(5t + 2) = 48$ (b) $3(2r + 4) = 30$ (c) $2(2b + 2) = 22$
   (d) $2(3w - 6) = 27$ (e) $3(4x - 2) = 24$ (f) $5(2y + 11) = 40$
   (g) $6(2k - 1) = 36$ (h) $3(2a - 13) = 18$

When two brackets are involved, expand both brackets then collect like terms before solving.

> Like terms are terms of the same kind. In Example 9 there are only terms in m and number terms.

EXAMPLE 9

Solve $2(2m + 10) = 12(m - 1)$.

$$2(2m + 10) = 12(m - 1)$$
$$4m + 20 = 12m - 12$$
$$20 + 12 = 12m - 4m$$
$$32 = 8m$$
$$m = 4$$

> Expand the brackets on both sides of the equation and collect like terms.

> Collect terms in m on the RHS because $12m$ on the RHS is greater than $4m$ on the LHS. This keeps the m term positive.

When an equation involves fractions, it can be transformed into an equation without fractions by multiplying all terms by the LCM of the numbers in the denominators.

> LCM means Lowest Common Multiple.

EXAMPLE 10

Solve the equation $\dfrac{x + 17}{4} = x + 2$.

$$\frac{x + 17}{4} = x + 2$$
$$\frac{4(x + 17)}{4} = 4(x + 2)$$
$$x + 17 = 4x + 8$$
$$17 - 8 = 4x - x$$
$$9 = 3x$$
$$x = 3$$

> Multiply both sides by 4, collect like terms and then finally divide by 3.

> Note the use of brackets.

> Collect the terms in x on the RHS and the numbers on the LHS.
> $4x$ on the RHS is greater than x on the LHS.

EXAMPLE 11

Solve the equation $\dfrac{x-6}{3} = \dfrac{x+4}{5}$.

$\dfrac{x-6}{3} = \dfrac{x+4}{5}$

$\dfrac{15(x-6)}{3} = \dfrac{15(x+4)}{5}$

$5(x-6) = 3(x+4)$

$5x - 30 = 3x + 12$

$5x - 3x = 12 + 30$

$2x = 42$

$x = 21$

Look at the denominators.
3 and 5 have a LCM of 15 so multiply both sides of the equation by 15.

Note the use of brackets. Always put them in when you multiply in this way.

Then solve using the method shown in Example 9.

 EXAMPLE 12

Solve the equation $\dfrac{2x+3}{6} + \dfrac{x-2}{3} = \dfrac{5}{2}$.

$\dfrac{6(2x+3)}{6} + \dfrac{6(x-2)}{3} = \dfrac{6(5)}{2}$

$2x + 3 + 2(x-2) = 15$

$2x + 3 + 2x - 4 = 15$

$4x - 1 = 15$

$4x = 16$

$x = 4$

The LCM here is 6.

Note the use of brackets.

The most common mistake is to forget to multiply all terms by the LCM.

This means the number on the RHS as well as the terms on the LHS.

 EXERCISE 7E

1 Solve these equations.
   (a) $2a + 4 = 5(a - 1)$
   (b) $3(d - 2) = 2d - 1$
   (c) $5(x + 3) = 11x + 3$
   (d) $12p + 3 = 3(p + 7)$
   (e) $4t + 3 = 3(2t - 3)$
   (f) $3b - 4 = 2(2b - 7)$
   (g) $8(3g - 1) = 15g + 10$
   (h) $3(2k + 6) = 17k + 7$
   (i) $2(y + 5) = 3y + 12$
   (j) $5r + 3 = 4(2r + 3)$

2 Solve the following equations by expanding both brackets.
   (a) $2(b + 1) = 8(2b - 5)$
   (b) $5(4a + 7) = 3(8a + 9)$
   (c) $6(x - 2) = 3(3x - 8)$
   (d) $5(2p + 2) = 6(p + 5)$
   (e) $9(3s - 4) = 5(4s - 3)$
   (f) $4(10t - 7) = 3(6t - 2)$
   (g) $4(2w + 2) = 2(5w + 7)$
   (h) $3(3y - 2) = 7(y - 2)$

Use Example 9 to help.

3 Solve these equations.

(a) $\dfrac{d + 3}{15} = 3 - d$

(b) $\dfrac{6y - 5}{5} = y + 3$

(c) $\dfrac{3x - 1}{8} = x - 2$

(d) $\dfrac{6 + a}{2} = a + 4$

(e) $\dfrac{c - 8}{4} = c + 1$

(f) $\dfrac{10 - b}{3} = 12 + b$

Use Example 10 to help.

4 Solve these equations.

(a) $\dfrac{x + 1}{3} = \dfrac{x - 1}{4}$

(b) $\dfrac{2x - 1}{3} = \dfrac{x}{2}$

(c) $\dfrac{3x + 1}{5} = \dfrac{2x}{3}$

(d) $\dfrac{x + 3}{2} = \dfrac{x - 3}{5}$

(e) $\dfrac{x + 2}{7} = \dfrac{3x + 6}{5}$

(f) $\dfrac{8 - x}{2} = \dfrac{2x + 2}{5}$

Use Example 11 to help.

5 Solve these equations.

(a) $\dfrac{x + 1}{2} + \dfrac{x + 2}{5} = 3$

(b) $\dfrac{x + 2}{4} + \dfrac{x + 1}{7} = 3$

(c) $\dfrac{3x + 2}{5} + \dfrac{x + 2}{3} = 2$

(d) $\dfrac{3x - 1}{5} - \dfrac{x + 2}{3} = \dfrac{1}{5}$

(e) $\dfrac{x - 3}{4} - \dfrac{x + 3}{3} = 1$

(f) $\dfrac{2x + 5}{4} - \dfrac{x + 4}{3} = 2$

Use Example 12 to help.

7.3 Solving inequalities involving brackets

Inequalities can also involve brackets.

Remember that there is usually more than one answer when you solve an inequality and you need to state all possible values of the solution set.

 EXAMPLE 13

Solve these inequalities.

(a) $9 \leqslant 3(y - 1)$ (b) $3(2x - 5) > 2(x + 4)$

(a)
$$9 \leqslant 3(y - 1)$$
$$9 \leqslant 3y - 3$$
$$9 + 3 \leqslant 3y$$
$$12 \leqslant 3y$$
$$4 \leqslant y$$

(b)
$$3(2x - 5) > 2(x + 4)$$
$$6x - 15 > 2x + 8$$
$$6x - 2x > 8 + 15$$
$$4x > 23$$
$$x > \tfrac{23}{4}$$
$$x > 5\tfrac{3}{4}$$

You must remember to keep the inequality sign in your answer.

For example, if you leave (a) as $4 = y$ you will lose a mark because you have not included *all* possible values of y.

If you are asked for integer solutions to (b) the final answer will be $x \geqslant 6$.

EXAMPLE 14

n is an integer.
List the values of *n* such that $-11 < 2(n - 3) < 1$.

$$-11 < 2(n - 3) < 1$$
$$-11 < 2n - 6 < 1$$
$$-11 + 6 < 2n < 1 + 6$$
$$-5 < 2n < 7$$
$$-2.5 < n < 3.5$$

Values of *n* are $-2, -1, 0, 1, 2, 3$

This is a double inequality.
Expand the bracket.
Add 6 throughout.

Remember to list the integer solutions as you were asked to in the question.
Remember to include 0.

 EXERCISE 7F

1 Solve these inequalities.
  (a) $2(x - 7) \leqslant 8$
  (b) $7 < 2(m + 5)$
  (c) $4(3w - 1) > 20$
  (d) $3(2y + 1) \leqslant -15$
  (e) $2(p - 3) > 4 + 3p$
  (f) $1 - 5k < 2(5 + 2k)$
  (g) $5(x - 1) \geqslant 3(x + 2)$
  (h) $2(n + 5) \leqslant 3(2n - 2)$

2 Solve these inequalities then list the integer solutions.
  (a) $-4 \leqslant 2x \leqslant 8$
  (b) $-6 < 3y < 15$
  (c) $-8 \leqslant 4n < 17$
  (d) $-12 < 6m \leqslant 30$
  (e) $-5 < 2(t + 1) < 7$
  (f) $-3 < 3(x - 4) < 6$
  (g) $-6 \leqslant 5(y + 1) \leqslant 11$
  (h) $-17 < 2(2x - 3) \leqslant 10$

7.4 Factorising by removing a common factor

Factorising an algebraic expression is the opposite of expanding brackets. To factorise an expression, look for a **common factor** – that is, a number that divides into all the terms in the expression. To factorise completely, use the HCF of the terms.

HCF means highest common factor.

2 is a factor of 6*x*.
2 is also a factor of 10.
So 2 is a common factor of 6*x* and 10.

For example,

  $6x + 10$ can be written as $2(3x + 5)$

  because $6x = 2 \times 3x$

  and $10 = 2 \times 5$

Notice that the common factor is the term outside the bracket.

EXAMPLE 15

Copy and complete these.

(a) $3t + 15 = 3(\square + 5)$ **(b)** $4n + 12 = \square(n + 3)$

(a) $3t + 15 = 3(t + 5)$

(b) $4n + 12 = 4(n + 3)$

Because $3 \times t = 3t$ (and $3 \times 5 = 15$)

$4 \times n = 4n$ and $4 \times 3 = 12$

 EXAMPLE 16

Factorise these expressions.

(a) $5a + 20$ **(b)** $4x - 12$ **(c)** $x^2 + 7x$ **(d)** $6p^2q^2 - 9pq^3$

(a) $\quad\quad 5a + 20 = 5 \times a + 5 \times 4$

$\quad\quad\quad\quad\quad = 5(a + 4)$

$\quad\quad\quad\quad\quad = 5(a + 4)$

$\quad$ Check $5(a + 4) = 5 \times a + 5 \times 4$

$\quad\quad\quad\quad\quad\quad\quad = 5a + 20 \quad \checkmark$

5 is a factor of $5a$ $\quad 5a = 5 \times a$
5 is also a factor of 20 $\quad 20 = 5 \times 4$
So 5 is a common factor of $5a$ and 20 and is the term outside the bracket.

Check your answer by removing the brackets.

(b) $4x - 12 = 4 \times x - 4 \times 3$

$\quad\quad\quad\quad = 4(x - 3)$

$\quad\quad\quad\quad = 4(x - 3)$

2 is a factor of $4x$ and 12.
4 is also a common factor of $4x$ and 12. Use 4 because it is the highest common factor (HCF) of $4x$ and 12. Always look for the HCF.

(c) $x^2 + 7x = x \times x + x \times 7$

$\quad\quad\quad\quad = x(x + 7)$

$\quad\quad\quad\quad = x(x + 7)$

x is a common factor of x^2 and $7x$.

(d) $6p^2q^2 - 9pq^3$

$\quad = 3 \times 2 \times p \times p \times q \times q - 3 \times 3 \times p \times q \times q \times q$

$\quad = 3pq^2(2p - 3q)$

$\quad = 3pq^2(2p - 3q)$

The HCF is $3pq^2$.

EXERCISE 7G

1 Copy and complete these.

(a) $3x + 15 = 3(\square + 5)$ **(b)** $5a + 10 = 5(\square + 2)$

(c) $2x - 12 = 2(x - \square)$ **(d)** $4m - 16 = 4(m - \square)$

(e) $4t + 12 = \square(t + 3)$ **(f)** $3n + 18 = \square(n + 6)$

(g) $2b - 14 = \square(b - 7)$ **(h)** $4t - 20 = \square(t - 5)$

Use Example 15 to help.

Don't forget to check your answers by removing the brackets.

2 Factorise these expressions.

(a) $5p + 20$ (b) $2a + 12$ (c) $3y + 15$

(d) $7b + 21$ (e) $4q + 12p$ (f) $6k + 24l$

Use Example 16(a) to help.
Remember $5 = 5 \times 1$

3 Factorise these expressions.

(a) $4t - 12$ (b) $3x - 9$ (c) $5n - 20$

(d) $2b - 8$ (e) $6a - 18b$ (f) $7k - 7$

4 Factorise these expressions.

(a) $y^2 + 7y$ (b) $x^2 + 5x$ (c) $n^2 + n$

(d) $x^2 - 7x$ (e) $p^2 - 8p$ (f) $a^2 - ab$

Use Example 16(c) to help.
Remember $n = n \times 1$

5 Factorise these expressions.

(a) $6p + 4$ (b) $4a + 10$ (c) $6 - 4t$

(d) $12m - 8n$ (e) $25x + 15y$ (f) $12y - 9z$

Remember $6p = 2 \times 3p$

6 Factorise completely.

(a) $3x^2 - 6x$ (b) $8x^2 - xy$ (c) $8a + 4ab$

(d) $p^3 - 5p^2$ (e) $3t^3 + 6t^2$ (f) $10yz - 15y^2$

(g) $18a^2 + 12ab$ (h) $16p^2 - 12pq$

7 Factorise these expressions.

(a) $4ab^2 + 6ab^3$ (b) $10xy - 5x^2$

(c) $3p^2q - 6p^3q^2$ (d) $8mn^3 + 4n^2 - 6m^2n$

(e) $6h^2k - 12hk^3 - 18h^2k^2$

Use Example 16(a) to help. Look for the common factors in the terms.

Expanding two brackets

You can use a grid method to multiply two numbers.

For example,

34×57

×	50	7
30	1500	210
4	200	28

$34 \times 57 = (30 + 4) \times (50 + 7)$

$= 30 \times 50 + 30 \times 7 + 4 \times 50 + 4 \times 7$

$= 1500 + 210 + 200 + 28$

$= 1938$

You can also use a grid method when you multiply two brackets together. You have to **multiply each term in one bracket by each term in the other bracket**.

For example,

To expand and simplify $(x + 2)(x + 5)$

×	x	5
x	x^2	$5x$
2	$2x$	10

$(x + 2)(x + 5) = x \times x + x \times 5 + 2 \times x + 2 \times 5$

$= x^2 + 5x + 2x + 10$

$= x^2 + 7x + 10$

You simplify the final expression by collecting the like terms.
$5x + 2x = 7x$.

It is like working out the area of a rectangle of length $x + 5$ and width $x + 2$.

Total area $= (x + 2)(x + 5)$

$\qquad = x^2 + 5x + 2x + 10$

$\qquad = x^2 + 7x + 10$

	x	5
x	area $= x \times x$ $= x^2$	area $= x \times 5$ $= 5x$
2	area $= 2 \times x$ $= 2x$	area $= 2 \times 5$ $= 10$

 EXAMPLE 17

Expand and simplify these.

(a) $(a + 4)(a + 10)$

(b) $(t + 6)(t - 2)$

(a)

$\times$	a	10
a	a^2	$10a$
4	$4a$	40

$(a + 4)(a + 10) \quad = a \times a + a \times 10 + 4 \times a + 4 \times 10$

$\qquad\qquad\qquad\quad = a^2 + 10a + 4a + 40$

$\qquad\qquad\qquad\quad = a^2 + 14a + 40$

> Remember you can use a grid to help.

> Remember to multiply each term in the first bracket by each term in the second bracket.

(b)

$\times$	t	-2
t	t^2	$-2t$
6	$6t$	-12

$(t + 6)(t - 2) \quad = t \times t + t \times (-2) + 6 \times t + 6 \times (-2)$

$\qquad\qquad\qquad = t^2 - 2t + 6t - 12$

$\qquad\qquad\qquad = t^2 + 4t - 12$

> Remember you are multiplying by -2.
> $^+$ve $\times$ $^-$ve $=$ $^-$ve.

Look again at the last example.

$$(t + 6) \quad (t - 2) \quad \begin{aligned} &= t^2 - 2t + 6t - 12 \\ &= t^2 + 4t - 12 \end{aligned}$$

The	First terms in each bracket	multiply to give t^2.
The	Outside pair of terms	multiply to give $-2t$.
The	Inside pair of terms	multiply to give $+6t$.
The	Last terms in each bracket	multiply to give -12.

> This method is often known as FOIL and is another way of expanding brackets.

Expand and simplify.

1 $(a + 2)(a + 7)$ 2 $(x + 3)(x + 1)$ 3 $(x + 5)(x + 5)$

4 $(t + 5)(t - 2)$ 5 $(x + 7)(x - 4)$ 6 $(n - 5)(n + 8)$

7 $(x - 4)(x + 5)$ 8 $(p - 4)(p + 4)$ 9 $(x - 9)(x - 4)$

10 $(h - 3)(h - 8)$ 11 $(y - 3)(y - 3)$ 12 $(4 + a)(a + 7)$

13 $(m - 7)(8 + m)$ 14 $(6 + q)(7 + q)$ 15 $(d + 5)(4 - d)$

16 $(8 - x)(3 - x)$ 17 $(x - 12)(x - 7)$ 18 $(y - 16)(y + 6)$

> Be careful when there are negative signs — this is where a lot of mistakes are made.

Squaring an expression

You can use the same method of expanding two brackets for examples involving the square of an expression.

> To square an expression, write out the bracket twice and expand.

EXAMPLE 18

Expand and simplify $(x + 4)^2$.

$(x + 4)\ (x + 4)$

$(x + 4)^2 = (x + 4)(x + 4)$
$= x^2 + 4x + 4x + 16$
$= x^2 + 8x + 16$

> You need to multiply the expression $(x + 4)$ by itself so write down the bracket twice and expand as you did in Example 17 or use FOIL as in this example.

> Notice that you do not just square the x and the 4, there are two other terms in the expansion.

1 Expand and simplify.

(a) $(x + 5)^2$ (b) $(x + 6)^2$ (c) $(x - 3)^2$

(d) $(x + 1)^2$ (e) $(x - 4)^2$ (f) $(x - 5)^2$

(g) $(x + 7)^2$ (h) $(x - 8)^2$ (i) $(3 + x)^2$

(j) $(2 + x)^2$ (k) $(5 - x)^2$ (l) $(x + a)^2$

> In question 1, see if you can spot the pattern between the terms in the brackets and the final expression.

2 Copy and complete these by finding the correct number to go in each box.

(a) $(x + \square)^2 = x^2 + \square x + 36$ (b) $(x - \square)^2 = x^2 - \square x + 49$

(c) $(x + \square)^2 = x^2 + 18x + \square$ (d) $(x - \square)^2 = x^2 - 20x + \square$

3 Expand and simplify.

(a) $(x + 4)(x - 4)$ (b) $(x + 5)(x - 5)$ (c) $(x + 2)(x - 2)$

(d) $(x - 11)(x + 11)$ (e) $(x - 3)(x + 3)$ (f) $(x - 1)(x + 1)$

(g) $(x + 9)(x - 9)$ (h) $(x + a)(x - a)$ (i) $(t + x)(t - x)$

What happens to the x term when you multiply brackets of the form $(x + a)(x - a)$?

EXAMPLE 19

Expand and simplify $(3x - y)(x - 2y)$.

×	x	$-2y$
$3x$	$3x^2$	$-6xy$
$-y$	$-xy$	$2y^2$

$(3x - y)(x - 2y) = 3x^2 - 6xy - xy + 2y$
$= 3x^2 - 7xy + 2y^2$

Remember to multiply each term in the first bracket by each term in the second bracket.

Be careful when there are negative signs. This is where a lot of mistakes are made.
$^+\text{ve} \times {}^-\text{ve} = {}^-\text{ve}.$
$^-\text{ve} \times {}^-\text{ve} = {}^+\text{ve}.$

EXERCISE 7J

Expand and simplify.

1 $(3a + 2)(a + 4)$ **2** $(5x + 3)(x + 2)$ **3** $(2t + 3)(3t + 5)$

4 $(4y + 1)(2y + 7)$ **5** $(6x + 5)(2x + 3)$ **6** $(4x + 3)(x - 1)$

7 $(2z + 5)(3z - 2)$ **8** $(y + 1)(7y - 8)$ **9** $(3n - 5)(n + 8)$

10 $(3b - 5)(2b + 1)$ **11** $(p - 4)(7p + 3)$ **12** $(2z - 3)(3z - 4)$

13 $(5x - 9)(2x - 1)$ **14** $(2y - 3)(2y - 3)$ **15** $(2 + 3a)(4a + 5)$

16 $(3x + 4)^2$ **17** $(2x - 7)^2$ **18** $(5 - 4x)^2$

19 $(2x + 1)(2x - 1)$ **20** $(3y + 2)(3y - 2)$ **21** $(5n + 4)(5n - 4)$

22 $(3x + 5)(3x - 5)$ **23** $(1 + 2x)(1 - 2x)$ **24** $(3t + 2x)(3t - 2x)$

Can you see the connection between questions 19–24 and question 3 in Exercise 7I ?

1 Solve the inequality $7 - 5x \geq -17$, given that x is a **positive** integer. [3]

(CIE Paper 2, Nov 2000)

---

2 Solve the inequality $25 - 3x < 7$. [2]

(CIE Paper 2, Jun 2001)

---

3 Solve the inequality $3(x + 7) < 5x - 9$. [2]

(CIE Paper 2, Jun 2002)

---

4 **(a)** Solve the inequality $5 - \dfrac{2x}{3} > \dfrac{1}{2} + \dfrac{x}{4}$. [3]

(b) List the positive integers which satisfy the inequality $5 - \dfrac{2x}{3} > \dfrac{1}{2} + \dfrac{x}{4}$. [1]

(CIE Paper 2, Nov 2002)

---

5 Solve the equation $\dfrac{x}{4} - 8 = -2$. [2]

(CIE Paper 2, Jun 2004)

---

6 **(a)** Factorise completely $12x^2 - 3y^2$. [2]

(b) (i) Expand $(x - 3)^2$. [2]

(ii) $x^2 - 6x + 10$ is to be written in the form $(x - p)^2 + q$.
Find the values of p and q. [2]

(CIE Paper 2, Jun 2004)

---

7 Solve the equation $\dfrac{3x - 2}{5} = 8$. [2]

(CIE Paper 2, Nov 2004)

Chapter 8

Formulae

This chapter will show you how to
✔ write a formula from a problem
✔ substitute numbers into expressions and formulae
✔ change the subject of a formula

8.1 Formulae

Formulae is the plural of formula.

You will need to know
● the correct order of operations

Brackets → Indices → $\begin{array}{c}\text{Multiplication}\\\text{Division}\end{array}$ → $\begin{array}{c}\text{Addition}\\\text{Subtraction}\end{array}$

A **formula** is a general rule that shows how quantities (or **variables**) are related to each other.

For example,

$v = u + at$

This is a formula that shows the relationship between an object's final velocity, v, its initial velocity, u, its acceleration, a, and the time it has been moving, t.

Deriving formulae

When solving a problem, it often helps to write a formula to express the problem. Start by deciding on a letter to represent an unknown value.

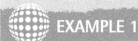 **EXAMPLE 1**

Alex buys x melons.
Each melon costs 45 cents.
Alex pays with a $5 note.
Write a formula for the change, C, in cents, Alex should receive.

---

x = number of melons
$C = 500 - 45x$

$5 = 500c$
The melons cost 45c each so the cost, in cents, for x melons is 45x.

1 Nilesh buys y mangoes.
   Each mango costs 48 cents.
   Nilesh pays with a $5 note.
   Write a formula for the change, C, in cents, Nilesh should receive.

2 Apples cost r cents each and bananas cost s cents each.
   Sam buys 7 apples and 5 bananas.
   Write a formula for the total cost, t, in cents, of these fruit.

3 To cook a chicken you allow 45 minutes per kg and then a
   further 20 minutes.
   Write a formula for the time, t, in minutes, to cook a chicken that
   weighs w kg.

4 To cook lamb you allow 30 minutes plus a further 65 minutes per kg.
   Write a formula for the time, t, in minutes, to cook a joint of lamb
   that weighs w kg.

5 A rectangle has a length of $3x + 1$ and a width of $x + 2$.
   Write down a formula for the perimeter, p, of this rectangle.

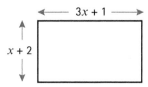

Substitution

This section shows you how to use substitution to find the values of
different algebraic expressions.

> Use mathematical operations in the correct order when substituting
> values into an algebraic expression.

 EXAMPLE 2

If $a = 5$, $b = 4$ and $c = 3$ work out the value of these expressions.

(a) $\dfrac{a + 3}{2}$ (b) $3b^2 - 1$ (c) $\dfrac{5c + 1}{2}$

(a) $\dfrac{a + 3}{2} = \dfrac{5 + 3}{2}$

$\qquad = 8 \div 2$

$\qquad = 4$

The dividing line acts like a bracket.
You must work out the numerator
first.

Remember $\dfrac{8}{2} = 8 \div 2$.

(b) $3b^2 - 1 = 3 \times 4^2 - 1$

$\qquad\quad = 3 \times 16 - 1$

$\qquad\quad = 48 - 1$

$\qquad\quad = 47$

You must work out the indices first
$(4^2 = 16)$, then the multiplication
(3×16), then
the subtraction $(48 - 1)$.

continued ▼

(c) $\dfrac{5c+1}{b} = \dfrac{5 \times 3 + 1}{4}$

$= \dfrac{15 + 1}{4}$

$= \dfrac{16}{4}$

$= 4$

EXERCISE 8B

1 If $r = 5$, $s = 4$ and $t = 3$, work out the value of these expressions.

(a) $\dfrac{r+3}{2}$ (b) $\dfrac{s+5}{3}$ (c) $\dfrac{t+7}{2}$

(d) $3r^2 + 1$ (e) $4t^2 - 6$ (f) $2s^2 + r$

(g) $4(5s + 1)$ (h) $t(r + s)$ (i) $5(2s - 3t)$

(j) $\dfrac{5t+1}{s}$ (k) $\dfrac{4r-2}{t}$ (l) $\dfrac{3s+t}{r}$

$3r^2 = 3 \times r^2 = 3 \times r \times r$

2 Copy and complete this table.

x	1	2	3	4	5
$x^2 + 2x$			15		

$3^2 + 2 \times 3 = 9 + 6 = 15$

3 Copy and complete this table.

x	3	4	3.5	3.7	3.8
$x^3 - x$		60			

Remember $x^3 = x \times x \times x$
$4^3 - 4 = 64 - 4 = 60$

4 If $A = 6$, $B = -4$, $C = 3$ and $D = 30$, work out the value of these expressions.

(a) $D(B + 7)$ (b) $A(B + 1)$ (c) $A^2 + 2B + C$

(d) $\dfrac{2A+3}{C}$ (e) $\dfrac{4B+D}{2}$ (f) $\dfrac{A^2+3B}{C}$

Substituting into formulae

 EXAMPLE 3

A formula for working out acceleration is

$$a = \frac{v - u}{t}$$

where v is the final velocity, u is the initial velocity and t is the time taken.

Work out the value of a when $v = 50$, $u = 10$, $t = 8$.

$$\begin{aligned} a &= \frac{v - u}{t} \\ &= \frac{50 - 10}{8} \\ &= 40 \div 8 \\ &= 5 \end{aligned}$$

Remember the line for division acts like a bracket. You must work out the numerator first.

 EXAMPLE 4

A formula for working out distance travelled is

$$s = ut + \tfrac{1}{2}at^2$$

where u is the initial velocity, a is the acceleration and t is the time taken.

Work out the value of s when $u = 3$, $a = 8$, $t = 5$.

$$\begin{aligned} s &= ut + \tfrac{1}{2}at^2 \\ &= 3 \times 5 + \tfrac{1}{2} \times 8 \times 5^2 \\ &= 15 + 4 \times 25 \\ &= 15 + 100 \\ &= 115 \end{aligned}$$

Do $5^2 = 25$ first;
then $3 \times 5 = 15$ and $\tfrac{1}{2} \times 8 = 4$;
then $4 \times 25 = 100$;
then $15 + 100 = 115$.

 EXERCISE 8C

1 Use the formula $a = \dfrac{v - u}{t}$ to work out the value of a when

   (a) $v = 15$, $u = 3$, $t = 2$ **(b)** $v = 29$, $u = 5$, $t = 6$
   (c) $v = 25$, $u = 7$, $t = 3$ **(d)** $v = 60$, $u = 10$, $t = 4$.

2 A person's Body Mass Index, b, is calculated using the formula

$$b = \frac{m}{h^2}$$

where m is their mass in kilograms and h is their height in metres.

Work out the value of b when

(a) $m = 70$, $h = 1.8$ (b) $m = 38$, $h = 1.4$

(c) $m = 85$, $h = 1.9$ (d) $m = 59$, $h = 1.7$.

3 The formula for the area of a trapezium is

$$A = \tfrac{1}{2}(a + b)h$$

Work out the value of A when

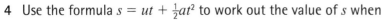

(a) $a = 10$, $b = 6$, $h = 4$ (b) $a = 13$, $b = 9$, $h = 8$

(c) $a = 9$, $b = 6$, $h = 4$ (d) $a = 15$, $b = 10$, $h = 6$.

4 Use the formula $s = ut + \tfrac{1}{2}at^2$ to work out the value of s when

(a) $u = 3$, $a = 10$, $t = 2$ (b) $u = 7$, $a = 6$, $t = 5$

(c) $u = 2.5$, $a = 5$, $t = 4$ (d) $u = -4$, $a = 8$, $t = 3$.

5 A formula for working out the velocity of a car is

$$v = \sqrt{u^2 + 2as}$$

where u is the initial velocity, a is the acceleration and s is the distance travelled.

Work out the value of v when

(a) $u = 3$, $a = 4$, $s = 5$ (b) $u = 6$, $a = 8$, $s = 4$

(c) $u = 9$, $a = 10$, $s = 2$ (d) $u = 7$, $a = 4$, $s = 15$.

6 A formula for the surface area of a cone, including the base, is

surface area of cone $= \pi r(r + l)$

where r is the radius and l is the slant height.

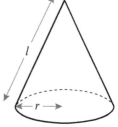

Work out the surface area of a cone with these dimensions.

(a) $r = 2$ cm, $l = 13$ cm   (b) $r = 4$ cm, $l = 10$ cm.

Give your answers to 3 s.f.

7 A formula for the total surface area of a cylinder is

surface area of cylinder $= 2\pi r(r + h)$

where r is the radius and h is the height.

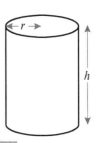

Work out the surface area of a cylinder with these dimensions.

(a) $r = 3.7$ cm, $h = 10.8$ cm   (b) $r = 4.2$ cm, $h = 4.1$ cm.

Give your answers to 3 s.f.

Using formulae

 EXAMPLE 5

The perimeter of a rectangle is given by $P = 2l + 2w$, where l is the length and w is the width.

Work out the value of l when $P = 24$ and $w = 5$.

$P = 2l + 2w$

$24 = 2l + 2 \times 5$

$24 = 2l + 10$

$24 - 10 = 2l$

$14 = 2l$

$7 = l$

Substitute the values you know, of P and w, into the formula, then solve the equation to find l.

 EXERCISE 8D

1   The formula for the area of a rectangle is $A = lw$, where l is the length and w is the width.
    Work out the value of w when
    (a) $A = 12$ and $l = 4$
    (b) $A = 36$ and $l = 9$
    (c) $A = 42$ and $l = 7$
    (d) $A = 60$ and $l = 15$.

2   The formula for the voltage, V, in an electrical circuit is $V = IR$, where I is the current and R is the resistance.
    Work these out.
    (a) The value of R when $V = 18$ and $I = 2$.
    (b) The value of R when $V = 35$ and $I = 5$.
    (c) The value of I when $V = 240$ and $R = 30$.
    (d) The value of I when $V = 240$ and $R = 40$.

3   The perimeter of a rectangle is given by

$$P = 2l + 2w$$

where l is the length and w is the width.
Use the formula to
(a) find l when $P = 18$ and $w = 4$.
(b) find l when $P = 32$ and $w = 7$.
(c) find w when $P = 60$ and $l = 17$.
(d) find w when $P = 50$ and $l = 13.5$.

4 Use the formula $v = u + at$
   (a) to find u when $v = 30$, $a = 8$, $t = 3$
   (b) to find a when $v = 54$, $u = 19$, $t = 7$
   (c) to find t when $v = 60$, $u = 15$, $a = 5$
   (d) to find u when $v = 20$, $a = 7$, $t = 4$.

8.2 Changing the subject of a formula

You will need to know that
● addition and subtraction are inverse operations
● multiplication and division are inverse operations
● squaring and finding the square root are inverse operations

The **subject** of a formula appears only once, on its own, on one side of the formula.

In the formula $v = u + at$ the variable v is called the subject of the formula.

P is the subject of the formula $P = 2l + 2w$.

P is on its own on one side of the formula.

You can **rearrange** a formula to make a different variable the subject.

 EXAMPLE 6

Rearrange $d = a + 8$ to make a the subject.

$d = a + 8$

$d - 8 = a$

You need to have a on its own on one side.

Subtract 8 from both sides as you would when solving an equation.

 EXAMPLE 7

Make x the subject of the formula $y = 5x - 2$.

$y = 5x - 2$

$y + 2 = 5x$

$\dfrac{y + 2}{5} = x$

Add 2 to both sides to leave $5x$ on its own.

Then divide both sides by 5 to leave x on its own.

EXAMPLE 8

Rearrange $P = 4g + 2h$ to make g the subject.

$P = 4g + 2h$

Subtract $2h$ from both sides.

$P - 2h = 4g$

$\dfrac{P - 2h}{4} = g$

Divide both sides by 4.

 EXAMPLE 9

Rearrange $V = \sqrt{(w + y)}$ to make w the subject.

$V = \sqrt{(w + y)}$

Square both sides first.

$V^2 = w + y$

$V^2 - y = w$

Then subtract y from both sides.

 EXAMPLE 10

Rearrange $p = \dfrac{q^2}{r} - s$ to make q the subject.

$p = \dfrac{q^2}{r} - s$

Add s to both sides to leave the term with q on its own.

$p + s = \dfrac{q^2}{r}$

$r(p + s) = q^2$

Multiply both sides by r.

$\pm \sqrt{r(p + s)} = q$

Square root both sides.

 EXERCISE 8E

1 Rearrange these formulae to make y the subject.

   (a) $x = 5y - 6$ **(b)** $x + 2y = 8$

   (c) $x + 3y - 8 = 0$ **(d)** $2x + 5y - 7 = 0$

   (e) $x - y = 4$ **(f)** $2x - 5y = 20$

2 Make x the subject of these formulae.

   (a) $y = 5x - 6$ **(b)** $y = \frac{1}{2}x - 8$

   (c) $y + \frac{1}{2}x = 2$ **(d)** $y - x = 7$

   (e) $2y + x = 9$ **(f)** $2y + 5x = 9$

3 Make r the subject of these formulae.

(a) $p = 3(4r + 5t)$

(b) $v = 5(7r + h)$

(c) $w = \dfrac{3r - 2s}{5}$

(d) $y = \dfrac{6p - 5r}{8}$

4 Rearrange these formulae to make a the subject.

(a) $b = \frac{1}{2}a + 6$

(b) $b = \frac{1}{2}a + 7$

(c) $b = \frac{1}{3}a - 1$

(d) $b = \frac{1}{4}a - 3$

(e) $b = 2(a + 1)$

(f) $b = 3(a - 5)$

> Multiply $\frac{1}{2}a$ by 2 to get a.

5 Rearrange these formulae to make x the subject.

(a) $3(x + y) = 5y$

(b) $2(x - y) = y + 5$

(c) $z = \dfrac{x}{y} - 5$

(d) $3p = \dfrac{2x}{q} - s$

6 Rearrange these formulae to make w the subject.

(a) $K = \sqrt{w + t}$

(b) $A = \sqrt{w - a}$

(c) $h = 2\sqrt{w} + l$

(d) $T = \sqrt{wr} + 5$

> Use Example 9 to help.

7 Rearrange these formulae to make r the subject.

(a) $t = \dfrac{r^2}{g} - m$

(b) $h = \dfrac{r^2}{4} + 3a$

(c) $V = \frac{1}{3}\pi r^2 h$

(d) $A = \pi(r^2 - s^2)$

> Use Example 10 to help.

8 A formula for the total surface area of a cylinder is

$$A = 2\pi r(r + h)$$

where r is the radius and h is the height.
Rearrange the formula to make h the subject.

9 A formula for the period of a pendulum is

$$T = 2\pi\sqrt{\dfrac{l}{g}}$$

Rearrange the formula to make l the subject.

> The period T is the time for one complete swing; l is the length and g is a constant.

10 The formula $F = 1.8C + 32$ can be used to convert degrees Celsius, $°C$, to degrees Fahrenheit, $°F$.

(a) Convert $15°C$ to degrees Fahrenheit.

(b) Rearrange the formula to make C the subject.

11 A formula is given as $v^2 = u^2 + 2as$.

(a) Find v when $u = 10$, $a = 4$ and $s = 12$.

(b) Rearrange the formula to make a the subject.

(c) Rearrange the formula to make u the subject.

12 A formula is given by

$$T = \sqrt{\dfrac{h^2 + g^2}{g^2}}$$

(a) Find T when $g = 10$ and $h = 2$.

(b) Rearrange the formula to make h the subject.

1   Make h the subject of the formula $g = \sqrt{h + i}$. [2]

(CIE Paper 2, Nov 2000)

2   Make y the subject of the formula $x = \dfrac{4 + \sqrt{y}}{3}$. [3]

(CIE Paper 2, Jun 2001)

3   Make x the subject of the formula $y = \dfrac{3x}{2} + 5$. [3]

(CIE Paper 2, Nov 2001)

4   Make V the subject of the formula $T = \dfrac{5}{V + 1}$. [3]

(CIE Paper 2, Jun 2002)

5   The surface area of a person's body, A square metres, is given by the formula
$$A = \sqrt{\dfrac{hm}{3600}}$$
where h is the height in centimetres and m is the mass in kilograms.
   (a) Dolores is 167 cm high and has a mass of 70 kg.
       Calculate the surface area of her body. [1]
   (b) Erik has a mass of 80 kg. Find his height if $A = 1.99$. [2]
   (c) Make h the subject of the formula. [3]

(CIE Paper 4, Nov 2003)

6   Make c the subject of the formula $b = \sqrt{3c - 5}$. [3]

(CIE Paper 2, Nov 2004)

Chapter 9

Indices

This chapter will show you how to

✔ calculate powers and roots

✔ revise, use and develop the laws of indices

9.1 Calculating powers and roots

You will need to know

● how to use index (power) notation.

Expressions such as 4^2 and 5^3 are examples of **index notation**.

This can be used to simplify numerical or algebraic expressions (for example $5 \times 5 \times 5 = 5^3$).

You can calculate any number raised to any power.

For example, $3^4 = 3 \times 3 \times 3 \times 3 = 81$
and $2^7 = 2 \times 2 \times 2 \times 2 \times 2 \times 2 \times 2 = 128$.

The above can be done without using a calculator, but a calculator is useful when dealing with decimal numbers.
There is a key on your calculator which will work out powers of any number.

To work out $(2.3)^6$ key in

which gives an answer of 148.035889

> Remember that calculators vary and this key sometimes has the x and the y the other way round. It may be a 'second function' key.

Negative indices

Indices can be negative, for example, 3^{-4}. You work this out in the same way as for positive indices. Key in

This gives an answer of 0.01234568...

> There is more about negative indices in Section 9.3.

Roots

Calculators usually have a key for working out roots. It is often the second function of the calculator key used for powers.

Your calculator has a key for working out powers or or

... and a key to work out roots

Remember that might be a combination of SHIFT or 2nd F and

So to work out $\sqrt[5]{360}$, you need to key

| 5 | | 3 | 6 | 0 | = |

which gives an answer of 3.2453...

EXERCISE 9A

1 Find the value of the following, giving your answer to 3 s.f.
   (a) 2^{12}
   (b) 7.2^4
   (c) -8^7
   (d) $(-2.9)^6$
   (e) $\sqrt[4]{81}$
   (f) $\sqrt[6]{300}$
   (g) $\sqrt[4]{100}$
   (h) $\sqrt[5]{-36.25}$
   (i) 3.7^{-3}
   (j) 6^{-2}

2 Which has the greater value of each pair?
   (a) 4^5 or 5^4
   (b) 3^9 or 9^3
   (c) $\sqrt[4]{4.9}$ or $\sqrt[5]{9.4}$

3 Complete the following calculations, giving your answer to 3 s.f.
   (a) $1.6^5 + 3.4^4$
   (b) $2.6^7 - \sqrt[5]{16\ 807}$
   (c) $\dfrac{(4.9)^8}{\sqrt[6]{4096}}$

4 A student calculates a number as 3.6^{15}.
   What is this value (to 3 s.f.)?

5 Calculate the following, giving your answers to 3 s.f.
   (a) $5^5 \times 3^4$
   (b) $5.6^{-6} \times \sqrt[4]{4.6}$
   (c) $(-8.2)^5 \div -4.1$
   (d) $\dfrac{-7^5 \times -6^6}{\sqrt[5]{9000}}$
   (e) $\dfrac{2^9 + 1^{-12}}{\sqrt[6]{52} + 14 + 1}$
   (f) $\dfrac{(-3.8)^4}{-2.9}$

6 Find the value of the following where $x = 4$ and $y = 5$.
   (a) x^5
   (b) y^6
   (c) 4^x
   (d) 7^y
   (e) x^y
   (f) $7x^y$

7 Sally is given a choice for her birthday. She can have
   2 to the power of the number of days in April (in cents),
   or $20 multiplied by the number of days in April.
   Which one should she take?

9.2 Multiplying and dividing expressions involving indices

You will need to know
● how to simplify fractions

 **EXAMPLE 1**

Simplify these.

(a) $4^3 \times 4^4$ (b) $r^3 \times r^2$ (c) $4h^2 \times 5h^4$

(a) $4^3 \times 4^4 = 4 \times 4 \times 4 \times 4 \times 4 \times 4 \times 4$
$\qquad = 4^7$

(b) $r^3 \times r^2 = r \times r \times r \times r \times r$
$\qquad = r^5$

(c) $4h^2 \times 5h^4 = 4 \times h \times h \times 5 \times h \times h \times h \times h$
$\qquad = 4 \times 5 \times h \times h \times h \times h \times h \times h$
$\qquad = 20 \times h^6$
$\qquad = 20h^6$

> Remember $r^3 = r \times r \times r$.

> The order in which you multiply does not matter, so you can rewrite this with the numbers first then the letters.

 **EXAMPLE 2**

Simplify these.

(a) $6^5 \div 6^2$ (b) $c^3 \div c^4$ (c) $10b^2 \div 5b^4$

(a) $6^5 \div 6^2 = \dfrac{6 \times 6 \times 6 \times 6 \times 6}{6 \times 6}$
$\qquad = \dfrac{6 \times 6 \times 6 \times \cancel{6} \times \cancel{6}}{\cancel{6} \times \cancel{6}}$
$\qquad = 6 \times 6 \times 6$
$\qquad = 6^3$

(b) $c^3 \div c^4 = \dfrac{c \times c \times c}{c \times c \times c \times c}$
$\qquad = \dfrac{\cancel{c}^1 \times \cancel{c}^1 \times \cancel{c}^1}{\cancel{c}^1 \times \cancel{c}^1 \times \cancel{c}^1 \times c}$
$\qquad = \dfrac{1}{c}$

(c) $10b^2 \div 5b^4 = \dfrac{10 \times b \times b}{5 \times b \times b \times b \times b}$
$\qquad = \dfrac{10 \times \cancel{b}^1 \times \cancel{b}^1}{5 \times b \times b \times \cancel{b}^1 \times \cancel{b}^1}$
$\qquad = \dfrac{10}{5 \times b \times b}$
$\qquad = \dfrac{10}{5b^2}$
$\qquad = \dfrac{2}{b^2}$

> Write the division as a fraction.
>
> Because the top and bottom of the fraction are both just multiplications, you can cancel any terms which are on both the top and bottom.

> Remember to divide the 10 by the 5.

EXERCISE 9B

1 Simplify each of these.
   (a) $12^2 \times 12^7$ (b) $45^3 \times 45^4$ (c) $6^2 \times 6^{10}$
   (d) $5^2 \times 5^3 \times 5^6$ (e) $7^1 \times 7^2 \times 7^5 \times 7^8$

2 Simplify each of these.

Remember $x = x^1$.

   (a) $a^3 \times a^2$ (b) $b^4 \times b^3$ (c) $c^2 \times c^4$ (d) $d^5 \times d^5$
   (e) $x^3 \times x$ (f) $y^2 \times y$ (g) $z \times z^4$ (h) $w \times w^3$

3 Simplify each of these.

Use Example 1 to help.

   (a) $2a^3 \times 3a^4$ (b) $5b^4 \times 3b^5$
   (c) $4c^2 \times c^6$ (d) $3d^4 \times 3d^4$

4 Can you see a quicker way to answer questions 2 and 3? If you can, describe it using an example to help.

5 Simplify each of these.

Use Example 2 to help.

   (a) $p^5 \div p^2$ (b) $q^6 \div q^2$ (c) $r^4 \div r^3$ (d) $s^6 \div s^3$
   (e) $e^2 \div e^5$ (f) $f^2 \div f^6$ (g) $g^3 \div g^4$ (h) $h \div h^6$

6 Simplify each of these.
   (a) $5x^5 \div x^2$ (b) $8y^6 \div 4y^2$ (c) $12r^4 \div 3r^3$ (d) $2s^2 \div 10s^5$

Use Example 2 to help.

7 Can you see a quicker way to answer questions 5 and 6? If you can, describe it using an example to help.

Remember $\frac{2}{10}$ simplifies to $\frac{1}{5}$.

9.3 Laws of indices

You may have noticed by now some of the rules that make it easier to simplify expressions involving indices. They are known as the **index laws** or **laws of indices**.

To multiply powers of the same number or variable, add the indices.

$$4^3 \times 4^2 = 4^{3+2}$$
$$= 4^5$$

$$x^3 \times x^2 = x^{3+2}$$
$$= x^5$$

$$4^3 \times 4^2 = 4 \times 4 \times 4 \times 4 \times 4$$
$$= 4^{3+2}$$
$$= 4^5$$

In general $x^m \times x^n = x^{m+n}$

To divide powers of the same number or variable, subtract the indices.

$$6^5 \div 6^3 = 6^{5-3}$$
$$= 6^2$$

$$t^5 \div t^3 = t^{5-3}$$
$$= t^2$$

$$6^5 \div 6^3 = \frac{6 \times 6 \times \cancel{6^1} \times \cancel{6^1} \times \cancel{6^1}}{\cancel{6^1} \times \cancel{6^1} \times \cancel{6^1}}$$
$$= 6^{5-3}$$
$$= 6^2$$

In general $x^m \div x^n = x^{m-n}$

Remember, the multiplication and division laws only work when the powers are of the *same* number or variable.

 EXAMPLE 3

Simplify.

(a) $5^2 \times 5^3$

(b) $3a^4 \times 5a^3$

(c) $g^3 \times g \times g^2$

(a) $5^2 \times 5^3 = 5^{2+3}$
$= 5^5$

(b) $3a^4 \times 5a^3 = 3 \times a^4 \times 5 \times a^3$
$= 3 \times 5 \times a^4 \times a^3$
$= 15 \times a^{4+3}$
$= 15a^7$

Multiply the numbers first then multiply the powers of a.

(c) $g^3 \times g \times g^2 = g^3 \times g^1 \times g^2$
$= g^{3+1+2}$
$= g^6$

Any value raised to the power 1 is itself.
$7^1 = 7; 5 = 5^1; x^1 = x; h = h^1$.
You don't normally write the power 1.

 EXAMPLE 4

Simplify.

(a) $3^6 \div 3^2$ **(b)** $x^3 \div x^5$ **(c)** $12b^5 \div 4b^3$ **(d)** $\dfrac{t^4 \times t}{t^3}$

(a) $3^6 \div 3^2 = 3^{6-2}$
$= 3^4$

(b) $x^3 \div x^5 = x^{3-5}$
$= x^{-2}$

You can have negative powers as well as positive ones.

(c) $12b^5 \div 4b^3 = \dfrac{12 \times b^5}{4 \times b^3}$
$= \dfrac{12}{4} \times \dfrac{b^5}{b^3}$
$= 3 \times b^{5-3}$
$= 3 \times b^2$
$= 3b^2$

As with the multiplication example, we can deal with the numbers first, $12 \div 4 = 3$; then deal with the letters, $b^5 \div b^3 = b^2$.

(d) $\dfrac{t^4 \times t}{t^3} = \dfrac{t^4 \times t^1}{t^3}$
$= \dfrac{t^5}{t^3}$
$= t^{5-3}$
$= t^2$

Simplify the top first, $t^4 \times t = t^5$; then deal with the division, $t^5 \div t^3 = t^2$.

Simplify each of these.

1 (a) $6^3 \times 6^4$ (b) $13^4 \times 13^8$ (c) $25^8 \times 25^9$
    (d) $5^4 \times 5^6 \times 5^7$ (e) $33 \times 33^6 \times 33^8$ (f) $12^3 \times 12^6 \times 12^9$

2 (a) $m^3 \times m^2$ (b) $a^4 \times a^3$ (c) $n^2 \times n^4$
    (d) $u^5 \times u^5$ (e) $t^3 \times t^6$

3 (a) $d^3 \times d$ (b) $a^2 \times a$ (c) $r \times r^4$
    (d) $e \times e^3$ (e) $t \times t^6$

4 (a) $2h^3 \times 3h^4$ (b) $5e^4 \times 3e^5$ (c) $4g^2 \times g^6$
    (d) $3r \times 3r^4$ (e) $6e^3 \times 4e$

5 (a) $a^5 \div a^2$ (b) $t^6 \div t^2$ (c) $e^4 \div e^3$
    (d) $s^6 \div s^3$ (e) $t^2 \div t^2$

6 (a) $e^2 \div e^5$ (b) $f^2 \div f^6$ (c) $g^3 \div g^4$
    (d) $h \div h^4$ (e) $w \div w^6$

7 (a) $5x^5 \div x^2$ (b) $6y^6 \div 2y^2$ (c) $12r^4 \div 4r^3$
    (d) $2s^2 \div 8s^5$ (e) $8t^4 \div 4t$

8 (a) $h^3 \times h^4 \times h^2$ (b) $e^4 \times e \times e^3$ (c) $4c^2 \times c^6 \times 6c$

9 (a) $\dfrac{d^4 \times d}{d^3}$ (b) $\dfrac{a^2 \times 3a^2}{a}$ (c) $\dfrac{4r \times 3r^2}{6r^2}$

Powers of 1 and 0

Any number or variable raised to the power 1 is equal to the number or variable itself.   Examples $3^1 = 3$, $x^1 = x$.

Any number or variable raised to the power 0 is equal to 1.
Examples $3^0 = 1$, $x^0 = 1$.

The following shows how the rule for a power of zero is obtained.

The division rule is 'subtract indices'. Look what happens when you apply it to this example

$$x^7 \div x^7 = x^{7-7} = x^0$$

But when you divide anything by itself you always get an answer of 1, which means that $x^0 = 1$.

EXAMPLE 5

Work out the value of these.

(a) 4^0 (b) $8k^0$ (c) $(3wz)^0$

In (b) it is only the k that is raised to power 0.

In (c) everything inside the bracket is raised to power 0 so the answer is simply 1.
(There is no term outside the bracket.)

(a) $4^0 = 1$

(b) $8k^0 = 8 \times k^0 = 8 \times 1 = 8$

(c) $(3wz)^0 = 1$

Negative indices and reciprocals

In the expression $\dfrac{1}{x^7}$, you can replace 1 with x^0. Then follow the index law for dividing.

$$\frac{1}{x^7} = 1 \div x^7 = x^0 \div x^7 = x^{0-7} = x^{-7}$$

This shows you that the **reciprocal** of a power is the same as that quantity raised to the equivalent negative power.

The reciprocal of x^n means '1 divided by x^n'.

$$\frac{1}{x^n} = x^{-n}$$

For example

$$\frac{1}{3^4} = 3^{-4} \qquad \frac{1}{x^4} = x^{-4} \qquad \frac{1}{y} = \frac{1}{y^1} = y^{-1} \qquad a^{-5} = \frac{1}{a^5}$$

x^{-n} can be read as the reciprocal of x^n, or $\dfrac{1}{x^n}$.

EXAMPLE 6

Work out the value of these.

(a) 9^{-2} (b) $3^{-3} \times 6^2$ (c) $(0.2)^{-4}$

The fraction in (b) has been written in its simplest form then as a mixed number.

(a) $9^{-2} = \dfrac{1}{9^2} = \dfrac{1}{81}$

(b) $3^{-3} \times 6^2 = \dfrac{1}{3^3} \times 6^2 = \dfrac{1}{27} \times 36 = \dfrac{36}{27} = \dfrac{4}{3} = 1\tfrac{1}{3}$

$0.0016 = \dfrac{16}{10\,000}$

(c) $(0.2)^{-4} = \dfrac{1}{(0.2)^4} = \dfrac{1}{0.0016} = \dfrac{10\,000}{16} = 625$

    or

$(0.2)^{-4} = (\tfrac{1}{5})^{-4} = (\tfrac{5}{1})^4 = 5^4 = 625$

Inverting the fraction and changing the negative power to a positive one is a very useful skill.

1 Work out the value of these.

(a) 12^1 (b) 7.6^0 (c) 1^{36} (d) $2.6^0 \times 9.7^1$

2 Write each of these in fraction form.

(a) 4^{-2} (b) 3^{-5} (c) 5^{-3} (d) 2^{-10}

3 Find the value of your answers to question 2, giving your answers in fraction form, e.g. $2^{-2} = \dfrac{1}{2^2} = \dfrac{1}{4}$.

4 Write each of these in negative index form.

(a) $\dfrac{1}{3^2}$ (b) $\dfrac{1}{6^3}$ (c) $\dfrac{1}{10^9}$ (d) $\dfrac{1}{8^4}$

5 Work these out.

(a) $4^{-2} \times 8^2$ (b) $7^3 \times 10^{-2}$ (c) $9^{-3} \div 3^{-2}$ (d) $(0.4)^4 \div 10^{-5}$

6 Work out the value of the following and then write a sentence about what you notice.

$\dfrac{1}{2^{-1}}$ $\dfrac{1}{2^{-2}}$ $\dfrac{1}{2^{-3}}$ $\dfrac{1}{2^{-4}}$

EXAMPLE 7

Write d^{-3} as a fraction and find its value when $d = 4$.

(a) $d^{-3} = \dfrac{1}{d^3}$

  when $d = 4$ $d^{-3} = \dfrac{1}{d^3}$

  $= \dfrac{1}{4^3}$

  $= \dfrac{1}{64}$

EXAMPLE 8

Write each of these using negative indices.

(a) $\dfrac{6}{a}$

(b) $\dfrac{12x^2}{3x^4}$

(a) $\dfrac{6}{a} = \dfrac{6}{a^1}$

  $= 6a^{-1}$

(b) $\dfrac{12x^2}{3x^4} = \dfrac{12}{3} \times x^{2-4}$

  $= 4x^{-2}$

Note that $a^{-1} = \dfrac{1}{a}$. This is very useful to remember.

Remember $x^m \div x^n = x^{m-n}$

EXERCISE 9E

1. Write each of these as a fraction.
   - (a) x^{-3}
   - (b) x^{-4}
   - (c) x^{-1}
   - (d) x^{-5}
   - (e) $5x^{-3}$
   - (f) $3x^{-2}$
   - (g) $6x^{-4}$
   - (h) $4x^{-1}$

2. Work out the value of each of the expressions in question 1 when $x = 2$.

3. Write each of these using negative indices.
   - (a) $\dfrac{1}{k^2}$
   - (b) $\dfrac{1}{e^5}$
   - (c) $\dfrac{1}{g}$
   - (d) $\dfrac{1}{x^n}$
   - (e) $\dfrac{6}{p}$
   - (f) $\dfrac{5}{a^3}$
   - (g) $\dfrac{4}{d^2}$
   - (h) $\dfrac{8}{h^m}$
   - (i) $\dfrac{3x^2}{x^4}$
   - (j) $\dfrac{12a^3}{3a^7}$
   - (k) $\dfrac{9b}{3b^2}$
   - (l) $\dfrac{4y^2}{6y^5}$

4. Simplify each of these and write your answer
   - (i) using negative indices
   - (ii) as a fraction.
   - (a) $e^2 \div e^5$
   - (b) $8s^3 \div s^4$
   - (c) $\dfrac{20f}{5f^3}$
   - (d) $\dfrac{12t^3}{15t^7}$
   - (e) $n^2 \times n^{-4}$
   - (f) $m^{-1} \times 3m^{-2}$
   - (g) $\dfrac{2a^2 \times 3a^2}{3a^6}$
   - (h) $\dfrac{5q \times 3q^2}{10q^3 \times q}$

Problems with more than one variable

 EXAMPLE 9

Simplify.
- (a) $3xy^2 \times 5xy$
- (b) $\dfrac{10a^3b^2}{2a^2b^2}$

(a) $3xy^2 \times 5xy = 3 \times x \times y^2 \times 5 \times x \times y$

$\qquad = 3 \times 5 \times x \times x \times y^2 \times y$

$\qquad = 15 \times x^2 \times y^3$

$\qquad = 15x^2y^3$

(b) $\dfrac{10a^3b^2}{2a^2b^2} = \dfrac{10 \times a^3 \times b^2}{2 \times a^2 \times b^2}$

$\qquad = \dfrac{10}{2} \times \dfrac{a^3}{a^2} \times \dfrac{b^2}{b^2}$

$\qquad = 5 \times a^1 \times 1$

$\qquad = 5a$

Deal with the numbers first, then each of the different letters in turn, first the xs then the ys.

Your answer does not need to show the intermediate lines of working.

Deal with the numbers first, then each of the different letters in turn, first the as then the bs.

$\dfrac{a^3}{a^2} = a^{3-2} = a^1$

$\dfrac{b^2}{b^2} = b^{2-2} = b^0 = 1$

1 Simplify these expressions.

(a) $4ab^2 \times 2ab$

(b) $3f^2g \times 7f^3g^2$

(c) $5xy^2 \times 4x^3y$

(d) $6p^4q^3 \times 6p^2q^2$

(e) $7r^2s \times 4s^5 \times 2r$

(f) $3c^3 \times 5cd \times 5d^4$

> Write the answers using negative indices *and* as algebraic fractions, where appropriate.

2 Simplify these expressions.

(a) $ab^2 \div a$

(b) $9f^2g \div 3f^2$

(c) $8xy^2 \div 4x$

(d) $6p^4q^3 \div 2p^2$

(e) $12r^2s^3 \div 4s^2$

(f) $7c^3d^4 \div 7d^3$

3 Simplify these expressions.

(a) $\dfrac{6x^3y^2}{3x^2y^2}$

(b) $\dfrac{4j^2k^4}{jk^2}$

(c) $\dfrac{6a^2b^3}{6a^2b}$

(d) $\dfrac{9m^4n^3}{3mn^3}$

(e) $\dfrac{4d^3e^2}{6(de)^3}$

(f) $\dfrac{16p^3q^4}{4p^3q^2}$

4 Match the expression on the left with the correct one from the right.

A	$3a^3b \times 2ab^2$
B	$a^2 \times 6b \times ab$
C	$12a^4b^4 \div 2a^2b$
D	$6a^2b^3 \div 3ab \times 2a$
E	$2a^3b^2 \times 6a^4b^2 \div 3a^3b$
F	$8a^2b^3 \times 3a^4b^2 \div 4a^3b$

G	$4a^4b^3$
H	$6a^4b^3$
I	$4a^2b^2$
J	$6a^3b^2$
K	$6a^3b^4$
L	$6a^2b^3$

5 Simplify these expressions.

(a) $\dfrac{6x^3y^2 \times 3x^2y}{9x^4y^2}$

(b) $\dfrac{4a^2b \times 6ab^3}{8a^3b^2}$

(c) $\dfrac{8c^3d^3}{2c^2d \times 2c^2d^3}$

(d) $\dfrac{9m^2n \times m^2n^2}{3m^2n^3 \times 2mn}$

6 Simplify these expressions.

(a) $\dfrac{4r^2st \times 6rs^2t}{12r^2s^2t}$

(b) $\dfrac{2x^3y^2z \times 10x^2yz}{5x^2yz^3}$

(c) $\dfrac{5abc \times 2b^2c^3 \times a^3bc}{3ab^3 \times 10ab^2c^2}$

7 If $s = 3$ and $t = 0.5$ find the value of the following

(a) s^{-2}

(b) t^{-4}

(c) $5s^3t^{-1}$

(d) $\dfrac{s^{-3}}{t}$

Power of a power

To raise a power of a number or variable to a further power multiply the indices.

$$(5^2)^3 = 5^{2 \times 3}$$
$$= 5^6$$

$$(p^2)^3 = p^{2 \times 3}$$
$$= p^6$$

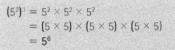

$$(5^2)^3 = 5^2 \times 5^2 \times 5^2$$
$$= (5 \times 5) \times (5 \times 5) \times (5 \times 5)$$
$$= 5^6$$

In general $(x^m)^n = x^{mn}$

EXAMPLE 10

Simplify these.

(a) $(r^3)^2$ **(b)** $(2k^2)^3$

(a) $(r^3)^2 = r^{3 \times 2}$
$$= r^6$$

(b) $(2k^2)^3 = 2^3 \times (k^2)^3$
$$= 8 \times k^{2 \times 3}$$
$$= 8 \times k^6$$
$$= 8k^6$$

Deal with the number first, $2^3 = 8$; then with the letter
$(k^2)^3 = k^{2 \times 3} = k^6.$

EXERCISE 9G

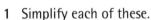

1 Simplify each of these.

    (a) $(p^3)^2$ **(b)** $(q^2)^4$ **(c)** $(r^3)^4$ **(d)** $(f^5)^3$ **(e)** $(d^4)^3$

2 Simplify each of these.

    (a) $(2j^2)^3$ **(b)** $(2m^3)^4$ **(c)** $(3w^5)^3$ **(d)** $(5x^4)^3$ **(e)** $(7d^5)^2$

3 Write the following as a single integer power of 8 where possible.

    (a) $8^5 \times 8^3$ **(b)** $8^3 \div 8^5$ **(c)** $8^4 + 8^6$

    (d) $8^2 \times 8^9 \times 8^3$ **(e)** $(8^3)^5$ **(f)** $\dfrac{8^4 \times 8^7}{8^3}$

    (g) $\dfrac{8 \times (8^2)^3}{8^6 \times 8^3}$ **(h)** $\dfrac{(8^3 \div 8^7) \times (8^3 \times 8^1)}{8}$

4 Write as a single integer power of 7 where possible.

    (a) $7^{-3} \times 7^{-2}$ **(b)** $7^{-3} \div 7^3$ **(c)** $(7^{-2})^3$

    (d) $7^{-3} - 7^3$ **(e)** $7^4 \div 7^{-3}$ **(f)** $\dfrac{7^{-2} \times 7^5 \times (7^4)^{-2}}{(7^{-3})^6}$

    (g) $\dfrac{1}{7^3} \times \dfrac{1}{7^7}$ **(h)** $\dfrac{1}{7^4} \times \dfrac{1}{7^2} \div \dfrac{1}{7^3}$

9.4 Expressions involving indices

In the rest of this section you will see how to develop the index laws so that you can handle quite complicated expressions involving indices.

Suppose you are asked to answer this question,

Work out the value of $5^{\frac{1}{2}} \times 5^{\frac{1}{2}}$

Use the law for multiplying powers $5^{\frac{1}{2}} \times 5^{\frac{1}{2}} = 5^{\frac{1}{2}+\frac{1}{2}} = 5^1 = 5$

This follows directly from the definition of a square root.

You can see that you have multiplied something by itself to get 5 so this means you must have started with the square root of 5.

This means that $\sqrt{5} = 5^{\frac{1}{2}}$

and the same is true for any square root, so that

$$\sqrt{7} = 7^{\frac{1}{2}} \quad \text{and} \quad \sqrt{20} = 20^{\frac{1}{2}} \quad \text{and} \quad \sqrt{x} = x^{\frac{1}{2}}.$$

In the same way can you see that since

$$x^{\frac{1}{3}} \times x^{\frac{1}{3}} \times x^{\frac{1}{3}} = x^{\frac{1}{3}+\frac{1}{3}+\frac{1}{3}} = x^1$$

then $x^{\frac{1}{3}}$ must be the cube root of x, i.e. $\sqrt[3]{x} = x^{\frac{1}{3}}$.

You can extend this idea to any fractional power.

In general $\sqrt[n]{x} = x^{\frac{1}{n}}$

EXAMPLE 11

Work out the value of

(a) $36^{\frac{1}{2}}$ (b) $81^{\frac{1}{4}}$ (c) $64^{\frac{1}{3}} \times 8^{-1}$

(a) $36^{\frac{1}{2}} = \sqrt{36} = 6$

(b) $81^{\frac{1}{4}} = \sqrt[4]{81} = 3$

(c) $64^{\frac{1}{3}} \times 8^{-1} = \sqrt[3]{64} \times \frac{1}{8^1} = 4 \times \frac{1}{8} = \frac{4}{8} = \frac{1}{2}$

For $\sqrt{36}$ give the positive square root.

Part (c) uses the rules for negative and fractional indices.

EXERCISE 9H

1 Work out the value of these.

(a) $25^{\frac{1}{2}}$ (b) $144^{\frac{1}{2}}$ (c) $27^{\frac{1}{3}}$

(d) $16^{\frac{1}{4}}$ (e) $216^{\frac{1}{3}}$ (f) $625^{\frac{1}{4}}$

(g) $100\,000^{\frac{1}{5}}$ (h) $(512/1000)^{\frac{1}{3}}$

2 Write the following using index notation.

(a) $\sqrt{875}$ (b) $\sqrt[4]{184}$ (c) $\sqrt[3]{89}$ (d) $\sqrt[8]{864}$

3 Work out the value of these.

(a) $25^{-\frac{1}{2}}$ (b) $32^{-\frac{1}{5}}$ (c) $81^{-\frac{1}{4}}$ (d) $1024^{-\frac{1}{10}}$

Finding $x^{\frac{m}{n}}$ where $m \neq 1$

You also need to know how to find the value of an expression such as $x^{\frac{m}{n}}$ where the power is a fraction with a number other than 1 in the numerator.

This is a combination of the 'power to a power' rule and the rule for roots.

> Always remember that the number on the top of the fraction is the power and the number on the bottom is the root.

$$x^{\frac{m}{n}} = (\sqrt[n]{x})^m \quad \text{or} \quad x^{\frac{m}{n}} = \sqrt[n]{(x^m)}$$

These rules are best remembered as

$x^{\frac{m}{n}} = (\sqrt[n]{x})^m$ 'take the root then raise to the power'

$x^{\frac{m}{n}} = \sqrt[n]{(x^m)}$ 'raise to the power then take the root'

You can see that these are the same in the following example,

$$(25^2)^{\frac{1}{2}} = 625^{\frac{1}{2}} = 25$$

and

$$(25^{\frac{1}{2}})^2 = 5^2 = 25$$

Using the rules you have learnt you can see why this works. The inverse of raising x to the power n (x^n) is raising x^n to the power $\dfrac{1}{n}$

$$(x^n)^{\frac{1}{n}} = x^{n \times \frac{1}{n}}$$
$$= x^{\frac{n}{n}}$$
$$= x^1$$
$$= x$$

> As $(x^m)^n = x^{m \times n}$

> As $\frac{n}{n} = 1$

> As $x^1 = x$

You will find that it is usually easier to do the first of these (i.e. root first then power), because it keeps the numbers smaller and so easier to handle.

⊕ EXAMPLE 12

Work out the value of

(a) $16^{\frac{3}{4}}$ (b) $125^{-\frac{2}{3}}$

(a) $16^{\frac{3}{4}} = (\sqrt[4]{16})^3$ or $\sqrt[4]{16^3}$

$(\sqrt[4]{16})^3 = (2)^3 = 8$

$(\sqrt[4]{16})^3 = \sqrt[4]{4096} = 8$

(b) $125^{-\frac{2}{3}} = \dfrac{1}{125^{\frac{2}{3}}} = \dfrac{1}{\sqrt[3]{(125)^2}} = \dfrac{1}{(5)^2} = \dfrac{1}{25}$

> $2^3 = 8$ is easy to do, $\sqrt[4]{4096} = 8$ is not one you would be expected to know!

> You should know that $\sqrt[3]{125} = 5$ because you are expected to know the cubes of 2, 3, 4, 5 and 10.

> Do not even try (b) the other way ... you would have to calculate 125^2!

Notice that (b) combines the rule for $x^{\frac{m}{n}}$ with the one for negative indices.

EXAMPLE 13

Find the value of n in each of the following.

(a) $2^n = \dfrac{1}{32}$ (b) $9^n = 3$ (c) $4^{n+1} = 2^8$

(a) $2^n = \dfrac{1}{32}$ $32 = 2^5$ so $\dfrac{1}{32} = \dfrac{1}{2^5} = 2^{-5}$ giving $n = -5$

(b) $9^n = 3$ $\sqrt{9} = 3$ so $9^{\frac{1}{2}} = 3$ giving $n = \frac{1}{2}$

(c) $4^{n+1} = 2^8$ $2^8 = 256$ and $256 = 4^4$ so $4^{n+1} = 4^4$

   giving $n + 1 = 4$ and so $n = 3$

In (c) it is easier to work out the value of 2^8 first, then think what power of 4 will be needed to give 256.

EXERCISE 9I

1 Work out the value of these.
   (a) $125^{\frac{2}{3}}$ (b) $64^{\frac{2}{3}}$ (c) $81^{\frac{1}{4}}$ (d) $1296^{\frac{3}{4}}$
   (e) $729^{\frac{5}{6}}$ (f) $343^{-\frac{2}{3}}$ (g) $32^{\frac{7}{5}}$ (h) $625^{-1.25}$

Change the decimal into a fraction.

2 Write these using index notation.
   (a) $\sqrt{52^3}$ (b) $\sqrt[3]{79^2}$ (c) $\sqrt[5]{143^3}$ (d) $\sqrt[4]{728^3}$

3 Which is greater?
   (a) $2401^{\frac{3}{4}}$ or $729^{\frac{2}{3}}$ (b) $216^{\frac{2}{3}}$ or $256^{\frac{3}{4}}$ (c) $3375^{\frac{2}{3}}$ or $3125^{\frac{4}{5}}$

4 Complete these calculations.
   (a) $8^{\frac{2}{3}} \times 81^{\frac{1}{4}}$ (b) $512^{\frac{2}{3}} \div 128^{\frac{3}{7}}$
   (c) $1728^{\frac{2}{3}} \times 729^{\frac{2}{3}} \div 10^{\frac{2}{3}}$

5 Find the value of n in each of these.
   (a) $2^n = 128$ (b) $5^n = \frac{1}{3125}$
   (c) $81^n = 3$ (d) $25^{n-1} = 5^6$
   (e) $64^n = 4$ (f) $8^{2n+1} = 2^{15}$
   (g) $4^{3n-2} = 16^2$ (h) $8^n = 2^{-9}$

6 (a) Draw the graph of $y = 2^x$ for values of x from -2 to 3.
      (Use a scale of 2 cm to 1 unit.)
   (b) Estimate the square root of 2 from your graph.

7 Find the value of a and b.
   (a) $8^{\frac{a}{b}} = 4$ (b) $1024^{\frac{a}{b}} = 8$ (c) $625^{\frac{a}{b}} = 125$

EXAMINATION QUESTIONS

1 **(a)** Write $(8x^4y)^2$ without brackets. [1]

    (b) Simplify $(8x^4y)^2 \div x^2y^{-1}$. [2]

(CIE Paper 2, Jun 2000)

---

2 Find the value of x, y and z when

    (a) $3^x = 1$, [1]

    (b) $10^x = 0.01$, [1]

    (c) $16^z = 2$. [1]

(CIE Paper 2, Jun 2000)

---

3 Find the value of $\left(\dfrac{9}{4}\right)^{\frac{-3}{2}}$, giving your answer as an **exact fraction**. [2]

(CIE Paper 2, Nov 2000)

---

4 In computing terms, a "kilobyte" is 2^{10} bytes and each **byte** is 8 **bits**.

    (a) 1 kilobyte is 2^x **bits**. Find x. [1]

    (b) 4 kilobytes is 2^y **bits**. Find y. [1]

(CIE Paper 2, Nov 2001)

---

5 Find the **exact** value of

    (a) 3^{-2}, [1]

    (b) $(1\frac{7}{9})^{\frac{1}{2}}$. [2]

(CIE Paper 2, Nov 2002)

---

6 **(a)** $3^x = \frac{1}{3}$. Write down the value of x. [1]

    (b) $5^y = k$. Find 5^{y+1}, in terms of k. [1]

(CIE Paper 2, Nov 2003)

---

7 Simplify $\frac{2}{3}p^{12} \times \frac{3}{4}p^8$. [2]

(CIE Paper 2, Jun 2004)

Chapter 10

Probability

This chapter will show you how to
- ✔ define and use probability
- ✔ draw tree diagrams
- ✔ solve conditional probability problems

10.1 Probability

An **event**, such as throwing a dice, can have different **outcomes**.

You can describe the chances of an outcome using words such as *certain*, *likely*, *even*, *unlikely* and *impossible*.

> The **probability scale** uses numbers between 0 and 1.

$0 \leqslant$ probability $\leqslant 1$.

The connection between the values on the probability scale and the descriptive words is shown below

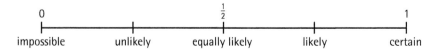

You can write probability as a fraction, a decimal or a percentage.

Converting between fractions, decimals and percentages was covered in Chapter 3.

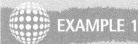 **EXAMPLE 1**

What is the probability of obtaining a Head when you toss a fair coin?

$$p(H) = p(T) = \tfrac{1}{2}$$
$$= 0.5$$

A fair coin is one where Head and Tail are equally likely.

p(H) is shorthand for the probability of throwing a head, and p(T) for the probability of throwing a tail.

The result which actually occurs is called an **outcome**.

Only two outcomes are possible when tossing a coin.

The probability of throwing a 3 on a fair six-sided dice must be one out of six, since there are six faces and six numbers (six possible outcomes). We write this as

$p(3) = \frac{1}{6}$

You must write a probability as a fraction or a decimal, *not* 1 out of 6 or 1 : 6.

$$\text{Probability} = \frac{\text{number of successful outcomes}}{\text{total number of possible outcomes}}$$

 EXAMPLE 2

A fair eight-sided (octahedral) dice is thrown.
Find the probability of obtaining
(a) a 3   (b) a prime number.

(a) The probability $p(3) = \frac{1}{8}$.

The value 3 can only occur once so there is only 1 successful outcome. The list of possible outcomes is 1, 2, 3, 4, 5, 6, 7 or 8 so 8 possible outcomes altogether.

(b) The probability $p(\text{prime}) = \frac{4}{8} = \frac{1}{2}$.

The only prime number values are 2, 3, 5 and 7, so there are 4 successful outcomes.

 EXERCISE 10A

1 A class of students sat a test paper and scored the following marks.

   13 13 21 11 19 7 12 17 16 19 22 13

   The pass mark for the test was 14.
   What is the probability that a student chosen at random
   (a) passed   (b) failed
   (c) scored more than 18   (d) scored 15?

2 A number is chosen at random from the integers 8 to 15 inclusive.
   What is the probability that the number is
   (a) even   (b) a multiple of 5
   (c) square   (d) prime?

3 A bag contains 8 red and 4 yellow sweets.
   (a) Julio takes a sweet at random and eats it. What is the probability that it is yellow?
   (b) Sabina now chooses a sweet at random. What is the probability that it is red?

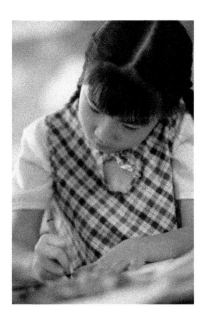

4   A survey of the methods of travel for a class of 30 gave
    these results.

Bus	Walk	Cycle	Car
7	8	5	10

What is the probability that a student chosen at random travels
to school

(a) by bus   (b) on wheels   (c) by train?

5   A bag contains 16 balls numbered 1 to 16 and is to be used to
    choose teams for a competition.
    The first ball chosen at random is numbered 15.
    What is the probability that the next ball chosen at random will be
    numbered 4?

6   A set of cards is numbered from 10 to 20 inclusive. A card is drawn
    at random. Find the probability that it is

(a) an odd number   (b) an even number

(c) a square number.

7   An ordinary six-sided dice is thrown. What is the probability of

(a) throwing a 2

(b) obtaining an even number

(c) throwing a number less than 4

(d) landing on a 3 or a 5

(e) not obtaining a 6?

8   In a bag of 16 sweets there are 11 blue and 5 red. What is the
    probability of picking out

(a) a blue sweet   (b) a red sweet

(c) a green sweet   (d) a blue or red sweet?

10.2 Mutually exclusive outcomes

When you toss a coin you can get either a Head (H) *or* Tail (T) but
not both at the same time. Obtaining a Head excludes a Tail. Such
outcomes are called **mutually exclusive** outcomes. If you get one
outcome you cannot get the other outcome.

Notice it is the word 'or' that is important here.

In addition, there are no other possibilities, apart from Head or Tail.
The outcomes Head and Tail are **exhaustive**. This means that the sum
of the probabilities is 1.

If you know that outcomes are mutually exclusive and exhaustive, you
can easily calculate the probabilities.

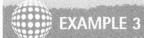 **EXAMPLE 3**

Work out the probability of obtaining a Head (H) or a Tail (T) when tossing a coin.

We know that $p(H) = p(T) = \frac{1}{2}$.

The probability of obtaining a Head or a Tail is
$$p(H \text{ or } T) = p(H) + p(T) = \frac{1}{2} + \frac{1}{2} = \frac{2}{2} = 1.$$

The key word used here is 'or'. As long as the outcomes are mutually exclusive, this means 'add' the probabilities.

For any two outcomes, say A and B, that are mutually exclusive and exhaustive,
$$p(A \text{ or } B) = p(A) + p(B) = 1$$

This is also true for more than two mutually exclusive exhaustive outcomes.

 EXAMPLE 4

A fair six-sided dice is thrown. What is the probability of getting a two or a four?

$p(2) = \frac{1}{6}$

$p(4) = \frac{1}{6}$

$p(2 \text{ or } 4) = \frac{1}{6} + \frac{1}{6}$

$= \frac{2}{6}$

$= \frac{1}{3}$

Add the probabilities.

The outcomes (2) and (4) are not exhaustive so the sum of the probabilities is less than 1.

 EXAMPLE 5

A spinner is divided into three equal sections coloured red, green and blue.
Find the probability that

(a) the spinner will land on red

(b) the spinner will not land on red.

All sectors are equal so they are all equally likely. The events are also mutually exclusive.

continued ▼

(a) $p(R) = \frac{1}{3}$

   Also $p(B) = p(G) = p(R) = \frac{1}{3}$.

(b) The probability that it will not land on red $p(\textbf{not } R)$ is the same as landing on Green **or** Blue $p(G \textbf{ or } B)$.

   $p(G \text{ or } B) = p(G) + p(B) = \frac{1}{3} + \frac{1}{3} = \frac{2}{3} = p(\text{not } R)$

Also $p(B) = p(G) = p(R) = \frac{1}{3}$

This is the same as
$1 - p(R) = 1 - \frac{1}{3} = \frac{1}{3}$
$p(\text{not } R) = 1 - p(R)$

For an event A, the probability of the event A *not* happening is given by

   $p(\text{not } A) = 1 - p(A)$

In probability you can use the word 'not' to indicate that the event will not happen.

EXERCISE 10B

1 One of the longest rivers in the world is the MISSISSIPPI. If one of these letters were chosen at random, what is the probability of

(a) choosing the letter I

(b) choosing the letter S

(c) choosing the letters M or P?

2 A fair six-sided dice is thrown. Work out the probability of

(a) throwing a 3   (b) not throwing a 1

(c) throwing a 3 or a 4   (d) not throwing a 2 or a 3.

3 A set of cards has the numbers 1 to 30 written on them. What is the probability of choosing

(a) a square number

(b a prime number

(c) a number >10?

4 A bag contains 5 green counters, 4 blue counters, 2 red counters and 3 yellow counters. What is the probability of

(a) picking a red counter

(b) picking a blue or green counter

(c) not picking a yellow counter

(d) not picking a green or red counter?

5 A bag contains 16 green, red and yellow marbles. The probability of picking a green marble is $p(G) = \frac{1}{4}$ and the probability of picking a red marble is $p(R) = \frac{3}{8}$.

(a) Work out the probability that

   (i) the marble picked will be yellow

   (ii) the marble will not be red or yellow.

(b) How many marbles of each colour are in the bag?

10.3 Listing outcomes

You should always record all the possible outcomes from a single event or two successive events in a systematic way. Use simple lists or **possibility diagrams** (two-way tables).

> The result which actually occurs is called an outcome. Only two outcomes are possible when tossing a coin – a Head or a Tail.

 **EXAMPLE 6**

Two coins (10c and 5c) are tossed at the same time. List all the possible outcomes.

Let H mean Heads and T mean Tails.
The outcomes are HH HT TH TT.
There are 4 possible outcomes in total.

> Notice that HT and TH are different because the H could be on the 10c coin and the T on the 5c coin or vice versa.

Another way of showing this information is in a **two-way table**.

		10c coin	
		H	T
5c coin	H	HH	HT
	T	TH	TT

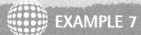 **EXAMPLE 7**

A four-sided spinner has 4 equal areas coloured red, blue, green and yellow. The spinner is spun and a coin is tossed.

List all the possible outcomes in a two-way table diagram.

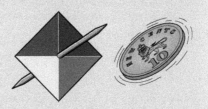

Let R, B, G and Y stand for Red, Blue, Green and Yellow.

		Spinner			
		R	B	G	Y
Coin	Heads (H)	R,H	B,H	G,H	Y,H
	Tails (T)	R,T	B,T	G,T	Y,T

> A possibility diagram is simply a two-way table. It is useful if there are a large number of outcomes.

There are 8 possible outcomes altogether.

1 Two dice, one red and one blue, are rolled at the same time.

(a) List all of the possible outcomes systematically.

(b) Complete a possibility diagram.

(c) Which method is better for recording the data?

2 Two spinners are spun at the same time and the two scores added.

(a) List all the possible outcomes.

(b) What is the probability that the final answer is negative?

3 In a game, you pick a ball from each box. To win a prize, you must select blue and a square number, or red and a prime.
List all the outcomes and work out the probability of winning.

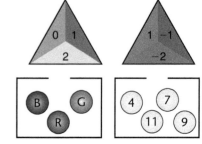

4 An ordinary six-sided dice is thrown. It is then thrown a second time. The scores are then added together. Construct a possibility diagram and from this work out

(a) the probability of the total being 11

(b) the probability of the total being less than 5.

5 Draw a possibility diagram to show the results when two dice, one green and one yellow are rolled.
Use your diagram to calculate the probability of

(a) a score of 8   (b) a score of 10

(c) a score of 10 or more   (d) a score of less than 3

6 Two spinners are used in a game and their scores are added.
If each spinner is numbered from 1 to 7, draw a possibility diagram to show the possible outcomes.
Use your diagram to find the probability that the total score is

(a) 10   (b) 1   (c) higher than 9

(d) less than 5   (e) prime   (f) square

7 Two six-sided dice are used in a board game.
Each player **multiplies** the scores on the two dice.
Some of the scores are shown below.
Copy and complete the possibility diagram.

		First dice					
		1	2	3	4	5	6
	1		2				6
	2			8			
	3			9			
Second dice	4	4					
	5					25	
	6		12				

Find the probability that the product of the scores is

(a) odd   **(b)** even   **(c)** less than 10

(d) a multiple of 5   **(e)** 6   **(f)** 40

10.4 Independent events and tree diagrams

When two or more events take place, they are **independent** if they have no effect on each other.

Examples are

- tossing a coin then tossing the coin again
- tossing a coin and rolling a dice
- rolling two dice together.

> Independent events can happen at the same time or one after the other.

For two independent events A and B, then

$$p(A \text{ and } B) = p(A) \times p(B)$$

and

the total number of outcomes =
total number of outcomes from event A ×
total number of outcomes from event B

> For two independent events, you multiply the probabilities of each outcome.

> The key word used here is 'and'. As long as the outcomes are independent, this means 'multiply' the probabilities.

The results from these events can be put into a **tree diagram**. In a tree diagram, each 'branch' of the tree represents one of the possible outcomes.

 **EXAMPLE 8**

The possibility diagram can have a number of forms.
Here is a different one from the two-way tables in examples 6 and 7.

Two six-sided dice numbered from 1 to 6 are thrown at the same time.
Draw a possibility diagram to show the outcomes.

		First dice					
		1	2	3	4	5	6
Second dice	1						
	2						
	3						
	4						
	5						
	6						

continued ▼

What you put in place of each cell depends on the question.
It might be 1,1 as in the tables in the previous example.

It might be the sum of the scores on the dice as shown in the next diagram.

First dice

		1	2	3	4	5	6
Second dice	**1**	2	3	4	5	6	7
	2	3	4	5	6	7	8
	3	4	5	6	7	8	9
	4	5	6	7	8	9	10
	5	6	7	8	9	10	11
	6	7	8	9	10	11	12

There are 36 outcomes.

You can find probabilities from this diagram.

(a) p(total score of 7) = $\frac{6}{36}$

(b) p(total score of more than 10) = $\frac{3}{36}$

There are 6 sevens shown in the green region.

There are 3 scores more than 10 in the blue region.

EXERCISE 10D

1 Hanif posts two letters.
The probability that a letter will be delivered the next day is 0.9.
Copy and complete the tree diagram below.
D stands for delivered the next day.
N stands for not delivered the next day.

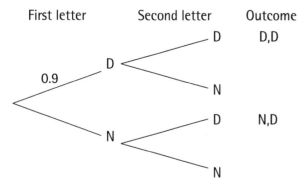

First letter	Second letter	Outcome	Probability
	D	D,D	$0.9 \times 0.9 = 0.81$
D	N		
N	D	N,D	
	N		

(a) What is the probability that neither of his letters is delivered the next day?

(b) What is the probability that one of his letters is delivered the next day?

2 Zainab and Renuka play tennis together and the probability that
   Zainab will win is $\frac{5}{6}$. They also play golf together and the probability
   that Renuka will win is $\frac{2}{3}$. Copy and complete the tree diagram.

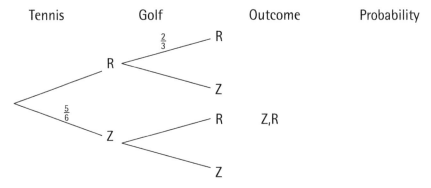

| Tennis | Golf | Outcome | Probability |

They decide to play a game of tennis and then a game of golf.

(a) What is the probability that Zainab will win both games?

(b) What is the probability that Renuka will win only one of the
    games?

3 A coloured hexagonal spinner has sections
   which are red or blue as shown. This spinner
   is used to play a game.

Copy and complete the tree diagram below.

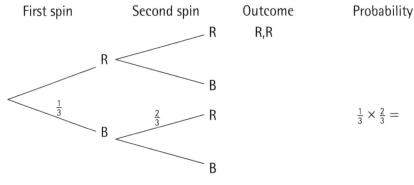

| First spin | Second spin | Outcome | Probability |

(a) What is the probability of the outcome being two blues?

(b) What is the probabilty of the outcome being one of each
    colour?

4 A coin and a three-sided spinner are used at the same time.

(a) Draw a tree diagram to show all the possible outcomes.

(b) What is the probability of getting a red and a tail?

5 A four-sided dice with the numbers 1, 2, 3, 4 and a spinner
   with three equal sectors coloured red, white and blue are
   thrown at the same time.

(a) Draw a tree diagram to show all the possible outcomes.

(b) What is the probability of getting a red or a white and an even
    number?

6   Peter takes two exams. The probability that he passes mathematics is 0.8. The probability that he passes history is 0.6. The results of the two exams are independent.

   (a) Draw a tree diagram to show all the possible outcomes.

   (b) What is the probability that   (i) he passes mathematics and fails history   (ii) he fails both subjects?

7   A bag contains 5 red counters and 3 green counters. A counter is taken at random from the bag and then replaced. Another counter is then taken from the bag.

   (a) Draw a tree diagram to show all the possible outcomes.

   (b) What is the probability of picking

      (i) two red counters (ii) two counters of the same colour

      (iii) at least one green counter?

8   An ordinary six-sided dice is tossed twice. Draw a tree diagram and show that the probability of obtaining just one six is $\frac{5}{18}$.

10.5 Conditional probability

The probability that one event occurs may depend upon another event having taken place. In this case the event is **conditional**. The second event is a **dependent event**.

In questions, look out for phrases such as 'without replacement' or 'not replaced', as these tell you that a second event is conditional.

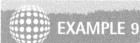 **EXAMPLE 9**

There are 6 red counters and 5 blue counters in a bag. A counter is taken at random from the bag and not replaced. A second counter is then taken out. What is the probability that they are both red ?

First counter $p(\text{red}) = \frac{6}{11}$

Second counter $p(\text{red}) = \frac{5}{10}$

The probability that both counters are red is
$p(\text{red and red}) = \frac{6}{11} \times \frac{5}{10} = \frac{30}{110} = \frac{3}{11}$

The events are clearly dependent.

After the first counter has been removed it is not replaced. There are now only ten counters in the bag.

When more than one probability is required, draw a tree diagram. Work out the conditional probabilities for each of the branches.

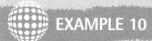

EXAMPLE 10

Juan has a drawer containing 4 pairs of white socks and 5 pairs of black socks. He takes two socks out of the drawer at random. Draw a probability tree diagram to show all the possible outcomes. Work out the probability that he takes out

(a) a pair of black socks   **(b)** a pair of white socks

(c) two socks of different colours.

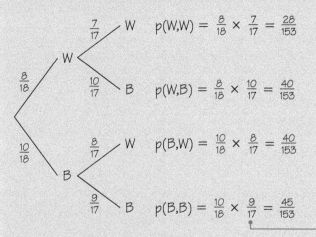

$$p(W,W) = \tfrac{8}{18} \times \tfrac{7}{17} = \tfrac{28}{153}$$

$$p(W,B) = \tfrac{8}{18} \times \tfrac{10}{17} = \tfrac{40}{153}$$

$$p(B,W) = \tfrac{10}{18} \times \tfrac{8}{17} = \tfrac{40}{153}$$

$$p(B,B) = \tfrac{10}{18} \times \tfrac{9}{17} = \tfrac{45}{153}$$

On the right of the tree diagram write out the conditional probabilities of each branch. Remember that the total probabilities from all the branches must add up to 1. This is always a good check.

The sum of all the conditional probabilities is

$$\tfrac{28}{153} + \tfrac{40}{153} + \tfrac{40}{153} + \tfrac{45}{153} = 1.$$

There are 17 socks left and 9 of them are black.

(a) Pair of black socks $p(B,B) = \tfrac{45}{153} = \tfrac{5}{17}$

(b) Pair of white socks $p(W,W) = \tfrac{28}{153}$

(c) Pair of different coloured socks is

$$p(B,W) + p(W,B) = \tfrac{40}{153} + \tfrac{40}{153} = \tfrac{80}{153}$$

You need not cancel probability fractions unless the question asks you to do so.

EXERCISE 10E

1 There are 5 black pens and 3 red pens in a drawer. A pen is taken and not replaced. A second pen is then taken.

(a) Draw a tree diagram showing all the possible outcomes.

(b) What is the probability that both pens taken will be red?

2 A bag contains 5 green balls and 4 blue balls. A ball is drawn at random and not replaced. A second ball is then picked from the bag. What is the probability that

(a) both balls are blue

(b) both balls are a different colour?

3 There are ten white carnations and six red roses. Sophie picks two flowers at random. Find the probability that they are

(a) different   (b) both roses.

4   A box contains 15 chocolates. Ten have hard centres and five have soft centres. Two chocolates are chosen at random.

(a) Draw a tree diagram to show all the possible outcomes.

(b) What is the probability that the chocolates chosen were

(i)   two hard centres   (ii) one of each kind

(iii) two of the same kind?

5   A bag contains 10 counters, 2 are red, 3 are blue and 5 are yellow. Stefan takes two counters out of the box, at random.

(a) Draw a tree diagram to show all the possible outcomes.

(b) What is the probability that he chooses

(i)   two yellow counters

(ii) two counters of the same colour

(iii) two counters of different colours

(iv) at least one red counter?

6   A bag contains 8 red and 4 yellow tomatoes. A tomato is chosen at random and eaten and then a second tomato is chosen at random. Draw a tree diagram to show all possible outcomes. What is the probability that the tomatoes chosen were

(a) both red   (b) one of each colour?

7   When Lee stays out late at night, the probability that he oversleeps the next morning is $\frac{1}{5}$. When he oversleeps the probability that he catches his train to work is $\frac{1}{8}$. When he does not oversleep he always catches the train to work.
Draw a tree diagram to show the possible outcomes.
What is the probability that Lee will miss his train?

8   Ahmed has the following coins in his pocket.

1 cent	10 cents	50 cents
3	6	1

Ahmed takes a coin out of his pocket at random and gives it to a friend.
He then chooses another coin at random.

Draw a tree diagram to show all possible outcomes.
What is the probability that the two coins are

(a) the same   (b) total 60 cents   (c) both 10 cents.

EXAMINATION QUESTIONS

1   Winston and Anthony take a driving test.
    The probability that Winston will pass is $\frac{3}{4}$ and the probability that Anthony will pass is $\frac{2}{3}$.
    (a) Which of them is more likely to pass?   [1]
    (b) Calculate the probability that they will both fail.   [2]
    (c) Calculate the probabilty that only one of them will pass.   [3]
    (d) If Winston fails he will take the test again.
        The probability that he will pass at any future attempt is $\frac{4}{5}$.
        (i)   Draw a tree diagram to show the probabilities of Winston passing or failing
              on each of his first three attempts.   [3]
        (ii) Calculate the probability that he will pass at his third attempt.   [2]
        (iii) Calculate the probability that he will not need more than three attempts to pass.   [3]

(CIE Paper 4, Jun 2000)

---

2   One teacher from Argentina, one from Brazil and three from Namibia attend an
    international conference. One of the five teachers is chosen at random to make a
    speech and one of the remaining four is chosen at random to write a report.
    (a) **Copy and complete** the probability tree diagram below, showing the countries from
        which the teachers were chosen.

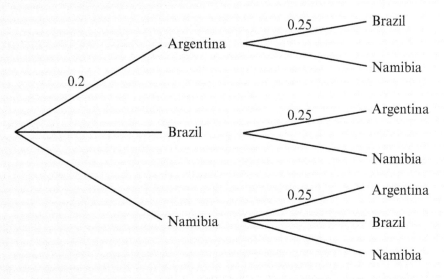

                                                                                                         [4]
    (b) Calculate the probability that
        (i)   both the chosen teachers were from Namibia,   [2]
        (ii) neither of the chosen teachers was from Namibia,   [3]
        (iii) the teacher from Brazil was not chosen.   [3]
    (c) One of the remaining three teachers is chosen at random to chair the conference
        Calculate the probability that this is the teacher from Brazil.   [2]

(CIE Paper 4, Nov 2000)

3

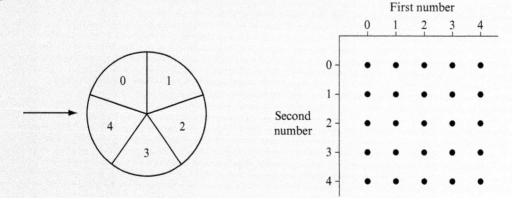

The wheel in Diagram 1 has one of the 0 to 4 in each of its five identical sectors.
The wheel is spun and when it stops the arrow points at a number.
All numbers are equally likely.
Diagram 2 shows the possible outcomes when the wheel is spun twice.

Find the probability that
(i) both numbers are 3, [1]
(ii) both numbers are the same, [2]
(iii) the sum of the two numbers is 6, [2]
(iv) the product of the two numbers is 8 or more, [2]
(v) the product of the two n umbers is less than the sum. [2]

(CIE Paper 4, Jun 2001)

4

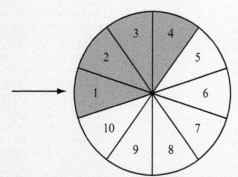

A wheel is divided into 10 sectors numbered 1 to 10 as shown in the diagram.
The sectors 1, 2 , 3 and 4 are shaded.
The wheel is spun twice and when it stops the fixed arrow points to one of the sectors.
(Each sector is equally likely.)
(a) The wheel is spun once so that one sector is selected. Find the probability that
   (i) the number in the sector is even, [1]
   (ii) the sector is shaded, [1]
   (iii) the number is even **or** the sector is shaded, [1]
   (iv) the number is odd **and** the sector is shaded. [1]

(b) The wheel is spun twice so that each time a sector is selected.
Find the probability that
(i)   both sectors are shaded, [2]
(ii) one sector is shaded and one is not, [2]
(iii) the sum of the numbers in the two sectors is greater than 20, [2]
(iv) the sum of the numbers in the two sectors is less than 4, [2]
(v)   the product of the numbers in the two sectors is a square number. [3]

(CIE Paper 4, Nov 2002)

---

5 There are two sets of road signals on the direct 12 kilometres route from Acity to Beetown.
The signals say either "GO" or "STOP".
The probabilities that the signals are "GO" when a car arrives are shown in the tree diagram.
(a) Copy and complete the tree diagram for a car driver travelling along this route.

1st signal   2nd signal

0.65 — GO

0.4 — GO

...... — STOP

0.45 — GO

...... — STOP

...... — STOP [3]

(b) Find the probability that a car driver
(i)   finds both signals are "GO", [3]
(ii) finds exactly one of the two signals is "GO", [2]
(iii) does not find two "STOP" signals. [2]

(CIE Paper 4, Jun 2003)

6

| A | D | A | M | D | A | N | I | E | L |

Adam writes his name on four red cards and Daniel writes his name on six white cards.
(a) One of the ten cards is chosen at random. Find the probability that
(i)   the letter on the card is D, [1]
(ii) the card is red, [1]
(iii) the card is red **or** the letter on the card is D, [1]
(iv) the card is red **and** the letter on the card is D, [1]
(v)   the card is red **and** the letter is N. [1]

(b) Adam chooses a card at random and then Daniel chooses one of the
remaining 9 cards at random.

Giving your answers as fractions, find the probability that the letters on
the two cards are

(i)   both D,   [2]
(ii) both A,   [2]
(iii) the same,   [2]
(iv) different.   [2]

(CIE Paper 4, Nov 2003)

7

A   B

Bag A contains 6 white beads and 3 black beads.
Bag B contains 6 white beads and 4 black beads.
One bead is chosen at random from each bag.
Find the probability that

(i)   both beads are black,   [2]
(ii) at least one of the two beads is white.   [2]

The beads are not replaced.
A second bead is chosen at random from each bag.
Find the probability that

(iii) all four beads are white,   [3]
(iv) the beads are not all the same colour.   [3]

(CIE paper 4, Jun 2004)

Chapter 11

Linear graphs

This chapter will show you how to
- ✔ describe and use the equation $y = mx + c$
- ✔ find equations of parallel and perpendicular lines through given points
- ✔ solve graphical inequalities
- ✔ interpret conversion graphs, distance–time and velocity–time graphs

11.1 Linear graphs

Any two points A and B on an x–y co-ordinate grid can be joined together to form a straight line. The section of line between A and B is called a **line segment**.

The straight line can also be extended beyond A and B and the resulting graph is called a **linear graph**.

When points lie on a straight line there is a connection between the **variables** x and y.

> A linear graph is simply the picture of a **linear equation**.

In a linear equation the highest power of x is 1. Examples of linear equations include $y = 2x$, $y = -3x + 2$, $2x + 3y = 5$, $y = -2$ and $x = 4$.

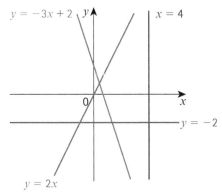

The two equations $y = -2$ and $x = 4$ do not contain a variable on the right-hand side. These equations represent straight line graphs parallel to the x-axis ($y = 0$) and parallel to the y-axis ($x = 0$).

> You need a minimum of three points to draw a straight line graph. Two points to define a straight line and a third point as a check.

To draw straight line graphs from a linear equation, first construct a table of results for values of x and y, then plot these on a graph.

EXAMPLE 1

Plot the graph of $y = x + 1$ for values $-2 \leqslant x \leqslant 2$.

When $x = -2$ $y = -2 + 1 = -1$
When $x = 0$ $y = 0 + 1 = 1$
When $x = 2$ $y = 2 + 1 = 3$

x	-2	0	2
y	-1	1	3

Substitute the given x values into the equation to find the corresponding y values.

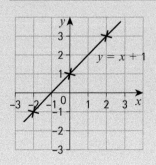

Plot these three points and join them up with a straight line. It is a good idea to draw your line beyond the end points. Always label your axes and label the line with the equation.

Guidelines to help you plot straight lines
- Choose a minimum of three values for x (always include 0).
- Put these values into the equation and work out the corresponding values for y.
- Write the results in a table.
- From the results, identify the extreme values for x and y and draw axes using these values.
- Plot the points from the table.
- Draw a straight line through all the points.
- Label the line with the equation.

EXERCISE 11A

1   Draw a co-ordinate grid with both the x-axis and y-axis from -5 to 5. On the grid draw and label the lines
   (a) $x = 4$ (b) $y = -1$ (c) $x = -5$ (d) $y = 4$.

2   In questions (a) to (f), use the same scale on both axes and draw x-axes and y-axes between -5 and $+5$.
   Draw these straight line graphs. For each one
   (i)   make a table of values, choosing at least three values of x
   (ii) work out the values of y using the equation of the line
   (iii) plot the points and draw a straight line through them.
   (a) $y = x - 3$ (b) $y = 2x + 3$ (c) $y = 4 - x$
   (d) $y = 3x - 1$ (e) $y = 2 - 2x$ (f) $y = 1 - \frac{1}{2}x$

3 On squared paper draw x and y axes from -6 to 6.
Using x-values of -3, 0 and 3 find the corresponding values of y
for the equation $y = x - 2$.
Put these results into a table and plot them on the graph.

4 On squared paper, draw x and y axes from -10 to 10.
Using the x values -5, 0 and 3, find the corresponding values for y
for the equation $y = 2x + 3$.
Put these results into a table and plot the graph.

5 Using x values of -4, 0 and 2, find the corresponding values of
y for the equation $y = -x + 4$.
Draw an appropriate co-ordinate grid and plot these results.

6 Draw the graph of $y = 3x - 1$.

7 Using the same scale on both axes, draw x and y axes from -3 to $+3$.
Draw the graphs of $y = x$ and $y = -x$ on the same co-ordinate grid.
What do you notice about these graphs?

8 Using the same scale on both axes, draw x and y axes from -5 to
$+5$. Draw the graphs of $y = 2x - 1$ and $y = \frac{1}{2}x + 2$ on the same
co-ordinate grid.
Write down the co-ordinates of the point where these graphs meet.

Finding the mid-point of a line

You can find the **mid-point** of a line segment AB, if you know
the co-ordinates of A and B.
If A is at (x_1, y_1) and B is point (x_2, y_2), the mid-point is
$$\left(\frac{x_1 + x_2}{2}, \frac{y_1 + y_2}{2} \right)$$

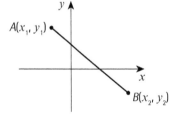

⬤ EXAMPLE 2

Work out the co-ordinates of the mid-point of the line segment RS
where R has co-ordinates $(1, 7)$ and S $(4, 6)$.

Mid-point is $\left(\dfrac{1 + 4}{2}, \dfrac{7 + 6}{2} \right)$

$\quad\quad\quad = \left(\dfrac{5}{2}, \dfrac{13}{2} \right)$

$\quad\quad\quad = (2\tfrac{1}{2}, 6\tfrac{1}{2})$

1   Write down the co-ordinates of the end points for each of the
    following line segments. For each line segment work out the
    co-ordinates of the mid-point.

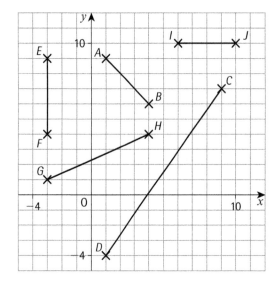

There is more on the distance
between two points in Chapter 17.

2   Without drawing these line segments, work out their mid-points.
    (a) $A(1, 1)$ $B(8, 1)$ (b) $C(7 ,9)$ $D(7, 2)$
    (c) $E(2, 3)$ $F(5, 9)$ (d) $G(-4, 5)$ $H(2, 5)$
    (e) $I(-2, 2)$ $J(3, -3)$

11.2 Finding equations of straight lines

Here, the slope of the line, from left to right,
is upwards.
The ratio

$$\frac{\text{vertical distance}}{\text{horizontal distance}}$$

gives a measure of the steepness of the line and is called the **gradient**
of the line. It is denoted by the letter m. This line has a **positive
gradient**.

If you have a line that slopes in the opposite direction,
then one of the values in the ratio will be negative.
This line has a **negative gradient**.

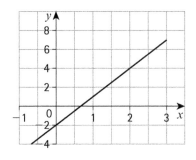

In simple terms, 3 up for every 1 across.

Gradient = amount of increase in y-value for unit increase in x-value.

x	0	1	2	3
y	-2	1	4	7

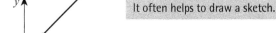

Look at the table of values for this line. You can see that each time the x-value increases by 1, the y-value increases by 3. This means that the gradient of the graph is 3.

For a line that passes through any two points $A(x_1, y_1)$ and $B(x_2, y_2)$ the gradient, m, is given by the expression

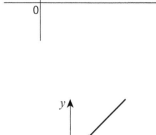

$$m = \frac{y_2 - y_1}{x_2 - x_1} = \frac{\text{difference in } y\text{-values}}{\text{difference in } x\text{-values}}$$

For example, if A is $(-1, 1)$ and B is $(1, 5)$ then,

$$m = \frac{5 - 1}{1 - (-1)} = \frac{4}{2} = 2$$

The place where the line crosses the y-axis is the **y-intercept** and is denoted by c.

It is the value of y when $x = 0$.
For this graph $c = 3$

Straight lines that pass through the negative part of the y-axis will have negative intercept values. Lines that pass through the origin have an intercept value of zero.

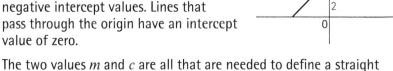

It often helps to draw a sketch.

The two values m and c are all that are needed to define a straight line.

All equations of straight lines have the same general form

$$y = mx + c$$

where m is the gradient of the line and c is the y-intercept.

For the line segment joining $A(-1, 1)$ and $B(1, 5)$ the equation is

$$y = 2x + 3$$

You can find the equation of any straight line if you know the co-ordinates of any two points on the line.

⬤ EXAMPLE 3

A line passes through the points $A(-4, 5)$ and $B(2, -10)$. Find

(a) the gradient of the line

(b) the equation of the line.

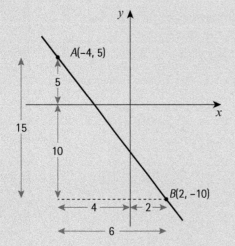

First draw a sketch.

(a) Difference in y-values $= 5 - (-10) = 5 + 10 = 15$

Difference in x-values $= -4 - 2 = -6$

Gradient, $m = \dfrac{\text{Difference in } y\text{-values}}{\text{Difference in } x\text{-values}} = \dfrac{15}{-6} = -\dfrac{5}{2}$

To find the gradient, find the difference between the y-values and the difference between the x-values.

(b) $y = -\dfrac{5}{2}x + c$

This line passes through point A with x-value -4 and y-value 5.

$5 = -\dfrac{5}{2}(-4) + c$

$5 = 10 + c$

$c = -5$

The value of c could have been obtained by using the other point $B(2, -10)$.

The equation of the straight line is

$y = -\dfrac{5}{2}x - 5$

Now combine the results of m and c into one equation. Don't forget the y and x!

Parallel lines

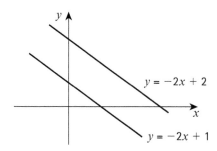

$y = -2x + 2$

$y = -2x + 1$

Parallel lines have the same gradient.

The graph above shows two lines both with $m = -2$.

EXAMPLE 4

Find the equation of the line parallel to $y = -\frac{5}{2}x - 5$ that passes through the point $B(4, 3)$.

Gradient of line, $m = -\frac{5}{2}$

The equation of the parallel line is

$$y = -\frac{5}{2}x + c$$

and this passes through point B with x-value 4 and y-value 3

$$3 \quad = -\frac{5}{2}(4) + c$$
$$3 \quad = -10 + c$$
$$c \quad = 13$$

The equation of the parallel line is

$$y \quad = -\frac{5}{2}x + 13$$

Form the general equation of this line.

Now work out the value of c knowing that the line passes through the point $B(4, 3)$.

Now substitute the value of c back into the general equation.

EXERCISE 11C

1 Find the gradient of the lines joining the points
   (a) $(1, 2)$ and $(5, 10)$
   (b) $(-1, 6)$ and $(2, -3)$
   (c) $(-4, -1)$ and $(0, -2)$

2 A line has a gradient of -2 and passes through the point with co-ordinate $(4, 6)$. Find the equation of the line.

3 A line has a gradient of $m = \frac{1}{3}$ and passes through the point $(-3, 5)$. Find the equation of the line.

4 Find **(i)** the gradients of the lines and **(ii)** the equation of the lines that pass through the following points.

(a) $A(5, 2)$ $B(4, 1)$ (b) $C(-6, -4)$ $D(-3, -7)$

(c) $E(1, 4)$ $F(6, 3)$ (d) $G(-2, 6)$ $H(-1, -7)$

5 A line passes through the origin and is parallel to the line with equation $y = 5 - 2x$. Find the equation of the line.

6 A line is parallel to the line with equation $y = 4x - 3$ and crosses the y-axis at $y = 7$. Find the equation of the line.

7 **Without plotting** these straight lines, identify which lines are parallel to the line $y = x - 1$.

(a) $y = x + 1$ (b) $y = x - 7$ (c) $y = 2x - 1$

(d) $2y = x - 1$ (e) $y = x + \frac{1}{2}$

8 **Without plotting** these straight lines, identify which lines are parallel to $y = -3x - 2$.

(a) $y = 3x - 2$ (b) $y = -3x + 2$ (c) $y = -2x - 3$

(d) $y = -2 - 3x$ (e) $y = 2 + 3x$

11.3 Using the general equation $y = mx + c$

The equation of a straight line is $y = x + 2$. The gradient m of this line is 1 and the y-intercept value is 2. Both of these values can be obtained directly from the equation.

The gradient is given by the value of the number in front of the 'x' (the **coefficient** of x). It is important to include the sign. For the line $y = x + 2$, the gradient is 1. For an equation $y = -2x - 5$ the gradient is -2.

> In algebra you write x to represent $1x$ and $-x$ to represent $-1x$.

The y-intercept, c, is given by the number term. In the equation $y = x + 1$ the intercept, c, is $+1$, and in the equation $y = -2x - 5$ the intercept, c, is -5.

> It is important to include the sign in the values of both m and c.

EXAMPLE 5

State the gradients and intercept values for the equations

(a) $y = x + 8$ (b) $y = -3x + 3$

(c) $y = -\frac{1}{2}x - 5$ (d) $y = 2.6x + 0.4$

> Gradients and intercepts can also be fractions and decimals. Remember to include the sign in front of the gradient and intercept.

(a) gradient $= 1$,   intercept $= 8$

(b) gradient $= -3$,   intercept $= 3$

(c) gradient $= -\frac{1}{2}$,   intercept $= -5$

(d) gradient $= 2.6$,   intercept $= 0.4$

You can easily find the gradient, m, and the intecept, c, provided the equation of the straight line is in the form

$$y = mx + c$$

This is not always the case. You may need to rearrange an equation to make y the subject of the equation. Then you can find the values of m and c directly. The values of m and c may also help you plot the graph.

You need to be aware that equations can be presented in a variety of ways.

 EXAMPLE 6

Rearrange these equations into the form $y = $ ____.

(a) $y - x = 1$ (b) $-x = 1 - y$ (c) $y - x - 1 = 0$

___

(a)
$$y - x = 1$$
$$y - x + x = 1 + x$$
$$y = 1 + x$$
$$y = x + 1$$

(b)
$$-x = 1 - y$$
$$-x + y = 1 - y + y$$
$$-x + y = 1$$
$$-x + x + y = 1 + x$$
$$y = 1 + x$$
$$y = x + 1$$

Do the same to both sides.

(c)
$$y - x - 1 = 0$$
$$y - x + x - 1 + 1 = 0 + x + 1$$
$$y = x + 1$$

 EXAMPLE 7

Write the following equations in the form $y = mx + c$.

(a) $2y = 6x - 12$ (b) $5y = -10x + 20$

___

(a) $2y = 6x - 12$
$$y = \frac{6x}{2} - \frac{12}{2}$$
$$y = 3x - 6$$

Divide both sides by 2.

(b) $5y = -10x + 20$
$$y = -\frac{10x}{5} + \frac{20}{5}$$
$$y = -2x + 4$$

Divide both sides by 5.

 EXAMPLE 8

Find the gradient and intercept of these graphs.

(a) $3x = y - 5$ (b) $\frac{1}{3}y + \frac{1}{4}x + \frac{1}{6} = 0$

continued ▼

(a) $3x = y - 5$
         $3x + 5 = y$
             $y = 3x + 5$
         Gradient $= 3$; intercept $= 5$

(b) $\frac{1}{3}y + \frac{1}{4}x + \frac{1}{6} = 0$
         $4y + 3x + 2 = 0$
                 $4y = -3x - 2$
                   $y = -\frac{3}{4}x - \frac{1}{2}$
             Gradient $= -\frac{3}{4}$; intercept $= -\frac{1}{2}$

Add 5 to both sides and turn the equation around to make y the subject on the left hand side.

Remove fractional parts by multiplying throughout by the lowest common denominator, 12. Then make y the subject by dividing both sides by 4.

EXERCISE 11D

1 For the following equations write down the value of the gradient and intercept.

(a) $y = 3x + 2$ (b) $y = -x + 3$

(c) $y = 4x - 7$ (d) $y = -3x - 4$

(e) $y = \frac{2}{3}x + 8$ (f) $y = 0.8x - 0.3$

2 Rewrite the following equations in the form $y = mx + c$. For each one write down the value of the gradient and intercept.

(a) $3y = 9x + 18$ (b) $2y = -8x - 4$

(c) $8y = -24x + 8$ (d) $y - 7 = -2x$

(e) $2x + 6 = 2y$ (f) $-3x = 4 + y$

(g) $2y + 3x = 2$ (h) $x = -3y - 2$

(i) $4y + 2 + 3x = 0$ (j) $0.3x = 2.4 + 0.6y$

(k) $\frac{1}{2}x - \frac{1}{3}y = \frac{1}{4}$ (l) $\frac{1}{6}y - \frac{1}{2} + \frac{1}{3}x = 0$

11.4 Graphical inequalities

Inequalities often describe a range of values that can be represented on a number line.

Inequalities can also be represented by a **region** or area on a graph.

For the inequalities $\leqslant$ and $\geqslant$ the **boundary region** is indicated by a continuous line. For the inequalities $<$ and $>$ the boundary region is indicated by a dashed line.

EXAMPLE 9

Show the region $x \geqslant 2$.

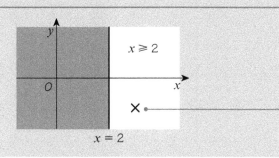

Begin by drawing the line $x = 2$. Then shade in the region that does not satisfy the inequality. This may be found by substituting co-ordinate values into the inequality to see if it is true for a given point.

For example, for this point $(3, -1)$, the x co-ordinate $\geqslant 2$.

You are expected to shade the *unwanted* region.

EXAMPLE 10

Show the region given by the inequality $y < 2x$.

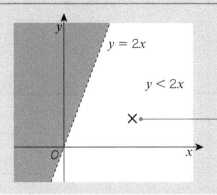

$< \text{ or } >$ ....

$\leqslant \text{ or } \geqslant$ _____

For example, for the point $(3, 1)$, $y = 1$ and $2x = 6$, so $y < 2x$.

Shade the *unwanted* region.

EXAMPLE 11

Show the region that satisfies the inequality $3x + y \leqslant 3$.

When $y = 0$, $x = 1$ and when $x = 0$, $y = 3$.

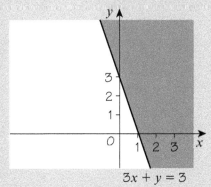

First draw the line $3x + y = 3$.

This line is easy to plot if you find the points where it crosses the x- and y-axes. These are found by putting $y = 0$ and working out x, then putting $x = 0$ and working out y.

It is not always obvious which side of the line should be shaded. Take a point e.g. the origin $(0, 0)$. Putting these values into the inequality gives $0 + 0 \leqslant 3$, which is true, so this point lies inside the required region.

Shade the *unwanted* region.

In some cases more than one inequality is given. In these cases the region that satisfies all inequalities simultaneously is the required region.

 EXAMPLE 12

Draw a graph that shows the region satisfying the following inequalities.

$x < 7, y \geqslant 1, y < x - 3$

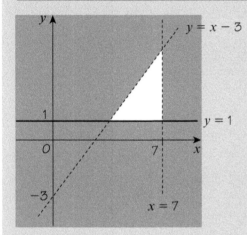

Begin by drawing the lines $x = 7$, $y = 1$ and $y = x - 3$.

The region required is
$x < 7$ to the left of the dashed line $x = 7$
$y \geqslant 1$ above the solid line $y = 1$
$y < x - 3$ below the dashed line $y = x - 3$
Only those points on the line $y = 1$ within the unshaded region can be included.

Shade the *unwanted* region.

EXERCISE 11E

1 For the following graphs, write down the inequalities which describe the **unshaded** region.

(a)
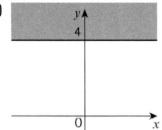

(b)
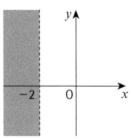

(c)
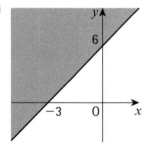

(d)
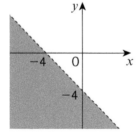

2 In the following questions draw graphs to show the region that satisfies the inequality.

(a) $x \leq 2$ (b) $y > -2$ (c) $-1 < x \leq 4$

(d) $0 \leq y \leq 3$ (e) $y \geq 3x$ (f) $y < 3x + 2$

(g) $y \geq x - 5$ (h) $2x + y < 3$

3 Show by shading the region which satisfies the following inequalities.

(a) $x < 4$ and $x + y \geq 2$ (b) $y \leq 3$ and $2x + y \geq 1$

4 Show the region bounded by the inequalities $x \geq -2$, $y < 7$ and $x + y > 1$.

5 The region R is shown unshaded. Write down the three inequalities which together describe the **unshaded** region.

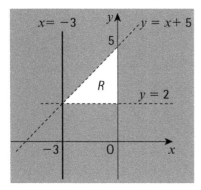

6 Using a scale of 2 cm to 1 unit on each axis, draw the lines $x + y = 6$, $y = x$ and $y = 4$.
Identify and label the region R which satisfies the inequalities $x + y \leq 6$, $y \leq x$ and $y \leq 4$.

7 Using the same procedure as in question 6 identify and label the region R which satisfies the inequalities $x + y < 5$, $y < 2x$ and $y > x$.

8 Using the same procedure as in question 6 identify and label the region R which satisfies the inequalities $x + y > 4$, $x + y < 6$, $y < 2$ and $x < 4$.

11.5 Linear programming

You may need a table of values.

We can use the techniques of drawing inequalitites to solve problems. This is known as linear programming.

 EXAMPLE 13

A furniture company has two types of trucks to deliver furniture. Type R can carry 7 tonnes and type T can carry 14 tonnes. The company has 210 tonnes of furniture to deliver.

The company has 35 type R and 10 type T trucks. Running costs are $200 for a type R and $500 for a type T. The company has a budget of $8000 for the delivery.

If x type R and y type T trucks are used, write down four inequalities which represent this information.

What is the smallest number of trucks that can be used?

7 tonnes in each type R truck and 14 tonnes in each type T truck must deliver at least 210 tonnes of furniture.

Carrying capacity gives $\quad 7x + 14y \geqslant 210$

Number of type R gives $\quad x \leqslant 35$

Number of type T gives $\quad y \leqslant 10$

Running costs gives $\quad 200x + 500y \leqslant 8000$

The company has up to 35 type R trucks.

The company has up to 10 type T trucks.

Each type R costs $200 and each type T costs $500 to run and the company has a maximum of $5000 to spend on the delivery.

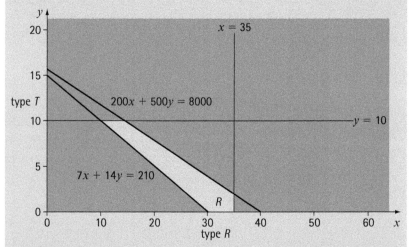

Shade the *unwanted* region.

The solution must be in the unshaded region. We are looking for the lowest combination of $x + y$ inside the region. By checking all solutions in this region we can see that this occurs at (10,10) which means that 20 trucks is the smallest number of vehicles that can be used.

EXERCISE 11F

1   An airline has a contract to fly 1200 people and 90 tonnes of luggage. It has two types of aircraft available, a Stork which can carry 100 people and and 12 tonnes of luggage or a Crane which can carry 160 people and 6 tonnes of luggage.

If x Storks and y Cranes are available, show that $5x + 8y \geqslant 60$ and $2x + y \geqslant 15$. Due to servicing requirements, the company only has 8 Storks and 7 Cranes available. Write down two more inequalities to show this information.

Draw a graph to show all this information and use it to find the smallest number of aircraft that can be used.

2   A parcel company has a contract to deliver 3600 parcels, using trucks which can take 600 parcels and vans which can take 240 parcels. The cost of each journey by truck is $200 and by van is $160. The budget for the delivery is $1760. Due to driver shortages the company must use more vans than trucks.

If x trucks and y vans are used, show that $5x + 2y \geqslant 30$ and $5x + 4y \leqslant 44$ and write down a third inequality.

Represent these inequalities on a graph and show the region which satisfies all three inequalities. Find the minimum number of trucks and vans that the company will need.

Shade the unwanted region.

3   A car hire company intends to replace at least 16 of its cars with new ones.

It has two sizes of car, small and large. The small cars cost $12 000 and the large car costs $15 000 to buy new and the company has $240 000 to spend. The company knows that it will need at least 8 but not more than 12 new, large cars .

If the company buys x small and y large cars, show that $4x + 5y \leqslant 80$ and write down two more inequalities.

Show, by shading the unwanted region in which the solution to these inequalities can be found.

What is the largest number of cars that the company can buy?

11.6 Conversion graphs

A **conversion graph** is used to convert one type of measurement into another type of measurement, usually with different units. Conversion graphs can be linear or curved. Only linear graphs are covered in this chapter.

Curved conversion graphs are covered in Chapter 20.

EXAMPLE 14

(a) Construct a table to show the conversion between degrees Celsius (°C) and degrees Fahrenheit (°F) for values $-40 \leqslant C \leqslant 100$.
Use the equation
$$F = 2C + 30$$

(b) Draw a conversion graph.

(c) What is the temperature in °F when it is 10°C?

(d) If the temperature is 160°F what is this in °C?

The accurate equation is $F = 1.8C + 32$ but this has been simplified here to make the graph easier to plot.

continued ▼

(a)

C	-40	-20	0	20	40	60	80	100
2C	-80	-40	0	40	80	120	160	200
+30	30	30	30	30	30	30	30	30
F	-50	-10	30	70	110	150	190	230

(b)

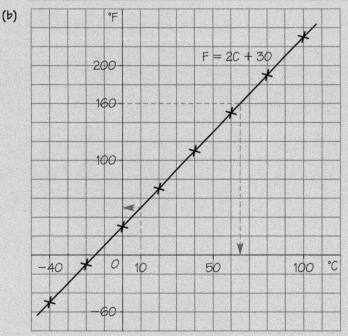

Draw dashed lines on the graph at 10°C and 160°F to meet the conversion line. From these points draw dashed lines to meet the axes and read off the answers.

≈ means approximately equal to.

(c) 10°C ≈ 50°F **(d)** 160°F ≈ 65°C

EXERCISE 11G

1 Copy and complete the conversion table between km and miles using the conversion 5 miles = 8 km.

miles (x)	0	5	10	20	50	100
km (y)		8			80	

Draw a conversion graph with x-values from 0 to 100 miles and y-values from 0 to 200 km.

(a) How many miles are there in 75 km?

(b) How many km are there in 75 miles?

2 Copy and complete the conversion table between centimetres and inches. Give your values correct to 1 d.p.

cm	0				12.5		25	
inches	0	1	2	3	5	6	10	12

Draw a conversion graph between cm and inches. From your graph work out

(a) how many cm there are in 4 inches,

(b) how many inches there are in 20 cm.

11.7 Graphs describing journeys

Distance–time graphs

Always plot time on the horizontal axis (the x-axis) and distance on the vertical axis (the y-axis). You can use **distance–time graphs** to work out the **speed** for part of a journey.

$$\text{Speed} = \frac{\text{distance}}{\text{time}}$$

If distance is measured in metres and time in seconds then the units of speed are metres per second or m/s. Other units of speed are kilometres per hour (km/h).

You can also use a distance–time graph to work out an **average speed** for a journey.

$$\text{Average speed} = \frac{\text{total distance}}{\text{total time}}$$

> m/s can also be represented by ms⁻¹ and km/h by kmh⁻¹ or kph.

> Units for average speed are identical to those used for speed.

⬤ EXAMPLE 15

Part of Jen's cycle ride is shown in this distance–time graph.

(a) How long did Jen stop at (i) B and (ii) C?

(b) What was the speed between A and B?

(c) What was the average speed between A and D?

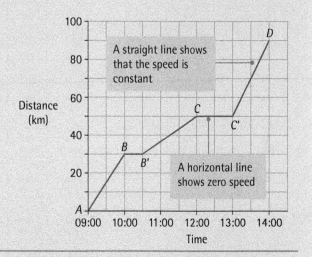

(a) (i) 30 mins   (ii) 1 hour

(b) Distance $AB = 30$ km   Time $= 1$ h

$$\text{Speed} = \frac{\text{distance}}{\text{time}} = \frac{30 \text{ km}}{1 \text{ h}} = 30 \text{ km/h}$$

(c) Total distance $= 90$ km and total time $= 5$ hours

$$\text{Average speed} = \frac{\text{total distance}}{\text{total time}}$$
$$= \frac{90 \text{ km}}{5 \text{ h}} = 18 \text{ km/h}$$

> Always write down the data you need from the graph.

> Average speed uses total distance and total time for the journey.

1 Chloë walks to school each morning, stopping off at the shop on the way. The distance–time graph shows her journey to school.

   (a) What time does she get to the shop?

   (b) How long does she spend in the shop?

   (c) How long does it take Chloe to walk to school?

   (d) What is her average walking speed?

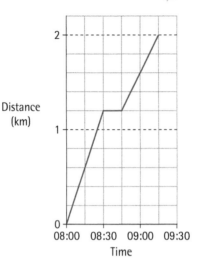

2 The distance–time graph shows the cycle journey that Imran undertook from home. He made two stops at shops on his journey before returning home.

   (a) How long did Imran's cycle ride take?

   (b) Which part of his journey did he travel at the greatest speed?

   (c) How can you tell?

   (d) What was his average speed for the whole cycle ride?

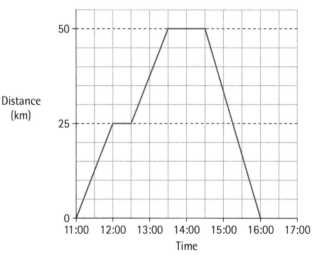

3 Glyn walked to the village shop, a distance of 800 m.
   It took him 10 minutes to get there and he was in the shop for 5 minutes.
   He then walked to the Post Office, another 200 m.
   This took 3 minutes and he was in the Post Office for 6 minutes.
   He then walked back home which took 16 minutes.

   (a) Draw a distance–time graph for his journey.

   (b) How fast did he walk to the shop?

   (c) What was his average speed for the whole journey?

4 Marcus leaves home at 08.15 and walks 400 m to the bus stop in 6 minutes. He waits 5 minutes for the bus to arrive. The bus journey is 4000 m and the bus arrives near school at 08.38.
   He then walks another 100 m to school in 2 minutes.

   > Do the same as you did for question 3 in questions 4 and 5.
   >
   > Plan sensible scales for the axes.

   (a) Draw a distance–time graph for his journey.

   (b) What was the average speed of the bus in metres per minute?

   (c) Convert this speed to km/h.

5   Alison went to town in her car. She drove the 12 miles into town in 25 minutes. She was in town for $1\frac{1}{4}$ hours then left to drive home. After 20 minutes of her journey home, 9 miles from town, she stopped at her Aunt's house and stayed for $\frac{1}{2}$ hour. She then continued her journey home, taking another 10 minutes.

(a) Draw a distance–time graph for her journey.

(b) What was her average speed in mph on the way to town?

Speed–time graphs

On a **speed–time graph** plot time on the x-axis and plot speed on the y-axis. The gradient gives the rate of change of speed, or **acceleration**. Constant acceleration gives a straight line.

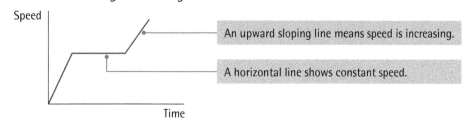

An upward sloping line means speed is increasing.

A horizontal line shows constant speed.

$$\text{Acceleration} = \frac{\text{change in speed}}{\text{time taken}}$$

If the speed is measured in metres per second (m/s) and time in seconds (s) the units of acceleration are metres per second per second or m/s² (ms^{-2}). A positive value for acceleration involves speeding up. A negative value involves slowing down (or **deceleration**).

The *area* under a speed–time graph gives the distance travelled.

Working out areas under a speed–time graph usually involves working out the areas of trapeziums, rectangles or triangles.

EXAMPLE 16

A car starts out from rest and travels, at constant acceleration, 75 m in 5 seconds before continuing its journey at a constant speed for a further 30 seconds. After this time it slows down uniformly, taking 10 seconds to come to a complete stop. Draw the speed–time graph for this journey. From the graph find

(a) the acceleration in the first 5 seconds

(b) the deceleration

(c) the total distance travelled.

'Slows down uniformly' means that the deceleration is constant.

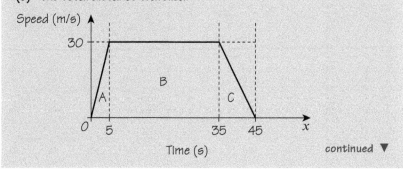

continued ▼

(a) Acceleration $= \dfrac{speed}{time} = \dfrac{30 \text{ m/s}}{5 \text{ s}} = 6 \text{ m/s}^2$

(b) Deceleration $= \dfrac{30 \text{ m/s}}{10 \text{ s}} = 3 \text{ m/s}^2$

(c) Total distance travelled

$= $ area of A $+$ area of B $+$ area of C

$= \left(\dfrac{30 \times 5}{2} \right) + (30 \times 30) + \left(\dfrac{30 \times 10}{2} \right)$ m

$= 75 + 900 + 150$ m

$= 1125$ m

The area can be worked out by adding the area of two triangles and a rectangle or by working out the area of a trapezium.
Area of the trapezium
$= \frac{1}{2}(a + b)h$
$= \frac{1}{2}(30 + 45) \times 30$
$= 1125$ m

EXERCISE 11I

1 The diagram shows a speed–time graph of the first 30 seconds of a car journey.

   (a) Work out the acceleration of the car in the first 10 seconds.

   (b) How far did the car travel altogether?

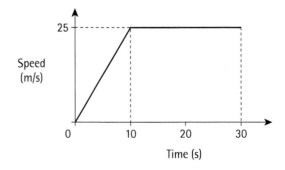

2 The diagram shows a speed–time graph for a car journey. From the graph find

   (a) the total distance travelled

   (b) the average speed for the whole journey

   (c) the distance travelled in the first 10 seconds

   (d) the deceleration of the car.

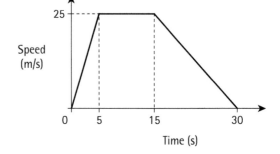

3 The speed-time graph shows a short section of a ski run. Use the graph to work out

   (a) the initial acceleration,

   (b) the deceleration at the end,

   (c) the total distance travelled,

   (d) the average speed.

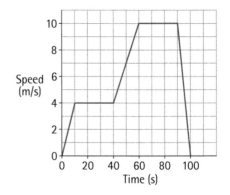

4 The speed-time graph shows part of a train journey between two stations.

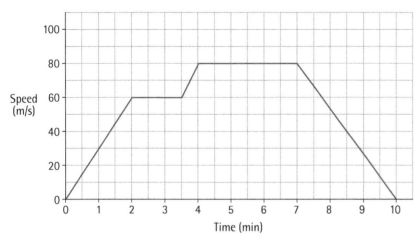

Work out

(a) the acceleration of the train as it left the first station,

(b) the deceleration of the train as it arrived at the second station,

(c) the maximum speed during the journey,

(d) the distance between the two stations.

5 The diagram shows the speed-time graph for a cable car journey from Mount Faber to Sentosa in Singapore.

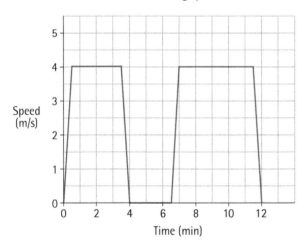

(a) The cable car stopped at Jardine Steps. How many minutes was the stop?

(b) Calculate the acceleration of the cable car as it left Mount Faber.

(c) What was the maximum speed of the cable car during the journey?

(d) Work out the total distance travelled by the cable car between Mount Faber and Sentosa.

(e) Calculate the average speed of the cable car for the whole journey.

1

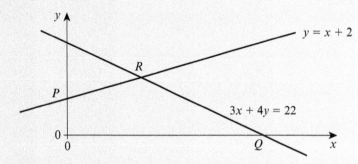

NOT TO SCALE

The line $y = x + 2$ cuts the y-axis at P. The line $3x + 4y = 22$ cuts the x-axis at Q.
The two lines intersect at R.

(a) Find the co-ordinates of
    (i) P,   [1]
    (ii) Q,   [2]
    (iii) R.   [3]

(b) $x > 0$ is one of four inequalities which define the region $OPRQ$.
    Write down the other three inequalities.   [3]

(CIE Paper 4, Jun 2000)

2

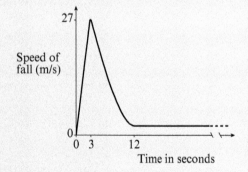

NOT TO SCALE

Simon jumps from a balloon. He falls faster and faster with constant acceleration
until after 3 seconds he opens his parachute. His speed decreases for the next 9 seconds
and then remains constant until he lands. The speed–time graph shows this.

(a) For the first 3 seconds, calculate
    (i)   his acceleration,   [1]
    (ii) the distance he falls.   [1]

(b) The total distance Simon falls in the first 12 seconds is 112 m. His constant speed
    after that is 2 m/s. Calculate in minutes and seconds the total time for his jump
    if the balloon was 1000 metres above the ground.   [2]

(CIE Paper 2, Jun 2000)

3

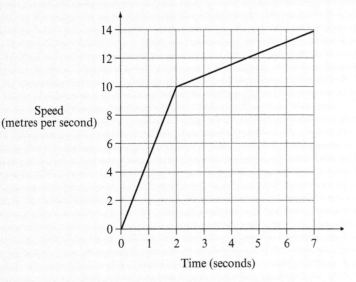

A car starts from rest. The speed–time graph shows the first 7 seconds of its journey.
Calculate

(a) the acceleration between 2 and 7 seconds,   [1]

(b) the distance travelled by the car during the first 7 seconds.   [2]

(CIE Paper 2, Nov 2000)

4

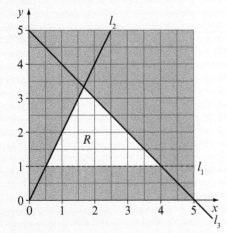

(a) Find the equations of the lines l_1, l_2 and l_3.   [3]

(b) The unshaded region, labelled R, is defined by three inequalities.
Write down the three inequalities.   [2]

(CIE Paper 2, Nov 2000)

5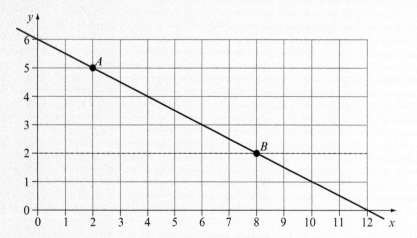

Answer this question without using graph paper.

A is the point $(2, 5)$ and B is the point $(8, 2)$.

(a) Find the equation of the line AB. [2]

(b) Calculate the length of the line AB, giving your answer correct to 2 d.p. [2]

(c) Find the co-ordinates of the point C such that A is the mid-point of BC. [2]

(d) Point D lies on the line $y = 2$ and has co-ordinates $(x, 2)$.
Find two possible values of x if the area of triangle ABD is 15 cm². [3]

(CIE Paper 4, Jun 2001)

---

6 There are x girls and y boys in a school choir.

(a) **(i)** The number of girls is more than 1.5 times the number of boys in the choir.
Show that $y < \frac{2}{3}x$. [1]

(ii) There are more than 12 girls in the choir.
There are more than 5 boys in the choir.
The maximum number of children in the choir is 35.
Write down three more inequalities. [3]

(b) **(i)** Using a scale of 2 cm to represent 5 children on each axis, draw an x-axis
for $0 \leqslant x \leqslant 40$ and a y-axis for $0 \leqslant y \leqslant 40$. [1]

(ii) Draw 4 lines on your graph to represent the inequalities in part (a).
Shade the **unwanted** region. [7]

(c) The school buys a uniform for each choir member.
A girl's uniform costs \$25. A boy's uniform costs \$20.
Find the maximum possible cost for the choir uniforms. Mark clearly the
point P on your graph which you use to calculate this cost. [3]

(CIE Paper 4, Nov 2001)

7

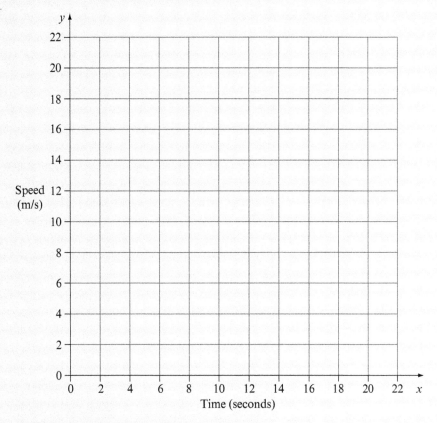

Time (seconds)

(Copy the diagram onto squared paper)

A car starts from rest with a constant acceleration of 5 m/s² for 4 seconds.
Next it decelerates at 2 m/s² for 6 seconds.
Then it decelerates at d m/s² until it comes to rest 18 seconds from the start.

(a) Draw the speed-time graph for the car on your grid. [3]
(b) Find the value of d. [1]
(c) Calculate the distance which the car travels **while it is accelerating.** [1]

(CIE Paper 2, Nov 2001)

8

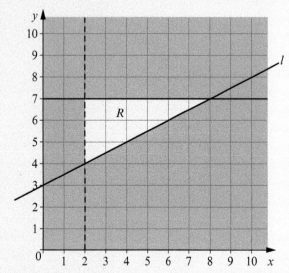

(a) Find the equation of the line l shown in the grid above. [2]
(b) Write down three inequalities which define the region R. [3]

(CIE Paper 2, Jun 2002)

9

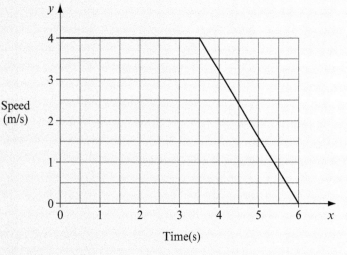

Time(s)

Ameni is cycling at 4 metres per second.
After 3.5 seconds she starts to decelerate and after a further 2.5 seconds she stops.
The diagram shows the speed-time graph for Ameni.
Calculate

(a) the constant deceleration, [1]
(b) the total distance travelled during the 6 seconds. [2]

(CIE Paper 2, Nov 2002)

Chapter 12

Ratio and proportion

This chapter will show you how to
✔ write, use and simplify ratios
✔ divide quantities in a given ratio
✔ solve problems using direct and inverse proportion
✔ apply ratios to problems involving scales and maps

12.1 Ratio

Writing and using ratios

A **ratio** compares two or more quantities.

A scale model of a car is labelled 1 : 18. This means that the length of any part of the real car is 18 times longer than the corresponding part on the model.

Part	Length on model	Length on actual car
Diameter of wheels	3 cm	3 cm × 18 = 54 cm
Length of car	26 cm	26 cm × 18 = 468 cm

1 : **18** is an example of a ratio.

A ratio is written with a : symbol between the numbers.
For 1 : 18, you say '1 to 18'.

⬤ EXAMPLE 1

A recipe for fudge pudding uses these ingredients

180 g of butter
150 g of sugar
120 g of dates

How much sugar and dates would you need if you used 270 g of butter?

---

270 g of butter = 1.5 × 180 g
Amount of sugar = 1.5 × 150 g = 225 g
Amount of dates = 1.5 × 120 g = 180 g

The multiplier is $\frac{270}{180} = 1.5$, so multiply the quantity of each ingredient by 1.5.

EXERCISE 12A

1   A cocktail uses cranberry juice, orange juice and tonic water in the ratio 5 : 3 : 1.

   (a) If I have 25 ml of tonic water, how much of the other ingredients will I need?

   (b) How much cocktail will I have altogether?

Find the total of all the ingredients.

2   A fruit stall sells 5 apples for every 3 oranges.

   (a) Apples come in boxes of 60. The stall has 4 boxes. How many oranges do they need?

   (b) One day the stall sells 42 oranges. How many apples do they sell?

3   Cupro-nickel is used to make key rings. It is made from mixing copper and nickel in the ratio 5 : 2.

   (a) How much copper would you need to mix with 3 kg of nickel?

   (b) How much nickel would you need to mix with 2 kg of copper?

4   Potting compost is made by mixing 8 kg of peat with 3 kg of sand.

   (a) How much sand would you need to mix with 20 kg of peat?

   (b) If I buy a 33 kg bag of compost, how much peat and sand will be in the bag?

5   A recipe for 500 ml of spaghetti sauce includes 150 g of meat, 250 g tomatoes, 75 g mushrooms and 25 g onions.

   (a) If I have only 200 g of tomatoes, how much of each other ingredient will I need?

   (b) How many millilitres of sauce would this make?

Simplifying ratios

You will need to know
● how to simplify fractions

You can simplify a ratio in the same way as you simplify fractions. For example, a 15 kg ingot of brass is made using 9 kg of copper and 6 kg of zinc.

These amounts can be written as a ratio 9 : 6 but this ratio can be simplified by dividing both numbers by 3 or by 6.
The two ratios 9 : 6 and 3 : 2 are equivalent.

$$\div 3 \left(\begin{array}{c} 9 \ : \ 6 \\ 3 \ : \ 2 \end{array} \right) \div 3$$

Here the simplest form of the ratio is 3 : 2. You could also say the ratio 3 : 2 is in its lowest terms.

A ratio is in its **simplest form** when the numbers in the ratio are **integers** and they have no common factor other than 1.

These rules are the same as the ones used for finding equivalent fractions.

EXAMPLE 2

Write these ratios in their lowest terms.

(a) $18 : 24 : 6$ (b) $1 \text{ kg} : 350 \text{ g}$ (c) $\frac{3}{4} : \frac{1}{3}$ (d) $2.7 : 3.6$

(a) $18 : 24 : 6$

     $= 3 : 4 : 1$ •————————————————— Divide by 6.

(b) $1 \text{ kg} : 350 \text{ g}$

     $= 1000 \text{ g} : 350 \text{ g}$ Units are not the same, change kg to g.

     $= 1000 : 350$ The units *must* be the same before you can simplify.

     $= 20 : 7$

(c) $\frac{3}{4} : \frac{1}{3}$ Find the LCM of the denominators (in this case 12).

     $= (\frac{3}{4} \times 12) : (\frac{1}{3} \times 12)$ Multiply both fractions by this number.

     $= 9 : 4$

(d) $2.7 : 3.6$

     $= 27 : 36$ •————————————————— Multiply by 10.

     $= 3 : 4$ •————————————————— Divide by 9.

EXERCISE 12B

1 Write these ratios in their lowest terms.

   (a) $9 : 15$ (b) $40 : 25$ (c) $48 : 36$

   (d) $120 : 70$ (e) $28 : 49$ (f) $1000 : 250$

2 Write these ratios in their simplest form.

   (a) $\$1 : 20¢$ (b) $6 \text{ mm} : 3 \text{ m}$ (c) $5\ell : 250 \text{ m}\ell$ Change each part into the same units first.

   (d) $300 \text{ m} : 2 \text{ km}$ (e) $75¢ : \$5$ (f) $350 \text{ g} : 2 \text{ kg}$

   (g) $\$3.50 : \$1.25$ (h) $45 \text{ cm} : 2 \text{ m}$ (i) $50 \text{ mm} : 1 \text{ m}$

3 Change these ratios into their simplest form.

   (a) $\frac{1}{2} : \frac{1}{4}$ (b) $\frac{2}{3} : \frac{3}{4}$ (c) $\frac{3}{5} : \frac{7}{10}$

   (d) $3.2 : 1.6$ (e) $5.4 : 1.8$ (f) $4.8 : 1.2$

4 A drink was made with $1\frac{1}{2}$ cups of lemonade and $\frac{1}{4}$ cup of blackcurrant cordial. Write the ratio of lemonade to blackcurrant in its lowest terms.

5 The cost of materials for a soft toy were: fabric \$3.20, stuffing \$1.20 and others 60¢. Write the ratio of the cost of fabric to stuffing to others in its lowest terms.

Writing a ratio as a fraction

You can use fractions to help you to solve ratio problems.

When items are divided in the ratio 2 : 3, the fraction $\frac{2}{3}$ gives you another method of solving the problem. This is used in method B in Example 3.

 EXAMPLE 3

In a school the ratio of boys to girls is 5 : 7.
There are 265 boys. How many girls are there?

Method A (using multiplying)

Suppose there are x girls.

The ratio $5 : 7 = 265 : x$

$265 \div 5 = 53$

$5 : 7 = (5 \times 53) : (7 \times 53) = 265 : 371$

There are 371 girls in the school.

> Multiply both sides of the ratio by 53.
> Multiplying both sides of a ratio by the same value gives an equivalent ratio.

Method B (using fractions)

Suppose there are x girls.

The ratio $5 : 7 = 265 : x$

$\frac{5}{7} = \frac{265}{x}$

$\frac{7}{5} = \frac{x}{265}$

$\frac{7 \times 265}{5} = x$

$x = 371$

There are 371 girls in the school.

> Inverting **both** sides of the equation gets the unknown (x) on the top, making it easier to solve.

> Multiply both sides by 265.
> See Chapter 8 for how to solve this kind of equation.

 EXERCISE 12C

1 At a football match the ratio of boys to men is 3 : 8. If there are 630 boys, how many men are there?

2 A piece of wood is cut into two pieces in the ratio 4 : 7.
   (a) If the shortest piece is 140 cm, how long is the longer piece?
   (b) How long was the original piece of wood?

3 A recipe for jam uses 125 g of fruit and 100 g of sugar.

   (a) What is the ratio of fruit to sugar in its lowest terms?

   (b) If I had 300 g of fruit how much sugar would I need?

   (c) What would be the total mass of the jam in part (b)?

4 In a box of strawberries the ratio of good to damaged fruit is 16 : 3.

   (a) If I found 18 damaged fruits, how many good ones did I have?

   (b) How many strawberries are in the box?

5 A celebrity magazine has pictures to print in the ratio of 3 : 2. If a magazine has 75 sections of pictures, how many sections of print does it have?

Writing a ratio in the form 1 : n or n : 1

Some ratios can easily be written in a form where one side of the ratio is 1.

For example, a ratio of 20 : 4 simplifies to 5 : 1.

Other ratios do not naturally simplify in this way.

For example, 12 : 8 simplifies to 3 : 2.

Remember that the numbers on each side must be integers with no common factors for a ratio to be in its simplest form.

If you are asked to write this ratio in the form n : 1 you cannot leave the answer as 3 : 2.

Look at which number has to be 1. Divide both sides of the ratio by that number.

12 : 8 = (12 ÷ 8) : (8 ÷ 8) = 1.5 : 1

All ratios can be written in the form 1 : n or n : 1.

This is called unitary form.

 EXAMPLE 4

Write these ratios in the form n : 1.

(a) 27 : 4   (b) 6 cm : 25 mm   (c) $2.38 : 85¢

(a) 27 : 4 = 6.75 : 1

Divide both sides by 4.

(b) 6 cm : 25 mm = 60 mm : 25 mm
              = 60 : 25 = 2.4 : 1

Divide both sides by 25.

Change of units needed in (b) and (c).

(c) $2.38 : 85¢ = 238¢ : 85¢ = 238 : 85
              = 2.8 : 1

Divide both sides by 85.

EXAMPLE 5

Write these ratios in the form 1 : *n*.

(a) 5 : 9   (b) 400 g : 1.3 kg   (c) 40 min : $1\frac{1}{4}$ h

---

(a) 5 : 9 = 1 : 1.8

| Divide both sides by 5. |

(b) 400 g : 1.3 kg = 400 g : 1300 g
$$= 400 : 1300 = 1 : 3.25$$

| Divide both sides by 400. |

| Change of units needed in (b) and (c). |

(c) 40 min : $1\frac{1}{4}$ h = 40 min : 75 min
$$= 40 : 75 = 1 : 1.875$$

| Divide both sides by 40. |

 EXERCISE 12D

1 Write the following ratios in the form *n* : 1.

  (a) 15 : 3   (b) 7 : 2

  (c) 9 : 4   (d) 12 : 5

  (e) 3 kg : 200 g   (f) 1 hour : 40 min

  (g) 5 m : 40 cm   (h) 1 day : 10 hours

  (i) 2.5 ℓ : 500 mℓ

2 Write the following ratios in the form 1 : *n*.

  (a) 16 : 24   (b) 45 : 54

  (c) 36 : 96   (d) 15 hours : 1 day

  (e) 5 days : 4 weeks   (f) 6 mm : 2.7 cm

  (g) 18 ℓ : 4500 mℓ (h) 5 cm : 15 mm

Dividing quantities in a given ratio

Ratios can be used to share quantities.

Ian and Simon share $60 so that Ian receives twice as much as Simon.

You can think of this as a ratio.   Ian : Simon = 2 : 1

Ian will get this much   Simon will get this much

where each bag of money contains the same amount.

To work out each man's share, you need to divide the money into 3 (2 + 1) equal **parts** (or **shares**).

$$1 \text{ part} = \$60 \div 3 = \$20$$

Ian receives $\qquad 2 \times \$20 = \$40$ 2 parts

Simon receives $\qquad 1 \times \$20 = \$20$ 1 part

Check $\qquad \$20 + \$40 = \$60$ ✓

> **To share quantities in a given ratio**
>
> (1) Work out the total number of equal parts.
> (2) Work out the amount in 1 part.
> (3) Work out the value of each share.

You can use this method to share amounts between more than two people.

EXAMPLE 6

The alloy Alnico is often used to make guitar pickups. It is made from five metals: cobalt, iron, nickel, aluminium and titanium in the ratio 6 : 5 : 3 : 1 : 1.

How many grams of each metal are there in 544 g of this alloy?

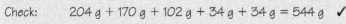

$$\text{Total number of parts} = 6 + 5 + 3 + 1 + 1 = 16 \text{ parts}$$
$$1 \text{ part} = 544 \text{ g} \div 16 = 34 \text{ g}$$

Cobalt	$= 6 \times 34\text{ g} = 204\text{ g}$	6 parts
Iron	$= 5 \times 34\text{ g} = 170\text{ g}$	5 parts
Nickel	$= 3 \times 34\text{ g} = 102\text{ g}$	3 parts
Aluminium	$= 1 \times 34\text{ g} = 34\text{ g}$	1 part
Titanium	$= 1 \times 34\text{ g} = 34\text{ g}$	1 part
Check:	$204\text{ g} + 170\text{ g} + 102\text{ g} + 34\text{ g} + 34\text{ g} = 544\text{ g}$ ✓	

Check that your final answers add up to the original amount.

EXERCISE 12E

1 Divide these amounts in the ratio given.
   (a) 50 in the ratio 3 : 2   (b) 30 in the ratio 3 : 7
   (c) 45 in the ratio 5 : 4   (d) 64 in the ratio 3 : 5

2 Divide each amount in the ratio given.
   (a) $200 in the ratio 9 : 1   (b) 125 g in the ratio 2 : 3
   (c) 600 m in the ratio 7 : 5   (d) 250 *l* in the ratio 16 : 9

3 Divide $120 in the ratio:
   (a) 7 : 3   (b) 1 : 3   (c) 3 : 2   (d) 5 : 7

4 The ratio of pupils to teachers for a school trip is 13 : 2.
If 135 people go on the trip, how many of them are teachers?

5 At a farm the ratio of black lambs to white lambs born is 2 : 9.
If 132 lambs are born one year, how many of them are black?

Increase or decrease in a given ratio.

6 A cocktail is made from orange juice, lemonade and lime juice in
the ratio 5 : 6 : 1. If I make 960 mℓ of cocktail, how much of each
ingredient will I need?

7 Concrete is made from cement, sand and gravel in the ratio
1 : 3 : 4. If I want to make 2 tonnes of concrete, how much of each
ingredient do I need?

8 Paulo is 18 years old, Johan is 15 years old and Sarah is 12 years
old. Their grandfather gives them $255 to be divided between them
in the ratio of their ages. How much will each of them receive?

12.2 Proportion

Direct proportion

Two quantities are in **direct proportion** if

- their ratio stays the same as they increase or decrease
- when one is zero, so is the other.

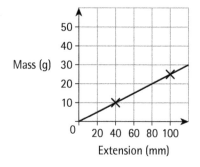

For example, a mass of 10 g attached to a spring stretches it by
40 mm. A mass of 25 g stretches the same spring by 100 mm.
The ratio mass : extension is

$$10 : 40 = 1 : 4 \quad \text{for the first mass}$$
$$25 : 100 = 1 : 4 \quad \text{for the second mass}$$

The ratio of mass : extension is the same. For a weight of 0 g the
extension is 0 m. So the two quantities (mass and extension) are in
direct proportion. If we plot the quantities on a graph, we get a
straight line through the origin.

You will find more about direct
proportion in Section 12.4.

⬤ EXAMPLE 7

The cost of 5 apples is $1.40. How much do 8 apples cost?

Suppose that 8 apples cost x cents.
$$5 : 140 = 8 : x$$
$$\frac{140}{5} = \frac{x}{8}$$
$$\frac{140 \times 8}{5} = x$$
$$x = 224$$

8 apples cost $2.24

Cost and number of apples are in
direct proportion. The ratio
number of apples : cost
must stay the same.

Work in cents for both costs.
Use the fractions method as in
Example 3.

Multiply both sides by 8.

Unitary method

Example 7 can be done by finding the cost of 1 apple.

This is called the **unitary method**.

> 5 apples cost $1.40 or 140¢
> 1 apple costs $\frac{140}{5} = 28¢$
> 8 apples cost $28 \times 8 = 224¢$ or $2.24

Notice how much easier this is and how it only takes three lines!

In the unitary method, you find the value of one unit of a quantity.

 **EXAMPLE 8**

Zainab has a part-time job.
She works for 15 hours a week and is paid $93.
Her employer wants her to work for 25 hours a week.
How much will Zainab be paid now?

First of all, find how much she is paid for **1** hour.

For 15 hours she is paid $93
For 1 hour she is paid $\frac{\$93}{15} = \$6.20$
For 25 hours she will get $25 \times \$6.20 = \$155$

To solve a *direct* proportion question you always do a *division* followed by a *multiplication*.

 EXERCISE 12F

1 If 8 pens cost $2.96, how much will 3 pens cost?

2 40 litres of petrol will take me 200 km.
How far can I go on 15 litres?

3 Five books weigh 450 g. How much would 18 books weigh?

4 Farah sews buttons onto trousers. She is paid $30 for sewing 200 buttons.
How much would she get for sewing 35 buttons?

5 6 packets of soap powder cost $7.38.
How much will 10 packets cost?

6 Jorina earns $67.20 for 12 hours' work. One week she works 17 hours. How much does she earn for that week?

7 A chocolate cake for 8 people uses 120 g of sugar.
How much sugar would you need for a cake for 15 people?

8 Omar walks 500 m to work and it takes him 8 minutes. If he continues to walk at the same speed,

(a) how far will he walk in 1 hour?

(b) how long will it take him to walk 2.25 km?

Inverse proportion

When two quantities are in direct proportion:

- as one increases, so does the other
- as one decreases, so does the other.

Suppose you travel from Hamburg to Kiel, a distance of 100 km.

If you travel at an average speed of 50 km/h it will take you 2 hours.

If you only average 40 km/h it will take you $2\frac{1}{2}$ hours.

The slower you travel, the more time it takes:

- as the speed decreases the time increases
- as the speed increases the time decreases.

$$\text{Time} = \frac{\text{distance}}{\text{speed}}$$

$$\frac{100}{50} = 2$$

$$\frac{100}{40} = 2\frac{1}{2}$$

If you *halve* the speed to 25 km/h you *double* the time to 4 hours.

> When two quantities are in **inverse proportion**, one quantity increases at the same rate as the other quantity decreases.

The best way to solve problems involving inverse proportion is to use the unitary method.

EXAMPLE 9

Two people take 6 hours to paint a fence.
How long will it take 3 people?

---

2 people take 6 hours
1 person takes 6 × 2 = 12 hours
3 people will take 12 ÷ 3 = 4 hours

Read the problem first and decide whether it is *direct* or *inverse* proportion.
Use your common sense!
The more people painting, the less time it takes.

Work out how long it will take 1 person.
1 person takes twice as long as 2 people.

EXAMPLE 10

Tarik is repaying a loan from a friend.
He agrees to pay $84 per month for 30 months.
If he can afford to pay $120 per month, how many months will it take to repay?

Paying $84 per month takes 30 months
Paying $1 per month takes (84 × 30) months
Paying $120 per month will take $\dfrac{84 \times 30}{120}$ months = 21 months

Repaying *more* each month will take *less* time, so this is inverse proportion.

210 years!

To solve *inverse* proportion questions you always do a *multiplication* followed by a *division*.

EXERCISE 12G

1 It takes 3 people 4 days to paint a shop.
How long would it take 1 person?

2 It takes 2 people 6 hours to make a suit.
How long would it take 3 people?

3 Eight horses need a trailer of hay to feed them for a week.
How many horses could this feed for 4 days?

4 It takes 5 bricklayers 4 days to build a house.
How long would it take 2 bricklayers?

5 It takes 3 pumps 15 hours to fill a swimming pool.
How many pumps would be needed to fill the pool in 9 hours?

6 A refugee camp has enough food for 400 people for 25 days. If the
food lasts only 20 days, how many people must be in the camp?

7 It takes 7 days for 6 people to dig a trench.
How long would it take 14 people?

8 In a library 48 paperback books 20 mm wide fit on a shelf.
How many books 24 mm wide would fit on the same shelf?

9 It takes 8 hours to fly to Chicago at a speed of 300 km/h.

(a) How long would it take to fly to Chicago at a speed of
400 km/h?

(b) If the journey took 12 hours, what speed was I travelling?

10 It takes 6 window cleaners 8 days to clean the windows of a hotel.

(a) How long would it take 4 window cleaners?

(b) The windows need to be cleaned in 3 days for a special event.
How many window cleaners are needed?

EXERCISE 12H

1 If 10 metres of material cost $23.50, what will 7 metres cost?

2 A man cuts a hedge in 45 minutes using a cutter with a blade
36 cm wide. How long would it take if the blade was only
15 cm wide?

3 It takes 200 tiles to tile a room when each tile covers 36 cm². If I
use tiles which cover 25 cm², how many tiles would I need?

4 Alan works for 9 hours a week in a shop. He is paid $45. He
increases his hours to 15. How much will he be paid?

5 It takes $2\frac{1}{2}$ hours to travel to London by train at an average speed
of 80 km/h. A new train travels at an average speed of 100 km/h.
How long will the journey to London take on the new train?

6 If 14 kg of potatoes cost $2.38, how much will 6 kg cost?

7 One load of feed lasts 40 sheep 9 days.
  (a) How many sheep could this load feed for 5 days?
  (b) For how many days could it feed 60 sheep?

8 In a hotel it takes a cleaner 24 minutes to clean 3 rooms.
  (a) How long will it take her to clean 16 rooms?
  (b) How many rooms can she clean in 4 hours?

12.3 Map scales

You will need to know
● how to convert between metric units of length

Map **scales** are written as ratios.

A scale of 1 : 50 000 means that 1 cm on the map represents
50 000 cm on the ground.

Always look carefully to see what
scale is being used.

When you answer questions involving map scales you need to:
● use the scale of the map
● convert between metric units of length so that your answer is
  in sensible units.

EXAMPLE 11

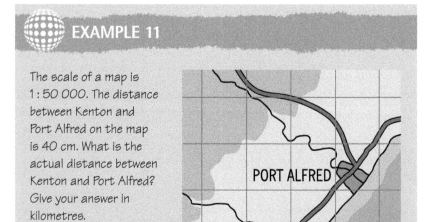

The scale of a map is
1 : 50 000. The distance
between Kenton and
Port Alfred on the map
is 40 cm. What is the
actual distance between
Kenton and Port Alfred?
Give your answer in
kilometres.

PORT ALFRED

KENTON-ON-SEA

Distance on map = 40 cm

Distance on the ground = 40 × 50 000 cm
$\qquad$ = 2 000 000 cm
$\qquad$ = 2 000 000 ÷ 100 m
$\qquad$ = 20 000 m
$\qquad$ = 20 000 ÷ 1000 km
$\qquad$ = 20 km

Work out the real distance in cm
then convert to km.

Each 1 cm on the map is 50 000 on
the ground.

1 m = 100 cm
1 km = 1000 m

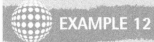 **EXAMPLE 12**

The distance between two towns is 24 km. How far apart will they be on a map of scale 1 : 180 000?

Distance on the ground = 24 km
$$= 24 \times 1000 \text{ m}$$
$$= 24\,000 \text{ m}$$
$$= 24\,000 \times 100 \text{ cm}$$
$$= 2\,400\,000 \text{ cm}$$

Distance on map $= \dfrac{2\,400\,000}{180\,000}$ cm = 13.3 cm (to 3 s.f.)

> Convert the real distance to cm before you divide by the scale of the map.

 EXERCISE 12I

1 The scale of a map is 1 : 25 000.
   Find the actual distance represented by these measurements on the map.
   (a) 4 cm   (b) 7 cm
   (c) 8 mm   (d) 12.5 cm

2 A map has scale 1 : 200 000.
   What measurement on the map will represent
   (a) 4 km   (b) 20 km
   (c) 15 km   (d) 12.5 km?

3 This motorway map has a scale of 1 : 3 000 000.
   (a) The distance on the map from Cair Faralel to Tashlan is 2.5 cm. How far is the actual distance?
   (b) Measure, in a straight line, the distance from Cair Faralel to Neruna. How far is the actual distance?

4 A map of Ireland has a scale of 1 : 500 000.
   What measurement on the map would represent these distances.
   (a) Waterford to Dundalk, 400 km
   (b) Wicklow to Carrigart, 320 km
   (c) Dublin to Tralee, 160 km?

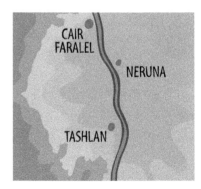

5 This map has a scale of 1 : 50 000. Use the map to work out the following distances.

(a) Between the ends of the 2 piers at Tynemouth.

(b) From Sharpness Point to Smuggler's Cave.

(c) The Ferry crossing of the Tyne.

(d) The combined length of both piers.

(e) From the Coast Guard Station (CG Sta) to the Coast Guard Lookout (CG Lookout).

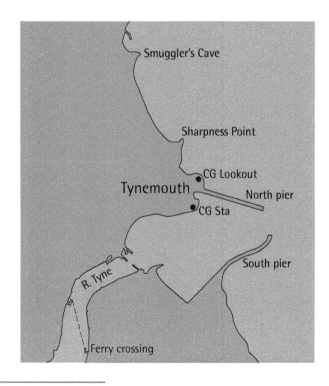

12.4 Variation

Direct variation

In Section 12.2 you saw that two quantities are in direct proportion if their ratio stays the same as they increase or decrease.
The example used was stretching a spring.

If no mass is attached to the spring, the extension is 0 m. This is important because two quantities can only be in direct proportion if **they are both zero at the same time.**

So the two conditions for direct proportion are

● if one quantity is zero then the other is also zero,
● their ratio stays the same as they increase or decrease.

This can be interpreted graphically, by plotting one quantity (or **variable**) against the other.

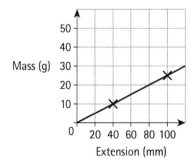

When two quantities are in direction proportion, their graph is a straight line passing through the origin.

In this case, the equation is $y = \dfrac{x}{4}$.

Suppose the gradient of the graph is k, then the equation of the graph will be $y = kx$

The symbol k is known as the **constant of proportionality**.

The gradient of the straight line and the constant of proportionality are always the same when two quantities are in direct proportion.

In this example, the relationship between these two quantities can be stated in several different ways, and you need to be familiar with all of them.

(1) y is directly proportional to x

(2) y varies directly as x

(3) $y \propto x$ where $\propto$ means 'is proportional to'

(4) $y = kx$ where k is the constant of proportionality

> Look back at Chapter 11 ... this is a graph of the form $y = mx + c$ where the value of c is zero. The value of the gradient k is $\dfrac{25}{100}$ or $\dfrac{1}{4}$, the same as the fractional equivalent of the ratio.

> Notice that (3) and (4) are almost the same, except that the symbol for proportionality ($\propto$) has been replaced by $= k$. Always use the $y = kx$ form in problems.

EXAMPLE 13

The volume of a solid ($V\,\text{cm}^3$) is directly proportional to the length of one of its sides ($l\,\text{cm}$). When $l = 12\,\text{cm}$, $V = 30\,\text{cm}^3$.

(a) Sketch a graph of this relationship.

(b) Find an equation connecting V and l.

(c) Find the volume when $l = 26\,\text{cm}$.

(d) Find the length of the solid when the volume is $37.5\,\text{cm}^3$.

(a)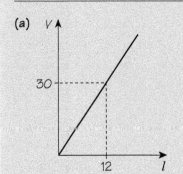

(b) Gradient $= \dfrac{30}{12} = 2.5 = k$

$V = 2.5\,l$

> $k = $ constant of proportionality.

(c) When $l = 26\,\text{cm}$

$V = 2.5 \times 26 = 65\,\text{cm}^3$

(d) When $V = 37.5\,\text{cm}^3$

$37.5 = 2.5 \times l$

$l = \dfrac{37.5}{2.5}$

$l = 15\,\text{cm}$

> When $l = 0$, $V = 0$.

The next example shows you how to handle questions when the information is given in the form of a table.

 **EXAMPLE 14**

In an experiment, the values of time (*T* min) and temperature (θ °C) were recorded in the following table.

Time (T min)	7.5	p	18
Temperature (θ °C)	16.35	25.07	q

If θ varies directly as *T*, find the missing values in the table.

$$7.5 : 16.35 = p : 25.07$$
$$\frac{7.5}{16.35} = \frac{p}{25.07}$$
$$\frac{7.5 \times 25.07}{16.35} = p$$
$$p = 11.5 \text{ minutes}$$

$$16.35 : 7.5 = q : 18$$
$$\frac{16.35}{7.5} = \frac{q}{18}$$
$$\frac{16.35 \times 18}{7.5} = q$$
$$q = 39.24°C$$

The ratio of time to temperature stays the same.

It is easier to use fractions.

The ratio/fraction can be written either way round.

You will need simple equation solving skills.

EXERCISE 12J

1 *y* varies directly as *x*. If *y* = 6 when *x* = 2 find
   (a) *y* when *x* = 5.5   (b) *x* when *y* = 12.

2 *w* is directly proportional to *t*. If *w* = 20 when *t* = 5 find
   (a) *w* when *t* = 7   (b) *t* when *w* = 18.

3 The table shows values of *h* and *p*.

h	1.4	5.2	a
p	b	18.2	39.55

If *h* ∝ *p* find the missing values *a* and *b*.

4 The surface area of a solid (*A* cm²) is directly proportional to the length of one of its sides (*l* cm).
   When *l* = 14, *A* = 33.6 cm².
   (a) Sketch a graph of the relationship between *l* and *A*.
   (b) Find an equation connecting *A* and *l*.
   (c) Find the area, *A*, when *l* = 19 cm.
   (d) Find the length, *l*, when *A* = 42 cm².

5 The table shows values of d and m.
Show that m is proportional to d.

d	4	6.5	11.7
m	2.32	3.77	6.786

6 The table shows values of c and N.
Is N directly proportional to c?
Give reasons for your answer.

c	3	7.2	12.5	20
N	4.8	11.52	18.25	32

7 The extension, e, of a spring is directly proportional to w, the
weight attached to the end of the spring.
When $w = 2.5$ kg, $e = 80$ mm.

(a) Find an equation connecting e and w.

(b) Find e when $w = 3.5$ kg.

(c) Find w when $e = 182.4$ mm.

Inverse variation

In Section 12.2 you saw that when one quantity increases at the same
rate as another quantity decreases, the two quantities are in inverse
proportion.

Example 9 asked this question:
Two people take 6 hours to paint a fence.
How long will it take 3 people?

You solved this by first finding how long it would take 1 person
(12 hours).
It is then easy to see that times for varying numbers of people will be.

Number of people (x)	1	2	3	4	6	8	9	12
Time (hours) (y)	12	6	4	3	2	$1\frac{1}{2}$	$1\frac{1}{3}$	1

Inverse proportion means that more
people take less time. For example,
9 people will do the job three times
faster than 3 people.

Notice that the product of any x–y pair is always 12 and the equation
of this relationship can be written as

$$xy = 12 \qquad y = \frac{12}{x}$$

A graph of these results looks like this:

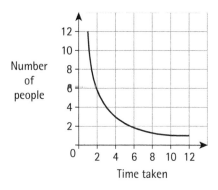

You can see that if the example stated that ...

Two people take **5** hours to paint a fence

... the equation would be $y = \dfrac{10}{x}$.

> One person will take 10 hours.

or if it is

Two people take **8** hours to paint a fence

then the equation would be $y = \dfrac{16}{x}$.

> One person will take 16 hours.

In this example, whatever the time is, the equation will always be of the form $y = \dfrac{k}{x}$

and the graph will be the same shape as the one above.

When two quantities behave in this way:

(1) y is inversely proportional to x

(2) y varies inversely as x

(3) $y \propto \dfrac{1}{x}$ where $\propto$ means 'is proportional to'

(4) $y = \dfrac{k}{x}$ where k is the constant of proportionality

> Notice that (3) and (4) are almost the same, except that the symbol for proportionality ($\propto$) has been replaced by $= k$. Always use the $y = \dfrac{k}{x}$ form in problems.

 EXAMPLE 15

In this table the two quantities x and y vary inversely.
Find the missing values, d and e.

x	d	7.5	16
y	20	8	e

$y = \dfrac{k}{x}$

$8 = \dfrac{k}{7.5}$

$8 \times 7.5 = k$ or $k = 60$

$y = \dfrac{60}{x}$

Using this equation, $20 = \dfrac{60}{d}$ which gives $d = 3$

$e = \dfrac{60}{16}$ which gives $e = 3.75$

> The two quantities x and y vary inversely so the equation connecting them must be $y = \dfrac{k}{x}$

> Use the pair of x and y values that you know, to find k.

> Notice that as x gets bigger, y gets smaller (and vice versa), which is what you would expect when two quantities vary inversely.

EXERCISE 12K

1   y varies inversely as x.
   If $y = 3$ when $x = 4$, find
   (a) y when $x = 24$ (b) x when $y = \frac{1}{3}$.

2   The table shows values of x and y, where x and y vary inversely.
   Find the missing values a and b.

x	0.5	2.5	a
y	b	6	1.2

3   If $h \propto \frac{1}{l}$ copy and complete this table of values.

l	0.2		0.6	1.5	3.6	
h		48	40			3.2

4   z is inversely proportional to w.
   $z = 54$ when $w = \frac{2}{3}$
   (a) Find an equation connecting z and w,
   (b) Find z when $w = 1.5$,
   (c) Find the possible values of w when $z = w$.

5   The table shows values of p and q.
   Is q inversely proportional to p?
   Give reasons for your answer.

p	0.6	2.4	9	30
q	18	4.5	1.2	0.36

6   In a physics experiment it is found that the volume (V cm³) of a gas
   varies inversely as its pressure (P bar).
   When the pressure is 1.6 bar the volume of the gas is 180 cm³.
   (a) Find an equation connecting V and P.
   (b) Find the volume when the pressure is 2.5 bar.
   (c) Find the pressure when the volume is 150 cm³.

Other kinds of variation

When two quantities are in direct proportion, their ratio stays the
same as they increase or decrease. So, for example, when one doubles
the other also doubles.
Sometimes two quantities increase together but not at the same rate.

EXAMPLE 16

y is proportional to x^2. If $y = 12$ when $x = 3$, find

(a) the value of y when $x = 9$

(b) the value of x when $y = 3$.

$y \propto x^2$ or

Using $y = 12$ when $x = 3$

$y = kx^2$

$12 = k \times 3^2$

$12 = k \times 9$

$\frac{12}{9} = k$

$k = \frac{4}{3}$

$y = \frac{4}{3}x^2$

(a) when $x = 9$ $y = \frac{4}{3} \times 9^2 = \frac{4}{3} \times 81 = 108$

(b) when $y = 3$ $3 = \frac{4}{3} \times x^2$

$\frac{9}{4} = x^2$

$x = \pm\frac{3}{2} = \pm 1\frac{1}{2}$

Use the $\propto$ notation to mean 'is proportional to' just as in the previous examples.
Then replace $\propto$ by $= k$, where k is the constant of proportionality.

Note that this time the equation contains x^2 because y is proportional to x^2.

Notice that there are **two** answers for x in part (b) since a square root has been taken.

Always start with a statement of proportionality.

(1) Use the given values of x and y to find the value of k, the constant of proportionality.
(2) Write down the equation connecting x and y using this value of k.
(3) Use the equation to calculate any answers required.

The most common ways that two quantities increase together, but not at the same rate, are shown in this table.

Variation		Equation
y is proportional to x^2 or y varies as x^2	$y \propto x^2$	$y = kx^2$
y is proportional to $\sqrt{x}$ or y varies as $\sqrt{x}$	$y \propto \sqrt{x}$	$y = k\sqrt{x}$
y is proportional to x^3 or y varies as x^3	$y \propto x^3$	$y = kx^3$

EXERCISE 12L

1 y is directly proportional to x^2. If $y = 20$ when $x = 2$, find
   (a) y when $x = 3$ (b) x when $y = 245$.

2 Q varies directly as m^2. If $Q = 48$ when $m = 4$,
   (a) find Q when $m = 1.5$ (b) m when $Q = 75$.

3 Given that $F \propto d^2$ copy and complete the table to find the missing values a and b.

d	6	8	a
F	126	b	423.5

4 y varies directly as $\sqrt{x}$
   If $y = 20$ when $x = 25$, find
   (a) y when $x = 81$ (b) x when $y = 12$.

5 Given that $y \propto x^3$ and $y = 162$ when $x = 3$.
   (a) Find an expression for y in terms of x.
   (b) Find y when $x = 4$.
   (c) Find x when $y = 750$.

6 The volume of a sphere is directly proportional to the cube of its radius.
   A sphere of radius 3 cm has a volume of 113.1 cm³. Find
   (a) the volume of a sphere of radius 2 cm
   (b) the radius of a sphere of volume 565.5 cm³.

7 In an experiment, measurements of Q and h were taken, as shown in this table.

h	3	6	7
Q	10.8	86.4	137.2

   Which of these laws fits the results?
   (A) $Q \propto \sqrt{h}$ (B) $Q \propto h^2$ (C) $Q \propto h^3$
   You must explain your answer.

___

When two quantities are in inverse proportion, one quantity increases at the same rate as the other quantity decreases.
So, for example, if one quantity doubles the other halves.
Sometimes two quantities are such that one increases and the other decreases **but not at the same rate.**

EXAMPLE 17

y is inversely proportional to the square root of x.
If $y = 8$ when $x = 9$, find

(a) the value of y when $x = 144$

(b) the value of x when $y = 6$.

$y \propto \dfrac{1}{\sqrt{x}}$　　or

$y = 8$ when $x = 9$

$y = \dfrac{k}{\sqrt{x}}$

$8 = \dfrac{k}{\sqrt{9}}$

$8 = \dfrac{k}{3}$

$8 \times 3 = k$

So　$k = 24$ and the equation is $y = \dfrac{24}{\sqrt{x}}$

(a)　when $x = 144$　$y = \dfrac{24}{\sqrt{144}} = \dfrac{24}{12} = 2$

(b)　when $y = 6$　　$6 = \dfrac{24}{\sqrt{x}}$

$\sqrt{x} = \dfrac{24}{6} = 4$

$x = 4^2 = 16$ •————————————— Square both sides.

> y is inversely proportional to the square root of x.
> Use the $\propto$ notation to mean 'is proportional to' just as in the previous examples.
> Then replace $\propto$ by $= k$, where k is the constant of proportionality.
>
> Note that this time the equation contains $\sqrt{x}$ and this term is in the denominator because y is **inversely** proportional to $\sqrt{x}$.

The most common ways that one quantity increases and the other decreases, but not at the same rate, are shown in this table.

Variation		Equation
y is inversely proportional to x^2 or y varies inversely as x^2	$y \propto \dfrac{1}{x^2}$	$y = \dfrac{k}{x^2}$
y is inversely proportional to $\sqrt{x}$ or y varies inversely as $\sqrt{x}$	$y = \dfrac{1}{\sqrt{x}}$	$y = \dfrac{k}{\sqrt{x}}$
y is inversely proportional to x^3 or y varies inversely as x^3	$y \propto \dfrac{1}{x^3}$	$y = \dfrac{k}{x^3}$

EXERCISE 12M

1   y is inversely proportional to $\sqrt{x}$.
    If $y = 1.8$ when $x = 100$, find
    (a) y when $x = 9$ (b) x when $y = 4.5$.

2   y varies inversely as x^2.
    If $y = 5$ when $x = 4$, find
    (a) y when $x = 10$ (b) x when $y = 20$.

3   If $y \propto \dfrac{1}{x^3}$ and $y = 6$ when $x = 2$, find
    (a) y when $x = \frac{1}{2}$ (b) x when $y = \frac{3}{4}$

4   W is inversely proportional to the square of m.
    If $W = 2.4$ when $m = 5$, find
    (a) an equation connecting W and m
    (b) W when $m = 6$
    (c) m when $W = 15$.

5   When a cylinder has a fixed volume, the radius, r cm, is inversely proportional to the square root of the height, h cm.
    When the height is 16 cm the radius is 5 cm.
    (a) Find the radius when the height is 4 cm.
    (b) Find the height when the radius is 10 cm.

6   The force of attraction, F newtons, between two magnets varies inversely as the square of the distance, d cm, between them.
    When the magnets are 5 cm apart the force of attraction is 3 newtons.
    (a) Find the force of attraction when the magnets are 2 cm apart.
    (b) How far apart are the magnets when the force of attraction is $\frac{1}{3}$ newton?

1 The brightness (B) of an object varies inversely as the square of the distance (d) of the object from a light.

When $d = 12$, $B = 2$.

(a) Find an equation connecting B and d.   [2]

(b) Find the value of B when $d = 3$.   [1]

(CIE Paper 2, Jun 2000)

2 A map has a scale of $1 : 250\,000$. Copy and complete the statement below.

1 centimetre on the map represents .... kilometres on the ground.   [1]

(CIE Paper 2, Jun 2001)

3 (a) One day Amit works from 08 00 until 17 00.

The time he spends on filing, computing, writing and having lunch is in the ratio.

Filing : Computing : Writing : Lunch = 2 : 5 : 4 : 1

Calculate the time he spends

(i)   writing,   [1]

(ii) having lunch, giving this answer in minutes.   [1]

(b) The amount earned by Amit, Bernard and Chris is in the ratio $2 : 5 : 3$.

Bernard earns $855 per week.

Calculate how much

(i)   Amit earns each week,   [1]

(ii) Chris earns each week.   [1]

(CIE Paper 4, Jun 2002)

4 The ratios of teachers : male students : female students in a school are $2 : 17 : 18$.

The total number of **students** is 665.

Find the number of **teachers**.   [2]

(CIE Paper 2, Jun 2003)

5 When cars go round a bend there is a force, F, between the tyres and the ground.

F varies directly as the square of the speed, v.

When $v = 40$, $F = 18$.

Find F when $v = 32$.   [3]

(CIE Paper 2, Nov 2003)

6 (a) Mohammed's height is 169 cm and Fatima's height is 156 cm.
    The frame sizes of their bikes are in the same ratio as their heights.
    The frame size of Mohammed's bike is 52 cm.
    Calculate the frame size of Fatima's bike. [2]
  (b) Fatima and Mohammed are members of a school team which takes part in a bike ride for charity.
    Fatima and Mohammed ride a total distance of 36 km.
    The ratio   distance Fatima rides : distance Mohammed rides = 11 : 9
    Work out the distance Fatima rides. [2]

(CIE Paper 4, Jun 2004)

---

7 The air resistance (R) to a car is proportional to the square of the speed (v).
  When $R = 1800$, $v = 30$.
  Calculate R when $v = 40$. [3]

(CIE Paper 2, Nov 2004)

---

8 Hassan sells fruit and vegetables at the market.
  (a) The mass of fruit and vegetables he sells is in the ratio

    fruit : vegetables = 5 : 7.

    Hassan sells 1.55 **tonnes** of vegetables.
    How many **kilograms** of fruit does he sell? [3]
  (b) The amount of money Hassan receives from selling fruit and vegetables is in the ratio

    fruit : vegetables = 9 : 8

    Hassan receives a **total** of $765 from selling fruit and vegetables.
    Calculate how much Hassan receives from selling fruit. [2]

(CIE Paper 4, Jun 2005)

---

9 The wavelength, w, of a radio signal is inversely proportional to its frequency, f.
  When $f = 200$, $w = 1500$
  (a) Find an equation connecting f and w. [2]
  (b) Find the value of f when $w = 600$. [1]

(CIE Paper 2, Jun 2005)

Chapter 13

Transformations

This chapter will show you how to
- ✔ recognise and use the six types of transformation – reflection, rotation, translation, enlargement, shear and stretch
- ✔ enlarge shapes with fractional and negative scale factors
- ✔ find the centre and scale factor of an enlargement
- ✔ use a combination of transformations

13.1 Transformations

A **transformation** changes the size or position of an object. The original shape is called the object and the transformed shape is called the **image**. You need to know about six types of transformation

- Reflection
- Rotation
- Translation
- Enlargement
- Shear
- Stretch

The first three of these – **reflection**, **rotation** and **translation** – only alter the *position* of an object. The size of the image and the object are identical – the image and object are **congruent**.

> You will find more about congruent and similar shapes in Chapter 14.

Enlargement alters not only the position of an object but also its size. The object and image are mathematically **similar**.

13.2 Reflection

You will need to know
- what is meant by a line of symmetry

> **Reflections** take place along a mirror line to produce a **mirror image**.

This image is exactly the same size and shape as the original shape (congruent) and points on the image are the same distance behind the **mirror line** as they are on the object in front of the mirror line.

A line connecting a point *P* on the object with the corresponding point *P'* on the image will always cross the mirror line at right-angles.

In a reflection

$PM = P'M$

Every point on an object is reflected in this way. When answering questions on reflecting 2-dimensional shapes, just consider the corners (vertices) of the object.

EXAMPLE 1

The object *ABCD* is reflected in a mirror line as shown. Draw the image of the object and label this *A'B'C'D'*.

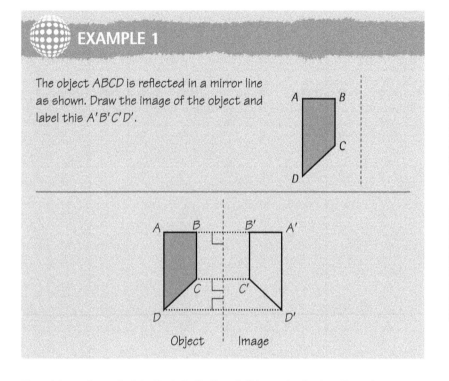

The shape of an object can be drawn on tracing paper. Turning the paper over and lining up the mirror line will allow you to draw the reflected image. This method will work in all questions on reflections.

Draw a line from *C* at right angles to the mirror line and continue the line to a point the same distance the other side and label it *C'*. Repeat this for points *A*, *B* and *D*. Now join the points in order with straight lines.

The object shape is labelled *A*, *B*, *C* and *D* in a clockwise direction. After reflection, the image shape is labelled *A'*, *B'*, *C'* and *D'* in an anticlockwise direction.

Object shapes can also cross a mirror line but the points are reflected in the same way.

EXAMPLE 2

The triangle *ABC* is reflected in the mirror line, *M*. Draw the reflection of this triangle and label it *A'B'C'*.

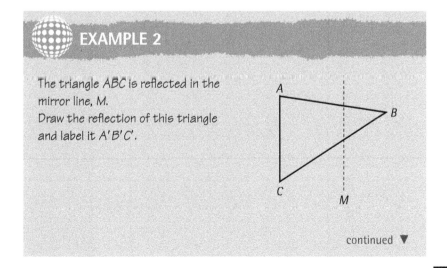

continued ▼

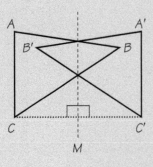

Draw a line from C at right angles to the mirror line and continue to the point C' at the same distance on the other side. Note that lines AB and A'B', and lines BC and B'C' cross exactly on the mirror line. This is always true for shapes that cross the mirror line.

Mirror lines can be vertical, horizontal or at an angle.

Mirror lines can be described with an equation, such as $x = 0$, $y = 4$, $y = x$.

Angled mirror lines need some care when constructing the image.

⬡ EXAMPLE 3

The trapezium ABCD is to be reflected in the diagonal mirror line as shown. Draw the image and label it A'B'C'D'.

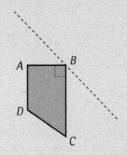

When the mirror line is sloping it is useful to rotate the page until the mirror line is vertical.

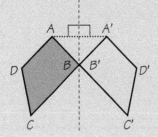

The mirror line is now vertical and the line AA' crosses the mirror line at right angles. Point B lies on the mirror line, so the image point B' also lies on the mirror line in the same position as B.

When you reflect an object on squared paper and in an angled mirror line, you may be able to count squares diagonally to find the position of an image point.

Do this for each point separately, then join up the points to produce the final image.

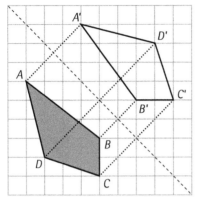

From A, count $1\frac{1}{2}$ squares diagonally to the mirror line. Count another $1\frac{1}{2}$ and mark the point A'. For B, count 1 square diagonally to the mirror line, then 1 more to B'. Find C' and D' in the same way. Note that AA' is perpendicular to the mirror line.

Sometimes you are given the object and image and asked to draw the mirror line.

You need to be able to reflect in the lines $y = x$ and $y = -x$. They are the lines at 45° to the co-ordinate axes.

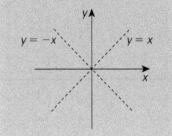

To describe a reflection fully you need to give the equation of the mirror line.

EXAMPLE 4

The diagram shows an object P and its image Q after reflection.

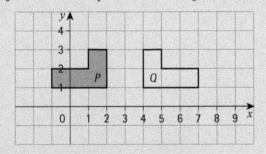

(a) Draw in the mirror line as a dashed line.

(b) What is the equation of this mirror line?

(a)

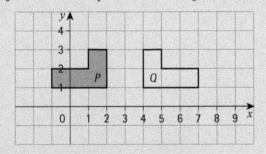

The mirror line must be the same distance from P as from Q.

(b) The equation of the mirror line is $x = 3$.

The mirror line is parallel to the y-axis. The x-values of all points on it are 3. So the equation is $x = 3$.

You will need squared paper for each question.

1 Each diagram shows a coloured object with its image. Copy these
   diagrams onto squared paper and draw in the mirror line
   in each case.

(a)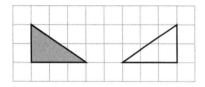

(b)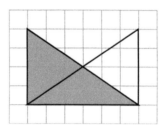

(c)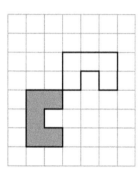

(d)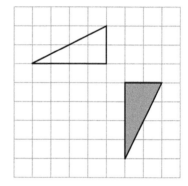

2 Copy these shapes and the dashed mirror line onto squared paper.
   Draw the reflected image in each case.

(a)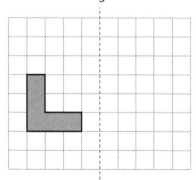

(b)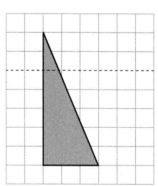

(c)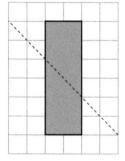

3 Copy the axes and triangle **A** onto squared paper.

Reflect triangle **A**

(a) in the *y*-axis and label the image **B**.

(b) in the *x*-axis and label it **C**.

(c) in the line $y = -x$ and label the image **D**.

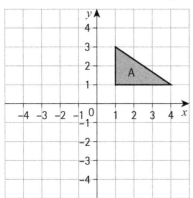

4 Copy the axes and the shape **P** onto squared paper.
Reflect the shape

(a) in the line $x = 1$ (b) in the line $y = x$.

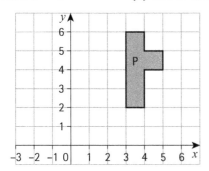

5 Copy the axes and polygon **A** onto squared paper.

(a) Reflect polygon **A** in the line $y = 1$. Label it **B**.

(b) Reflect polygon **A** in the line $y = x$. Label it **C**.

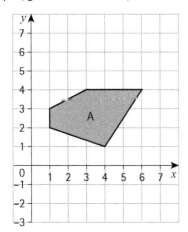

13.3 Rotation

A **rotation** turns an object either clockwise or anticlockwise through a given angle about a fixed point.

The fixed point is called the **centre of rotation**. It can be either inside or outside the object.

An object can be rotated through any angle (in degrees). Common rotations are **quarter turn** (90°), **half turn** (180°) and **three-quarter turn** (270°).

> Always look carefully to see whether the rotation is clockwise or anticlockwise.

⬤ EXAMPLE 5

Draw the image of this shape after it has been rotated through 90° anticlockwise about the centre of rotation at

(a) A **(b)** B **(c)** C.

The image after each rotation is shown shaded.

> Tracing paper is very useful in all questions on rotation.

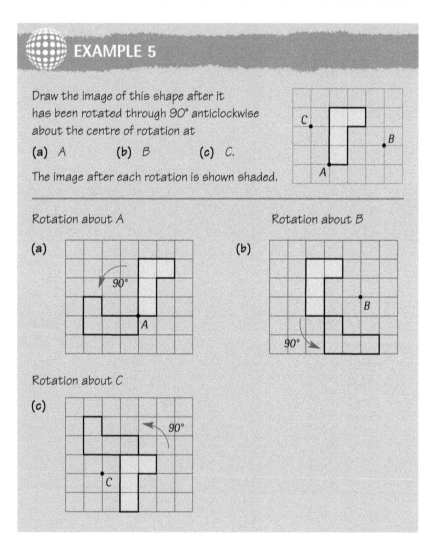

Rotation about A **(a)**

Rotation about B **(b)**

Rotation about C **(c)**

> Trace the shape and the centre of rotation on to tracing paper. Hold the centre of rotation fixed with your pencil point. Turn the tracing paper through the required angle.

> Draw the image you see on your diagram.

> The image formed after rotation is the same size and shape as the original object.

An object and its image after rotation are congruent.

EXAMPLE 6

Draw the image of the shape after rotation about P(1, −1) through

(a) a quarter of a turn anticlockwise

(b) rotation through 180° clockwise.

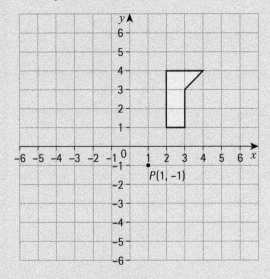

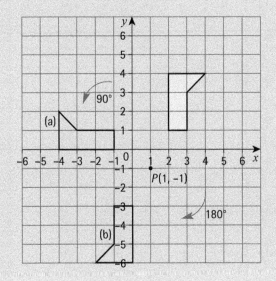

Use tracing paper to help you.

An image formed by a rotation through 180° clockwise is in the same position as an image formed by a rotation through 180° anticlockwise.
They are both 'half turns' and it doesn't matter which direction you turn.

To describe a rotation fully you need to give

● the centre of rotation

● the angle of turn

● the direction of turn

Clockwise or anticlockwise.

If you want to describe fully the rotation that takes shape *P* on to shape *Q*, the easiest way is to use tracing paper.

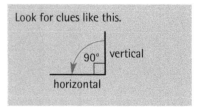

Place the tracing paper over the whole of the diagram and draw shape *P* on it.

The longest side of the diagram in shape *P* is vertical. The corresponding side in shape *Q* is horizontal. So the angle of rotation must be 90° (or 270° if you rotate in the opposite direction).

1 Try a point somewhere near *P* and *Q*. Put your pencil point on the point and hold it fixed.

2 Turn through 90° (or 270°) and see if shape *P* lands exactly on top of shape *Q*.

3 If it does not, try another centre of rotation. Keep trying different centres of rotation until shape *P* fits exactly on top of shape *Q*.

4 Describe the rotation, giving
  ● the angle
  ● the direction
  ● the centre of rotation (as co-ordinates).

The rotation that takes *P* to *Q* is 90° anticlockwise about point (2, 1).

Remember to ask for some tracing paper when you attempt any transformation question on the exam paper. It is particularly useful for rotation questions.

Look for clues like this.

90° vertical
horizontal

Once you have drawn the diagram, you can try several different centres of rotation quite quickly.

Notice that the centre of rotation lies on the perpendicular bisector of AA'. This is true for any pair of corresponding points.

EXERCISE 13B

1 Copy these shapes onto squared paper.

(a)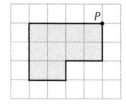

(b)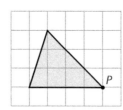

(c)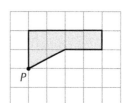

Draw the image after rotating each shape about the point *P* through
(i) a half turn clockwise
(ii) a quarter turn anticlockwise.

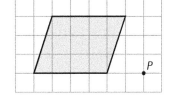

2 Copy this shape onto squared paper.

Draw the image of the shape after it has been rotated about the point *P* through

(a) 90° clockwise

(b) 180° anticlockwise

(c) three quarters of a turn clockwise.

3 On squared paper draw *x*- and *y*-axes going from −6 to +6. Copy this shape onto your axes.

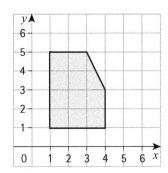

Draw the image of the shape after

(a) a quarter turn clockwise about the origin (0, 0). Label the image *A*.

(b) a quarter turn anticlockwise about the origin (0, 0). Label the image *B*.

(c) 180° rotation anticlockwise about the origin (0, 0). Label the image *C*.

4 Describe fully the transformation which maps shape *P* onto shape *Q*.

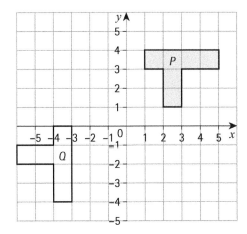

You need to give three pieces of information
● the amount of turn
● the direction of turn
● the centre of rotation.

Use tracing paper to help you.

13.4 Translation

A **translation** slides a shape from one position to another.

In a translation every point on the shape moves the same distance in the same direction.

To describe a translation you need to give the distance and the direction of the movement.

 **EXAMPLE 7**

Translate this shape 4 squares to the right and 2 squares up.

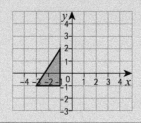

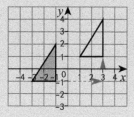

Choose any vertex of the shape and move this point 4 squares to the right and 2 squares up. Repeat this for the other vertices. Join up the vertices with straight lines.

An object and its image after a translation are congruent.

You can describe a translation by a **column vector**.

The translation in Example 7 has column vector $\begin{pmatrix} 4 \\ 2 \end{pmatrix}$.

Column vectors always have tall brackets round them.

The top number represents the movement in the x-direction and the bottom number represents the movement in the y-direction.

They are not fractions so do not draw a line between the numbers.

Notice that the translation to take the triangle back to its original position is $\begin{pmatrix} -4 \\ -2 \end{pmatrix}$.

Movements right and up are positive but left and down are negative.

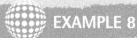

EXAMPLE 8

Translate this shape by the vector $\begin{pmatrix} -3 \\ -3 \end{pmatrix}$.

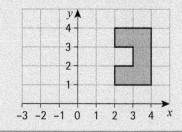

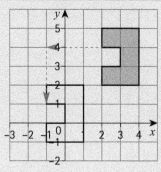

$\begin{pmatrix} -3 \\ -3 \end{pmatrix}$ means 3 squares *left* and 3 squares *down*.

EXERCISE 13C

1 Copy these shapes onto squared paper and translate them by the amounts shown.

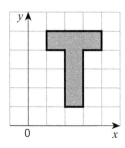 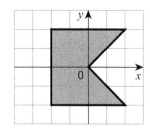

(a) $\begin{pmatrix} 3 \\ -2 \end{pmatrix}$ (b) $\begin{pmatrix} -4 \\ 2 \end{pmatrix}$ (c) $\begin{pmatrix} -5 \\ 0 \end{pmatrix}$ (d) $\begin{pmatrix} -1 \\ -6 \end{pmatrix}$ (e) $\begin{pmatrix} 0 \\ 3 \end{pmatrix}$

2 Copy this shape onto squared paper. A translation of the shape moves the point P to the point P' on the image. Draw the complete image. What is the column vector that describes the translation?

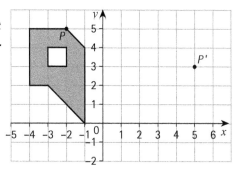

3 The triangle A is translated to new positions at B, C, D and E.
   Describe each transformation by giving the column vector.

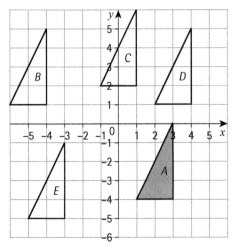

4 The letter N has vertices at positions A(0, 0), B(2, 4), C(4, 0) and
   D(4, 4). On an x–y grid with x and y between −6 and +6 plot these
   points and join the lines in order A to D.

   (a) Translate the letter N by the translation vector $\begin{pmatrix} -5 \\ 2 \end{pmatrix}$ followed

       by a second translation using the vector $\begin{pmatrix} 3 \\ -7 \end{pmatrix}$.

       Draw these new shapes on your diagram and label them
       A′B′C′D′ and A″B″C″D″.

   (b) What are the co-ordinates of the new vertex B″?

   (c) What single transformation vector could be used to describe
       the movement from ABCD to A″B″C″D″?

13.5 Enlargement

An **enlargement** changes the size of an object but not its shape.

The number of times the shape is enlarged is called the **scale factor** or
multiplier. This can be a whole number or a fraction.

In an enlargement, all the angles stay the same but all the lengths
are changed in the same **proportion**. The image is **similar** to the
object.

An enlargement by a scale factor of
a fraction less than 1 makes the
image smaller.

For help with proportionality see
Chapter 12.

EXAMPLE 9

Enlarge the rectangle ABCD by a
scale factor 2.

continued ▼

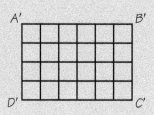

Similar shapes
● have equal angles
● have lengths in the same proportion.

Every length on the object is multiplied by 2 on the image.

$AB = 3$, so $A'B' = 2 \times 3 = 6$
$BC = 2$, so $B'C' = 2 \times 2 = 4$

EXAMPLE 10

What is the scale factor of the enlargement that takes shape A to shape B?

Compare the lengths of corresponding sides.

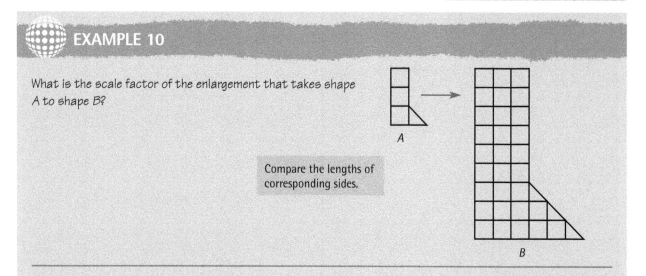

Shape A is only 1 square wide at the top.

Shape B is 3 squares wide at the top.
Shape A is 3 squares long.
Shape B is 9 squares long.

Shape B is 3 times longer and 3 times wider than shape A.

The scale factor is 3.

The final position of an enlargement is determined by the position of the **centre of enlargement**. In Examples 9 and 10 there is no centre of enlargement so the image can be drawn anywhere.

When you enlarge from a centre of enlargement, the distances from the centre to each point are multiplied by the scale factor.

If no centre of enlargement is given you can then draw the image close to the original shape.

EXAMPLE 11

Copy the triangle ABC. Enlarge the triangle by scale factor 2 using the point O as the centre of enlargement.

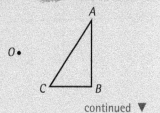

Multiply the distance OA by 2 to get OA', and similarly for the other vertices.
$OA' = 2 \times OA$
$OB' = 2 \times OB$
$OC' = 2 \times OC$

continued ▼

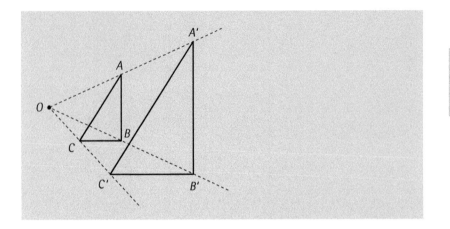

Always draw your diagram as accurately as possible using a pencil and ruler. Leave the construction lines on your diagram.

The centre of enlargement can be a point on the shape.

EXAMPLE 12

Enlarge the triangle by scale factor 3 using point *P* as the centre of enlargement.

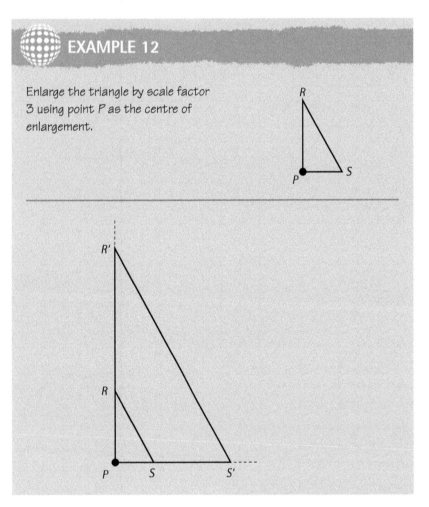

For an enlargement by a scale factor 3
$PR' = 3 \times PR$
$PS' = 3 \times PS$
The enlargement overlaps the original shape.

Sometimes the centre of enlargement is inside the shape.
Here, *ABCD* has been enlarged about centre *O*, by scale factor $\frac{1}{3}$.

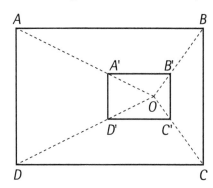

$OA' = \frac{1}{3}OA$
$OB' = \frac{1}{3}OB$
$OC' = \frac{1}{3}OC$
$OD' = \frac{1}{3}OD$

The enlargement is smaller than the original.

To describe an enlargement fully you need to give the scale factor and the centre of enlargement.

To find the position of the centre of enlargement, join vertices in the enlargement to the corresponding vertices in the original and continue these lines until they meet at a point.

This point is the centre of enlargement.

You draw in the construction lines for the enlargement.

EXAMPLE 13

Triangle *ABC* has been enlarged to produce the shaded triangle *A'B'C'*.

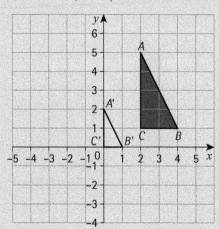

Note that we use the term 'enlarged' even though the new shape is smaller!

(a) What is the scale factor of the enlargement from *ABC* to *A'B'C'*?

(b) Mark on the grid the position of the centre of enlargement *P*, and give its co-ordinates.

This enlargement has made a smaller image so the scale factor must be less than 1.

continued ▼

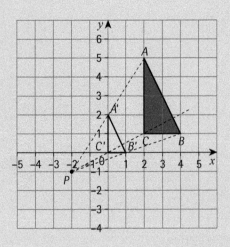

All lengths on triangle $A'B'C'$ are half the lengths on triangle ABC. So the scale factor is $\frac{1}{2}$.

Draw in the construction lines joining A to A', B to B' etc. These lines meet at point $P(-2, -1)$, the centre of enlargement.

(a) $C'A' = \frac{1}{2}C'A'$ and $C'B' = \frac{1}{2}C'B'$. The scale factor is $\frac{1}{2}$.

(b) The centre of enlargement is at $P(-2, -1)$.

Negative scale factor

An enlargement by a negative scale factor produces an image that is in the opposite direction to the object. The size of this image is given by the size of the scale factor.

EXAMPLE 14

Enlarge triangle PQR with a scale factor -1 using the centre of enlargement $C(-1, 1)$.

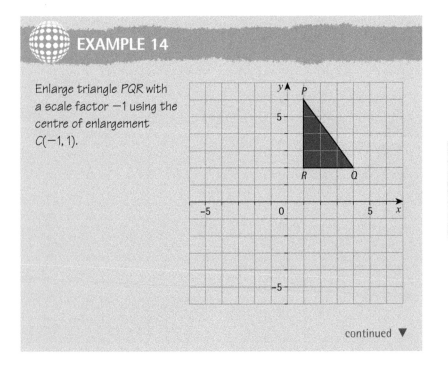

Mark the centre C at position $(-1, 1)$. Draw extended lines from each vertex through to the opposite side of C. For a scale factor -1 the length $PC = P'C$, $QC = Q'C$ and $RC = R'C$.

continued ▼

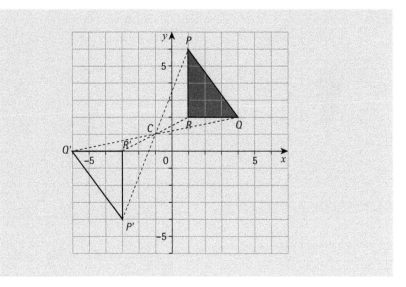

Label the image $P'Q'R'$. Leave your construction lines on the diagram.

For a scale factor of -2, $P'C = 2 \times PC$
$Q'C = 2 \times QC$
$R'C = 2 \times RC$

For a negative scale factor, the image is always 'upside down' in relation to the object.

... and so on for any other scale factor.

Scale factors and similarity

- A scale factor of 1 produces an image shape that is the same size as the object shape. The object and image shapes are *congruent*.

- A scale factor > 1 produces an image shape that is larger than the object shape and the two shapes are *similar*.

- A scale factor < 1 produces an image shape that is smaller than the object shape and the two shapes are *similar*.

- A negative scale factor produces an image 'upside down' in relation to the object and on the opposite side of the centre of enlargement. The size of the image is given by the size of the scale factor.

EXERCISE 13D

1 For each of the following shapes, work out the scale factor of the enlargement.

(a)
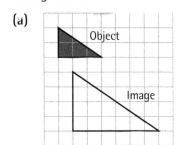

(b)
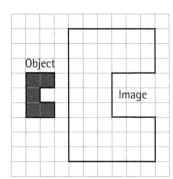

Use Example 10 to help you.

(c)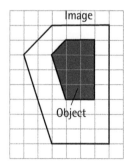

(d)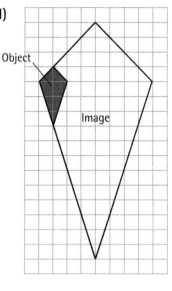

2 Copy each of the following shapes onto squared paper.
   Enlarge each one by scale factor 2.

> No centre of enlargement is given, so draw the enlargement close to the original shape.

(a)   (b)   (c)

3 Copy the following shapes onto squared paper.
   Enlarge each one by scale factor 2 from the centre of enlargement *C*.

(a)   (b)

4 The vertices of triangle *K* are (1, 1), (1, 2) and (4, 1).

   Copy the diagram.

   Enlarge the triangle *K* by scale factor 3 with (0, 0) as the centre of enlargement.

   What are the co-ordinates of the image triangle *K'*?

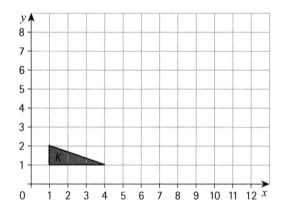

5 This right-angled triangle is to be enlarged by scale factor 4.

The centre of enlargement is at a point $P(1, 2)$.

Copy the diagram and draw the enlargement.

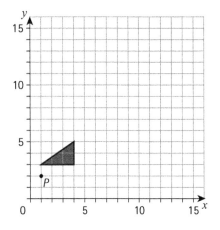

6 The rectangle X is enlarged to produce the image Y.

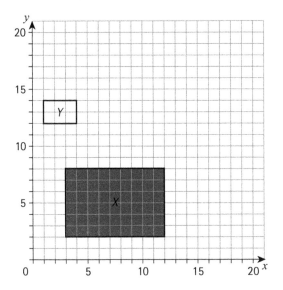

Use Example 13 to help you.

Copy the diagram.
(a) What is the scale factor of this enlargement?
(b) Construct lines to show the position of the centre of enlargement.
(c) What are the co-ordinates of the centre of enlargement?

7 Copy the shape below onto squared paper and draw an
   enlargement using a scale factor of $\frac{1}{3}$ about the point (4, 4).

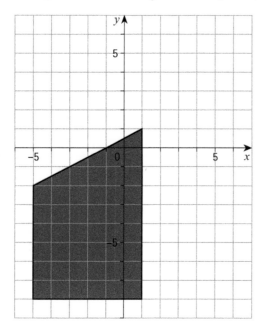

8 Copy the shape onto squared paper and draw an enlargement
   with a scale factor −2 about the origin.

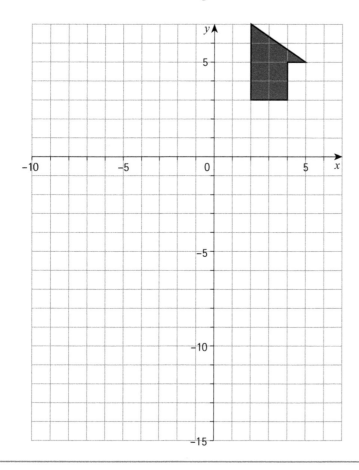

13.6 Stretch

One-way stretch

The following diagrams show how this transformation works.

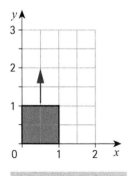 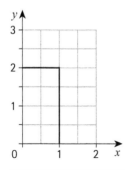 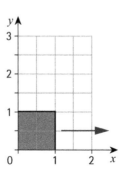 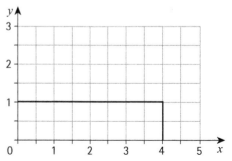

This is a square of side 1 unit placed at the origin.

This is a one-way stretch of the unit square, from the x-axis, parallel to the y-axis, of scale factor 2.

This is a square of side 1 unit placed at the origin.

This is a one-way stretch of the unit square, from the y-axis, parallel to the x-axis, of scale factor 4.

You can see that a one-way stretch is exactly that, a stretch in one direction only. The direction of the stretch is perpendicular to the invariant line. The scale factor of the stretch tells you the distance multiplier from the invariant line in the direction of the stretch.

To describe a one-way stretch you must give the scale factor, and the invariant line.

If the scale factor is negative, the stretch is in the opposite direction.

If the stretch is a fraction, smaller than 1, then the image will be smaller and nearer the invariant line.

EXAMPLE 15

For the triangle ABC, draw a one-way stretch of SF3 from the y-axis parallel to the x-axis.

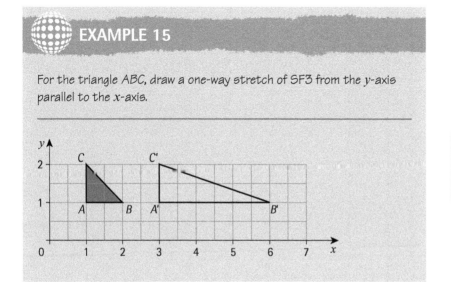

A is 1 unit from the invariant line (y-axis) so A' is 3 units from it. B is 2 units from the invariant line so B' is 6 units from it.

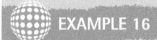

EXAMPLE 16

For the triangle ABC, draw a one way stretch SF −2 from the y-axis parallel to the x-axis.

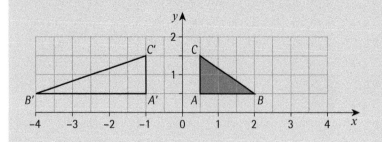

A is $\frac{1}{2}$ unit from the invariant line (y-axis) so A′ is −1 unit from it.
B is 2 units from the invariant line so B′ is −4 units from it.

 EXERCISE 13E

1 Copy the diagram onto squared paper.
Draw a one-way stretch, scale factor 4 from the y-axis.

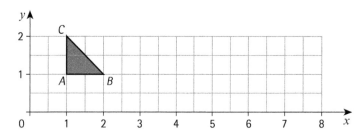

2 Copy the diagram onto squared paper.
Draw a one-way stretch, scale factor $\frac{1}{2}$ from the y-axis.

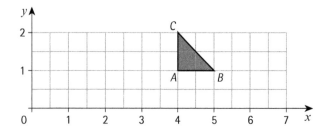

3 Copy the diagram onto squared paper.
   Draw a one-way stretch, scale factor 2 from the x-axis.

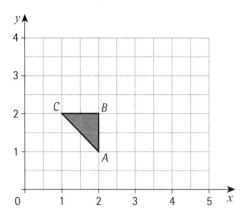

4 Copy the diagram onto squared paper.
   Draw a one-way stretch, scale factor $\frac{1}{2}$ from the x-axis.

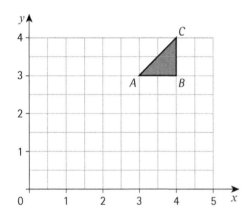

5 Copy the diagram onto squared paper.
   Draw a one-way stretch, scale factor -2 from the line $x = 1$.

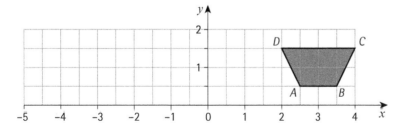

Two-way stretch

This is the result of applying two one-way stretches at right angles to each other.

The following diagrams show how this transformation works.

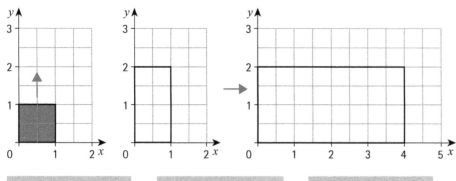

This is a square of side 1 unit placed at the origin.

This is a one-way stretch of the unit square, from the x-axis, parallel to the y-axis, of scale factor 2.

This is a one-way stretch of the previous diagram, from the y-axis, parallel to the x-axis, of scale factor 4.

You can see that a two-way stretch is two one-way stretches in two directions with different scale factors.

 EXERCISE 13F

Describe the stretches in each of the following diagrams.

1
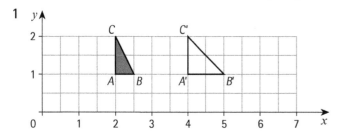

2
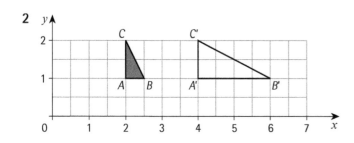

3

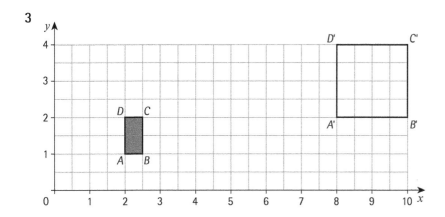

4

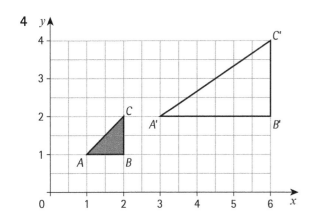

5

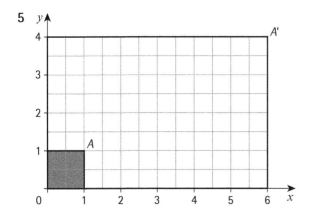

13.7 Shear

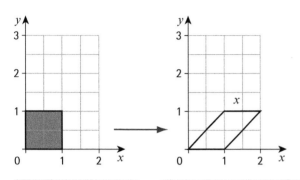

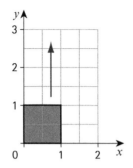

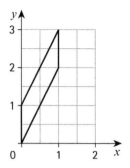

This is a square of side 1 unit placed at the origin.

This is a shear of the unit square, with the x-axis invariant of scale factor 1. Points on the unit square move parallel to the x-axis.

This is a square of side 1 unit placed at the origin.

This is a shear of the unit square with the y-axis invariant of scale factor 2. Points on the unit square move parallel to the y-axis.

The distance that a point moves is decided by the scale factor.

Measure the distance of the point from the invariant line and multiply by the scale factor. This will give the distance that the point moves parallel to the invariant line.

Points on the invariant line do not move.

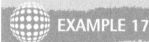 EXAMPLE 17

The shape shown is to be sheared by a scale factor 3 with the x-axis invariant.

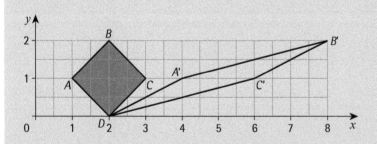

Point	Distance from line	Distance to move
A	1	3
B	2	6
C	1	3
D	0	0

To describe a shear fully you need to give the scale factor and the invariant line.

EXAMPLE 18

Shear the shape shown by a scale factor 2, with the line $y = 1$ invariant.

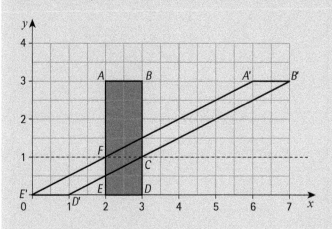

Point	Distance from line	Distance to move
A	2	4
B	2	4
C	0	0
D	-1	-2
E	-1	-2
F	0	0

Points on the invariant line do not move

EXERCISE 13G

1 Copy the diagram onto squared paper.
Shear the shape A with scale factor 4, x-axis invariant.

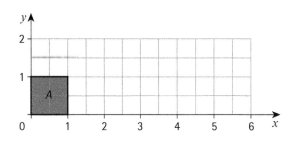

2 Copy the diagram onto squared paper.
Shear the shape B with scale factor 3, y-axis invariant.

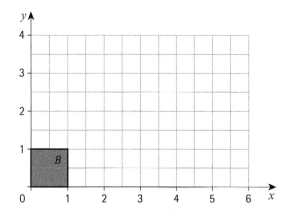

3 Copy the diagram onto squared paper.
   Shear the shape C with scale factor 3, x-axis invariant.

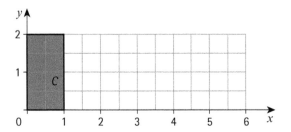

4 Copy the diagram onto squared paper.
   Shear the shape D with scale factor $1\frac{1}{2}$, y-axis invariant.

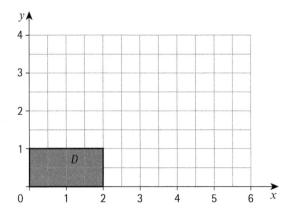

5 Copy the diagram onto squared paper.
   Shear the shape E with scale factor 2, $y = 2$ invariant.

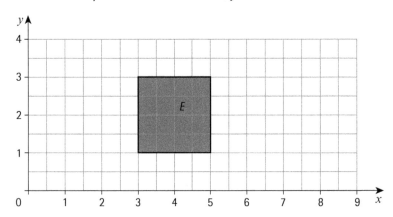

Points below the the invariant line move in the opposite direction to those above the invariant line.

6 Copy the diagram onto squared paper.
   Shear the shape F with scale factor 2, $y = 1$ invariant

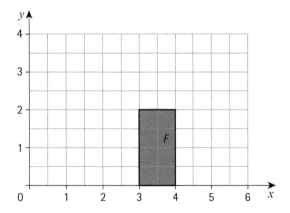

EXERCISE 13H

1

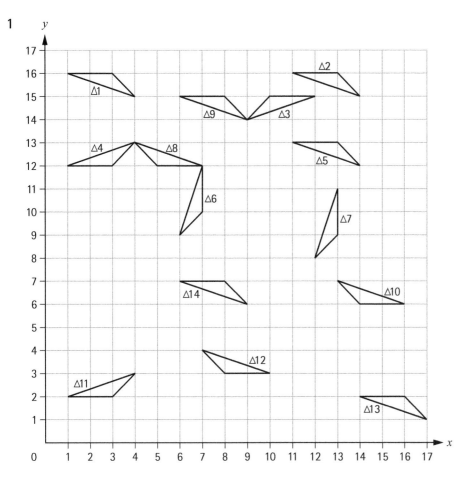

(a) Describe as fully as possible the transformation for these movements.

1 △1 to △2	**2** △1 to △4	**3** △3 to △9
4 △11 to △12	**5** △5 to △6	**6** △7 to △10
7 △10 to △12	**8** △13 to △14	**9** △4 to △8
10 △8 to △6	**11** △7 to △7	**12** △2 to △5

(b) **1** Draw axes so that values of x and y go from -5 to 5.

2 Draw and label the shape P which has co-ordinates $(4,-1)$, $(4,-3)$, $(2,-3)$, $(3,-2)$ and $(3,-1)$.

3 Draw and label the shape Q which has co-ordinates $(-1,1)$, $(-1,-1)$, $(-3,-1)$, $(-2,0)$ and $(-2,1)$.

4 Write down the transformation which maps shape P to shape Q.

2

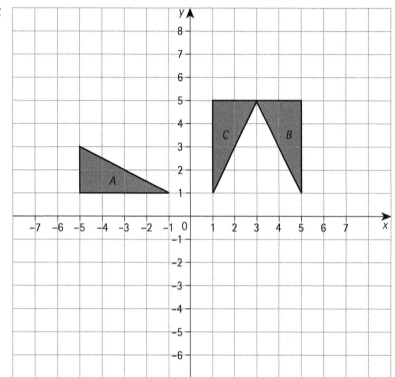

(a) Describe fully the single transformation which maps triangle C onto B.

(b) Describe fully the single transformation which maps triangle C onto A.

(c) Draw the reflection of triangle A in the x-axis. Label it D.

(d) Draw the translation of triangle B by the vector $\begin{pmatrix} -1 \\ -4 \end{pmatrix}$. Label it E.

(e) Draw the rotation of triangle C about the point (0,0) through 180°. Label it F.

(f) Draw the enlargement of triangle A, centre (5,−5), scale factor $\frac{1}{2}$. Label it G.

13.8 Combined transformations

Transformations can be performed one after the other.

 **EXAMPLE 19**

Reflect the object P about the y-axis (x = 0) and label it P'.
Now reflect P' about the line x = 4 and label this P''.

What single transformation takes P to P''?

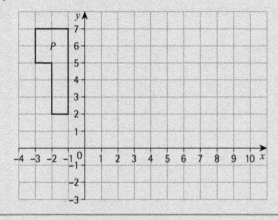

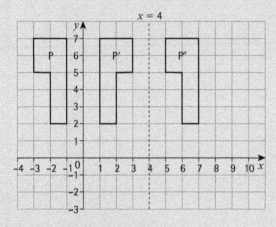

Draw on the mirror line
$x = 4$. Reflect the object in the
y-axis to give P'. Then reflect P' in
the line $x = 4$ to give P''.

P'' is a translation of P 8 units to the right.

It is a translation of $\begin{pmatrix} 8 \\ 0 \end{pmatrix}$.

EXAMPLE 20

Using the object shape P in Example 19, reflect P in the y-axis followed by a reflection in the line $y = x$.

What single transformation takes P to P''?

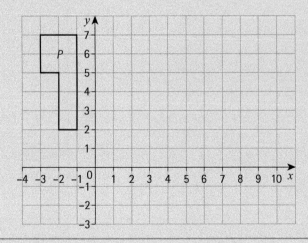

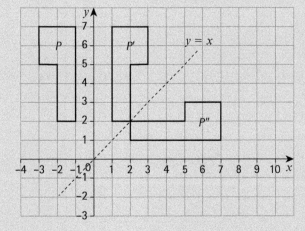

Draw on the mirror line $y = x$.

P'' is obtained by a rotation of P through 90° clockwise about the origin (0, 0).

The centre of rotation is the intersection of the two mirror lines $x = 0$ and $y = x$. The point of intersection is (0, 0).

A reflection followed by a second reflection along mirror lines that are parallel (Example 19) can be replaced by a single transformation involving a translation.

A reflection followed by a second reflection along mirror lines that are not parallel to each other (Example 20) can be replaced by a single transformation involving a rotation about the point of intersection of the two mirror lines.

EXERCISE 13I

1 Copy shape *D* onto squared paper. Reflect the shape in the *y*-axis (label *D'*) followed by a reflection in the *x*-axis (label *D"*).
Describe the single transformation that takes *D* to *D"*.

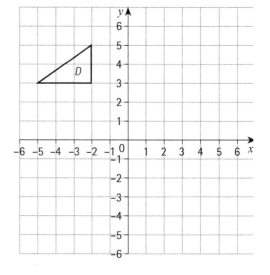

2 Construct a grid with *x*-axis as shown and *y*-axis from 0 to 10. Copy the object *E* and reflect the shape in the line *x* = −1. Label this *E'*. Now reflect shape *E'* in the *y*-axis and label this *E"*.
What is the single transformation that takes *E* to *E"*?

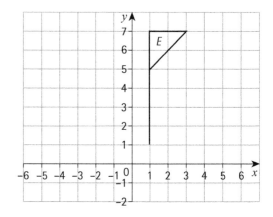

3 The object *T* is reflected in the line *y* = −*x* to produce an image *T'*. This image is now rotated a quarter of a turn anticlockwise about the origin to produce a second image *T"*.
What single transformation takes *T* to *T"*?

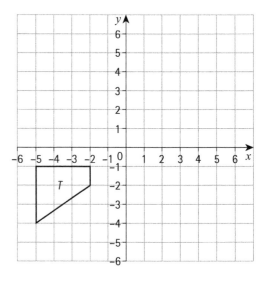

4 Draw axes with values of x and y between -4 and $+4$. On the grid draw the triangle ABC which has vertices at $A(2, 3)$, $B(3.5, 1.5)$ and $C(2.5, 1)$. On the same diagram

  (a) Rotate ABC 90° anticlockwise about the point $(0, 0)$. Label this shape L.

  (b) Reflect this new shape about the y-axis and label this triangle M.

  (c) Rotate this new shape 270° clockwise about the origin and label this N.

  (d) Describe the single transformation that takes ABC to N.

13.9 Using matrices

Some of the transformations that you have studied can be worked out using vectors or matrices.

Translation (T)

This is the only transformation that needs a vector to describe it because there are no invariant points. The notation to describe this is sometimes written

$$T: \begin{pmatrix} x \\ y \end{pmatrix} \rightarrow \begin{pmatrix} x \\ y \end{pmatrix} + \begin{pmatrix} p \\ q \end{pmatrix}$$

This is a formal way of saying that every point moves p units to the right and q units up.

See section 13.4.

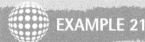 **EXAMPLE 21**

$$T: \begin{pmatrix} x \\ y \end{pmatrix} \rightarrow \begin{pmatrix} x \\ y \end{pmatrix} + \begin{pmatrix} -3 \\ -3 \end{pmatrix}.$$

All points on the diagram move 3 units left and 3 down.

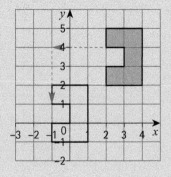

$\begin{pmatrix} -3 \\ -3 \end{pmatrix}$ means 3 squares *left* and 3 squares *down*.

Some of the transformations **on your syllabus** can be described with a 2×2 matrix.

We will use a formal description for these which reads

$$P: \begin{pmatrix} x \\ y \end{pmatrix} \rightarrow \begin{pmatrix} a & b \\ c & d \end{pmatrix}\begin{pmatrix} x \\ y \end{pmatrix}$$

where P is a transformation and (x, y) is any point on the diagram.

For example, to find out where the point A(3, 5) moves to

for the transformation $\begin{pmatrix} 2 & 0 \\ 0 & 2 \end{pmatrix}$ we work out $\begin{pmatrix} 2 & 0 \\ 0 & 2 \end{pmatrix}\begin{pmatrix} 3 \\ 5 \end{pmatrix}$

now $\begin{pmatrix} 2 & 0 \\ 0 & 2 \end{pmatrix}\begin{pmatrix} 3 \\ 5 \end{pmatrix} = \begin{pmatrix} 6 \\ 10 \end{pmatrix}$

so $A(3, 5) \rightarrow A'(6,10)$

This can be written $P(A) = A'$.

> A must be in a column.
> P and A must be in this order.

> See Chapter 1, Example 4.

Reflection (M)

EXAMPLE 22

The diagram shows a triangle ABC.

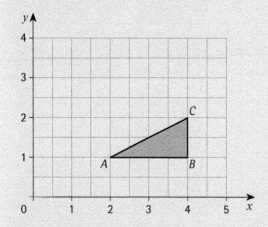

Draw the image of triangle ABC under the transformation

$$M = \begin{pmatrix} 0 & 1 \\ 1 & 0 \end{pmatrix}$$

The co-ordinates are A (2, 1), B (4, 1) and C (4, 2).

You can work out the image for each co-ordinate but it is possible to work out all three in one go.

> As shown above for P.

$$\begin{matrix} & A & B & C \\ \begin{pmatrix} 0 & 1 \\ 1 & 0 \end{pmatrix} & \begin{pmatrix} 2 & 4 & 4 \\ 1 & 1 & 2 \end{pmatrix} \end{matrix} = \begin{matrix} A' & B' & C' \\ \begin{pmatrix} 1 & 1 & 2 \\ 2 & 4 & 4 \end{pmatrix} \end{matrix}$$

The image will be at A' (1, 2), B' (1, 4) and C' (2, 4).

continued ▼

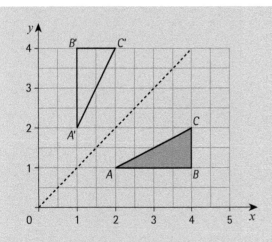

You can see that this triangle has been reflected in $y = x$.

There are 3 other reflections that can be worked out this way.

EXERCISE 13J

1 Copy the diagram and draw the image of triangle *ABC* under the transformation M$_1$ where

$$M_1 = \begin{pmatrix} 1 & 0 \\ 0 & -1 \end{pmatrix}$$

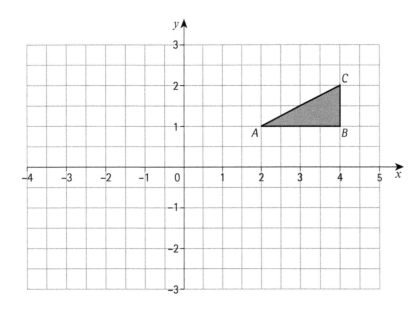

Describe the transformation.

2

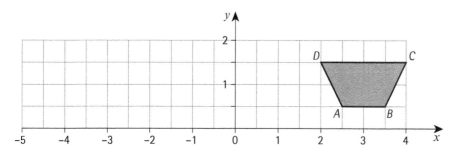

Copy the diagram and draw the image of trapezium *ABCD* under the transformation M_2 where

$$M_2 = \begin{pmatrix} -1 & 0 \\ 0 & 1 \end{pmatrix}$$

Describe the transformation.

3   Copy the diagram and draw the image of triangle *ABC* under the transformation M_3 where

$$M_3 = \begin{pmatrix} 0 & -1 \\ -1 & 0 \end{pmatrix}$$

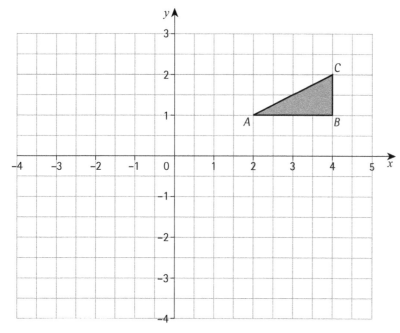

Describe the transformation.

Rotation (R)

These transformations will all have the centre of rotation at the origin.

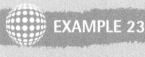

EXAMPLE 23

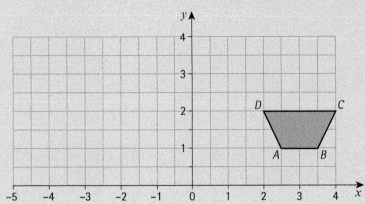

Draw the image of trapezium ABCD under the transformation

$$R = \begin{pmatrix} 0 & -1 \\ 1 & 0 \end{pmatrix}$$

The co-ordinates are $A(2\frac{1}{2}, 1)$, $B(3\frac{1}{2}, 1)$, $C(4, 2)$ and $D(2, 2)$.

$$\begin{pmatrix} 0 & -1 \\ 1 & 0 \end{pmatrix} \overset{A\ \ B\ \ C\ D}{\begin{pmatrix} 2\frac{1}{2} & 3\frac{1}{2} & 4 & 2 \\ 1 & 1 & 2 & 2 \end{pmatrix}} = \overset{A'\ \ B'\ \ C'\ \ D'}{\begin{pmatrix} -1 & -1 & -2 & -2 \\ 2\frac{1}{2} & 3\frac{1}{2} & 4 & 2 \end{pmatrix}}$$

The image will be at $A'(-1, 2\frac{1}{2})$, $B'(-1, 3\frac{1}{2})$, $C'(-2, 4)$ and $D'(-2, 2)$.

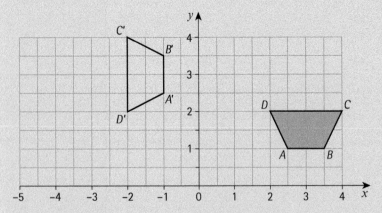

This is a rotation, centre O, through 90° anticlockwise.

EXERCISE 13K

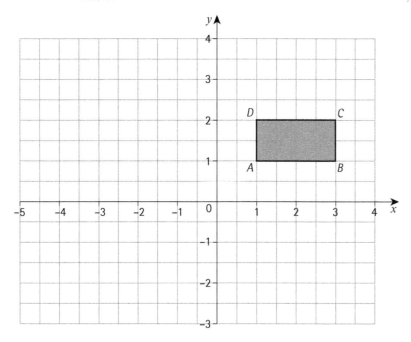

Copy the diagram onto squared paper. Draw the image of the rectangle under the following transformations.
Describe each transformation.

1 $R_1 = \begin{pmatrix} -1 & 0 \\ 0 & -1 \end{pmatrix}$

2 $R_2 = \begin{pmatrix} 0 & 1 \\ -1 & 0 \end{pmatrix}$

3 $R_3 = \begin{pmatrix} 0.6 & -0.8 \\ 0.8 & 0.6 \end{pmatrix}$

4 $R_4 = \begin{pmatrix} 0.866 & -0.5 \\ 0.5 & 0.866 \end{pmatrix}$

Enlargement (E)

These enlargements will all have the centre of the enlargement at O and scale factor k.

The matrices will all have the form

$E = \begin{pmatrix} k & 0 \\ 0 & k \end{pmatrix}$

(a) $0 < k < 1$ Image will be smaller than the object.
(b) $k > 1$ Image will be larger than the object.
(c) $k < 0$ Image will also be reflected in the origin.

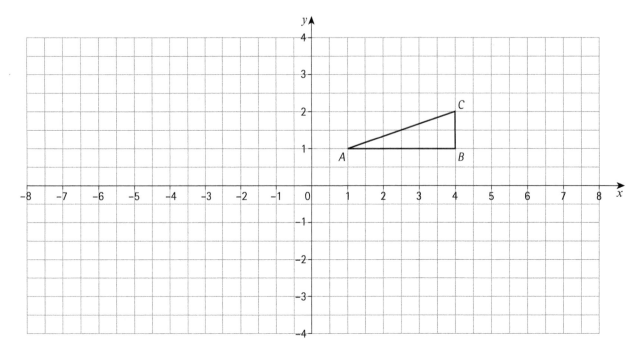

Copy the diagram onto squared paper. Draw the image of the triangle under the following transformations.

Describe each transformation.

1 $E_1 = \begin{pmatrix} 2 & 0 \\ 0 & 2 \end{pmatrix}$ 2 $E_2 = \begin{pmatrix} \frac{1}{2} & 0 \\ 0 & \frac{1}{2} \end{pmatrix}$ 3 $E_3 = \begin{pmatrix} -2 & 0 \\ 0 & -2 \end{pmatrix}$

Shear (H)

These shears will have either the x-axis or the y-axis invariant and scale factor k.

$H = \begin{pmatrix} 1 & k \\ 0 & 1 \end{pmatrix}$ or $H = \begin{pmatrix} 1 & 0 \\ k & 1 \end{pmatrix}$

Stretch (S)

These one-way stretches will be from the x-axis or the y-axis, scale factor k.

$S = \begin{pmatrix} k & 0 \\ 0 & 1 \end{pmatrix}$ or $S = \begin{pmatrix} 1 & 0 \\ 0 & k \end{pmatrix}$

You are not expected to learn all these different matrices.

You will be required to recognise the transformations.

Combined transformations

The notation that will be used will look like RM(P).

This means carry out the transformation M on the shape (or point) P then **followed by** the transformation R to the result. This is illustrated in the next example.

 EXAMPLE 24

Triangle ABC has vertices A(1, 1), B(4,1) and C(4,2).

Transformations $M = \begin{pmatrix} -1 & 0 \\ 0 & 1 \end{pmatrix}$ and $R = \begin{pmatrix} -1 & 0 \\ 0 & -1 \end{pmatrix}$ are given.

Draw the image of triangle ABC under the transformations RM.

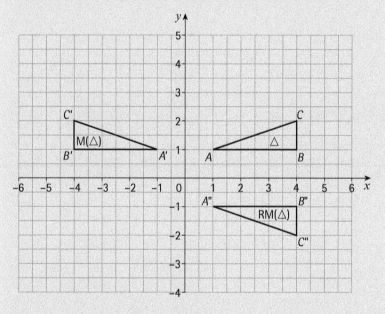

$$M(\triangle) = \begin{pmatrix} -1 & 0 \\ 0 & 1 \end{pmatrix}\overset{A\ B\ C}{\begin{pmatrix} 1 & 4 & 4 \\ 1 & 1 & 2 \end{pmatrix}} = \overset{A'\ B'\ C'}{\begin{pmatrix} -1 & -4 & -4 \\ 1 & 1 & 2 \end{pmatrix}}$$

$$RM(\triangle) = \begin{pmatrix} -1 & 0 \\ 0 & -1 \end{pmatrix}\overset{A'\ B'\ C'}{\begin{pmatrix} -1 & -4 & -4 \\ 1 & 1 & 2 \end{pmatrix}} = \overset{A''\ B''\ C''}{\begin{pmatrix} 1 & 4 & 4 \\ -1 & -1 & -2 \end{pmatrix}}$$

Place M first, followed by R.

You can see that M is a reflection in the y-axis, R is a rotation 180° about O and overall RM is a reflection in the x-axis.

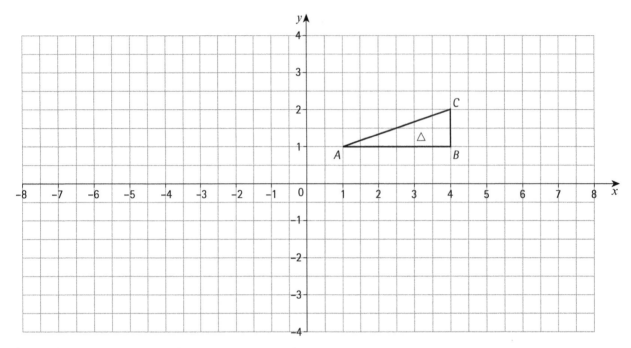

For each question copy the diagram onto squared paper.

Draw the image of the triangle under the following transformations.

1 MR($\triangle$) where $R = \begin{pmatrix} -1 & 0 \\ 0 & -1 \end{pmatrix}$ and $M = \begin{pmatrix} -1 & 0 \\ 0 & 1 \end{pmatrix}$

2 MN($\triangle$) where $M = \begin{pmatrix} -1 & 0 \\ 0 & 1 \end{pmatrix}$ and $N = \begin{pmatrix} 1 & 0 \\ 0 & -1 \end{pmatrix}$

3 MR($\triangle$) where $M = \begin{pmatrix} 0 & 1 \\ -1 & 0 \end{pmatrix}$ and $R = \begin{pmatrix} 0 & 1 \\ 1 & 0 \end{pmatrix}$

4 S_2S_1($\triangle$) where $S_1 = \begin{pmatrix} 2 & 0 \\ 0 & 1 \end{pmatrix}$ and $S_2 = \begin{pmatrix} 1 & 0 \\ 0 & 2 \end{pmatrix}$

5 E_1E_2($\triangle$) where $E_1 = \begin{pmatrix} 2 & 0 \\ 0 & 2 \end{pmatrix}$ and $E_2 = \begin{pmatrix} \frac{1}{2} & 0 \\ 0 & \frac{1}{2} \end{pmatrix}$

13.10 **Finding the matrix**

It will be necessary to work out the matrix when the transformation is written in words.

If you work out the following matrix product

$\begin{pmatrix} a & b \\ c & d \end{pmatrix} \begin{pmatrix} 1 \\ 0 \end{pmatrix}$ and $\begin{pmatrix} a & b \\ c & d \end{pmatrix} \begin{pmatrix} 0 \\ 1 \end{pmatrix}$

you will get the results

$\begin{pmatrix} a \\ c \end{pmatrix}$ and $\begin{pmatrix} b \\ d \end{pmatrix}$

this means that the matrix maps the vector

$$\binom{1}{0} \rightarrow \binom{a}{c} \text{ and } \binom{0}{1} \rightarrow \binom{b}{d}$$

Therefore if we know where these two vectors go to, then we can write down the matrix.

Sometimes known as base vectors I and J.

EXAMPLE 25

Find the matrix R for a rotation of 180° about O.

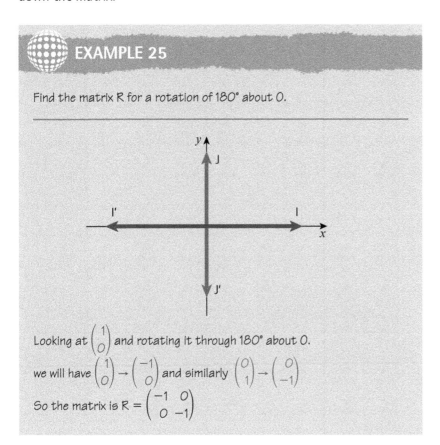

Looking at $\binom{1}{0}$ and rotating it through 180° about O.

we will have $\binom{1}{0} \rightarrow \binom{-1}{0}$ and similarly $\binom{0}{1} \rightarrow \binom{0}{-1}$

So the matrix is $R = \begin{pmatrix} -1 & 0 \\ 0 & -1 \end{pmatrix}$

EXERCISE 13N

Find the matrix for the following transformations.
Show all your working.

1 Rotation, centre (0,0) through 90° clockwise.

2 Enlargement SF5, centre (0,0).

3 Stretch SF4 from the y-axis.

4 Shear $y = 0$ invariant, SF2.

5 Reflection in $y = -x$.

6 Shear $y = 0$ invariant, SF4.

7 Enlargement SF$\frac{1}{2}$, centre (0,0).

8 Rotation 90° anticlockwise, centre (0,0).

9 Stretch SF1.5, from the x-axis.

10 Reflection in $x = 0$.

11 Reflection in $y = x$.

12 Shear, y-axis invariant, SF1.

13 Rotation 45° clockwise, centre (0,0).

14 Enlargement SF−2, centre (0,0).

1

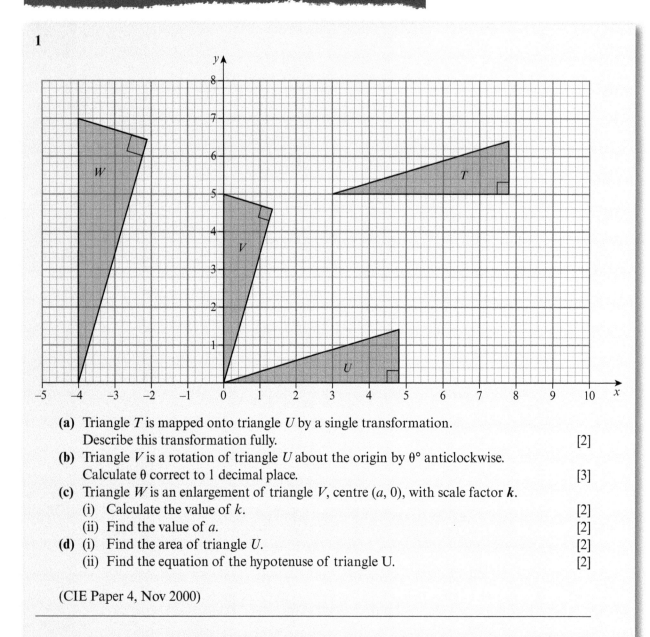

(a) Triangle T is mapped onto triangle U by a single transformation.
Describe this transformation fully. [2]

(b) Triangle V is a rotation of triangle U about the origin by $\theta°$ anticlockwise.
Calculate θ correct to 1 decimal place. [3]

(c) Triangle W is an enlargement of triangle V, centre $(a, 0)$, with scale factor k.
  (i) Calculate the value of k. [2]
  (ii) Find the value of a. [2]

(d) (i) Find the area of triangle U. [2]
  (ii) Find the equation of the hypotenuse of triangle U. [2]

(CIE Paper 4, Nov 2000)

2

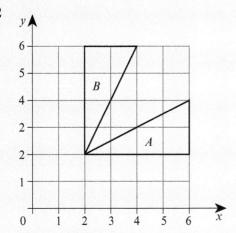

(a) Describe fully the single transformation which maps triangle *A* onto triangle *B*. [2]

(b) Find the 2 × 2 matrix which represents this transformation. [2]

(CIE Paper 2, Nov 2000)

3

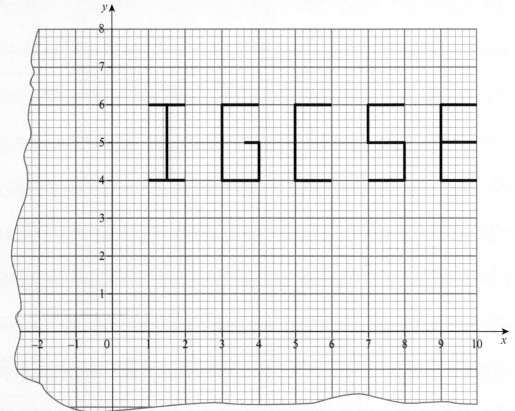

Answer the whole of this question on a sheet of graph paper.

(a) Using a scale of 1 centimetre to represent 1 unit on each axis, draw an x-axis for $-6 \leqslant x \leqslant 10$ and a y-axis for $-6 \leqslant y \leqslant 8$.

Copy the letters IGCSE accurately from the diagram above onto the **same position** on your graph paper. Each letter is 2 cm high and 1 cm wide.

[For example, the letter I lies in the rectangle $1 \leqslant x \leqslant 2$ and $4 \leqslant y \leqslant 6$.] [2]

(b) Draw accurately the image of your letters under the following transformations.

    (i) Rotate your letter I by 90° clockwise about the origin. [2]

    (ii) Reflect your letter G in the y-axis. [2]

    (iii) Enlarge your letter C, scale factor 4, centre (7, 7) [2]

    (iv) Translate your letter S by the vector $\begin{pmatrix} -3 \\ -4 \end{pmatrix}$. [2]

    (v) Stretch your letter E parallel to the y-axis, stretch factor 0.5, with the x-axis invariant. [2]

(c) (i) Find the transformation matrix **M** which represents a rotation by 90° clockwise about the origin. [2]

    (ii) Find the inverse matrix $\mathbf{M}^{-1}$ and describe in words the transformation which it represents. [3]

(CIE Paper 4, Jun 2001)

4

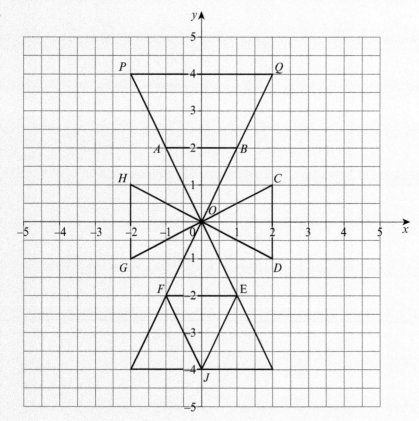

(a) Describe fully the single transformation which maps both
    (i)   *A* onto *C* **and** *B* onto *D*,   [2]
    (ii) *A* onto *D* **and** *B* onto *C*,   [2]
    (iii) *A* onto *P* **and** *B* onto *Q*.   [3]
(b) Describe fully a single transformation which maps triangle *OAB* onto *JFE*.   [2]

(c) The matrix **M** is $\begin{pmatrix} 0 & -1 \\ -1 & 0 \end{pmatrix}$

    (i)   Describe the transformation which **M** represents.   [2]
    (ii) Write down the co-ordinates of *P* after transformation by matrix **M**. [2]
(d) (i)   Write down the matrix R which represents a rotation by 90° clockwise
        about *O*.   [2]
    (ii) Write down the letter representing the new position of *F* after the
        transformation RM(*F*).   [2]

(CIE Paper 4, Jun 2002)

---

5   (a) 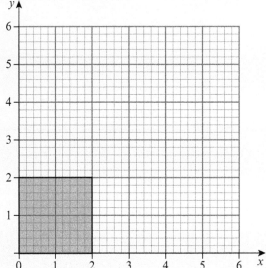

Copy **the diagram** and draw the shear of the shaded square with the *x*-axis
invariant and the point (0,2) mapping onto the point (3,2).   [2]

(b)

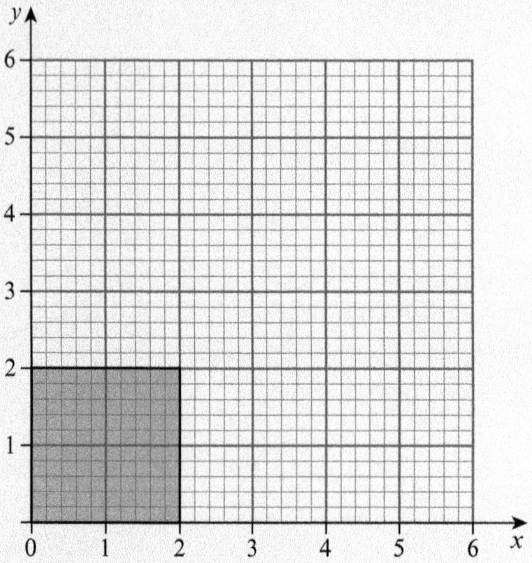

Make another copy of the diagram .
(i)   draw the one-way stretch of the shaded square
      with the x-axis invariant and the point $(0, 2)$ mapping onto $(0, 6)$. [2]
(ii) Write down the matrix of this stretch. [1]

(CIE Paper 2, Jun 2003)

Chapter 14

Congruency and similarity

This chapter will show you how to
✔ define congruency in triangles using the four definitions of SSS, SAS, ASA and RHS
✔ define similarity and use scale factors
✔ find areas and volumes of similar figures using scale factors

14.1 **Congruency and similarity**

You will need to know
● about ratio and proportion, right-angled triangles and enlargement

Congruent shapes are identical. Reflection, rotation and translation transformations all produce images that are congruent to the original objects.

Similar shapes have exactly the same shape but are not the same size.

All angles in the object and image are equal but all lengths are not. In similar shapes, corresponding lengths are in the same ratio or proportion.

This means they have exactly the same shape and are exactly the same size. All lengths and angles in the object and image are equal.

You may need to turn shapes over before they fit exactly. A reflection in a mirror line produces congruent shapes.

EXAMPLE 1

Which pair of shapes are congruent to shape A and which shapes are similar to shape A?

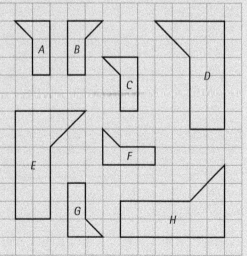

B, C, F and G are all congruent to A.
D, E and H are all similar to A.

Some images need to be translated, rotated or reflected.

The four conditions for congruent triangles are

(1) Three sides are equal (known as **S**ide, **S**ide, **S**ide – **SSS**).

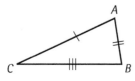 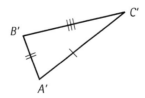

(2) Two sides are equal and the included angle is the same (known as **S**ide, **A**ngle, **S**ide – **SAS**).

> The *included* angle is the angle made by the two known sides.

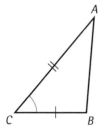 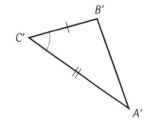

(3) Two angles are the same and a side is equal (known as **A**ngle, **S**ide, **A**ngle – **ASA**).

> Also called Side, Angle, Angle –SAA.

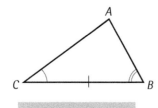 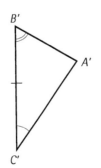

> *BC* and *B′C′* are the corresponding sides.

or

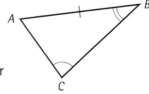 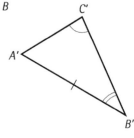

> *AB* and *A′B′* are the corresponding sides.

(4) A right angle, a hypotenuse and a side are equal (right angle, hypotenuse, side – **RHS**).

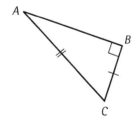 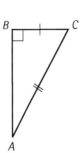

> The hypotenuse is the longest side of a right-angled triangle. It is always opposite the right angle.

> *BC* and *B′C′* are the corresponding sides.

There is one case where triangles are sometimes thought to be congruent, but they are not.
Look at these diagrams.

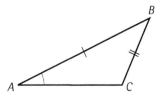 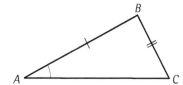

These triangles have two sides which are the same length and an angle which is the same size.
You might think that SSA is a condition for congruency, but one look at these triangles should convince you that it is not!

Try constructing a triangle with $AC = 8$ cm, $BC = 5$ cm and $B\hat{A}C = 30°$. Draw a line AB as your starting point.

 EXERCISE 14A

1 Look at the shapes in the diagram.
   (a) Write down the shapes that are congruent to shape A.
   (b) Write down the shapes that are similar to shape A.

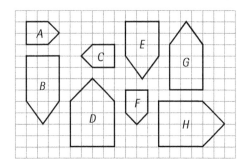

2 Copy this shape onto squared paper.
   On the same paper draw one shape that is similar and one shape that is congruent.

3 Look at the following figures. For each one write down the letters of the shapes that are similar to each other.

(a)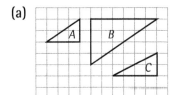

(b)

(c)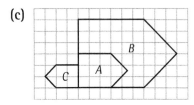

(d)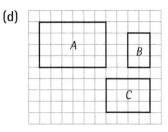

4 Look at the following pairs of triangles. State which pairs are
  congruent and give the appropriate reason.

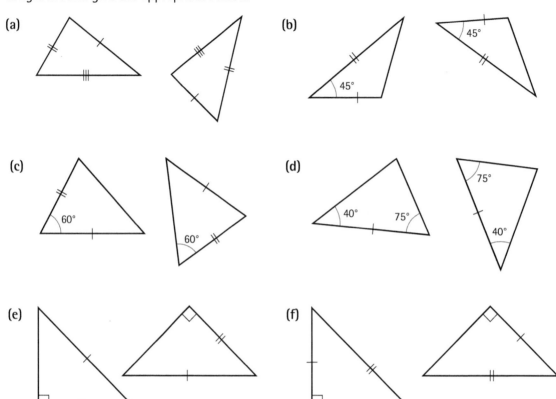

(a)

(b) 45° 45°

(c) 60° 60°

(d) 40° 75° 75° 40°

(e)

(f)

14.2 Similarity

Similar shapes have exactly the same shape but are not exactly the
same size. All angles in the object and image are equal but all lengths
are not.

Enlargement always produces an image that is similar to the object.

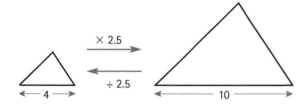

× 2.5

÷ 2.5

4

10

In similar shapes corresponding lengths are in the same **ratio** or
proportion. The ratio is the **scale factor** of the enlargement.

Ratio and proportion were covered
in Chapter 12.

The scale factor may sometimes be
called the linear scale factor (k).

For two shapes to be similar

- the corresponding angles must be equal.
- the ratios of corresponding sides must be the same.

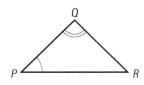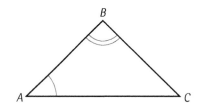

In the triangles *PQR* and *ABC*

angle QPR = angle BAC
angle RQP = angle CBA
angle PRQ = angle ACB

Always write the letters of the triangles above one another, to help you pick out the corresponding lengths and ratios.

So in this case $\dfrac{ABC}{PQR}$

from which you can pick out the three ratios

$$\frac{AB}{PQ} = \frac{BC}{QR} = \frac{CA}{RP}$$

This defines the scale factor, k, in going from triangle *PQR* to triangle *ABC*.

> It is important to obtain the correct scale factor by identifying in which direction you are going e.g.
>
> $PQR \rightarrow ABC$ is $k = \dfrac{AB}{PQ}$
>
> whereas
>
> $ABC \rightarrow PQR$ is $\dfrac{1}{k} = \dfrac{PQ}{AB}$.

⬤ EXAMPLE 2

The two triangles opposite are similar with equal angles as shown.
Find the unknown lengths x and y.

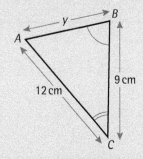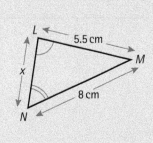

Method A

The triangles BAC and LMN are similar

$$\frac{LMN}{BAC}$$

The three equivalent ratios are

$$\frac{LN}{BC} = \frac{LM}{BA} = \frac{MN}{AC}$$

$$\frac{x}{9} = \frac{5.5}{y} = \frac{8}{12}$$

So $\quad x = \dfrac{72}{12} = 6$ cm and $y = \dfrac{5.5 \times 12}{8} = 8.25$ cm

> Notice how important it is to label the triangles accurately.
> angle L = angle B
> angle M = angle A
> angle N = angle C

> Using two equivalent fractions allows either x or y to be determined.

continued ▼

Method B

The triangles BAC and LMN are similar

$$\frac{BAC}{LMN}$$

The scale factor of the enlargement $= \frac{AC}{MN} = \frac{12}{8} = 1.5$

So $AB = 1.5 \times LM = 1.5 \times 5.5 = 8.25$ cm

and $LN = BC \div 1.5 = 9 \div 1.5 = 6$ cm.

Since $\triangle ABC$ is larger than $\triangle LMN$ the scale factor is worked out this way.

Lengths in $\triangle LMN \times 1.5$ = lengths in $\triangle ABC$.

Lengths in $\triangle ABC \div 1.5$ = lengths in $\triangle LMN$.

 ## EXAMPLE 3

Triangle ABC has AB = 9 cm.
A line PQ is drawn parallel to BC
so that PQ = 5 cm, AP = 6 cm
and PB = 3 cm.

Show that triangle APQ is
similar to triangle ABC.
Find the length BC.

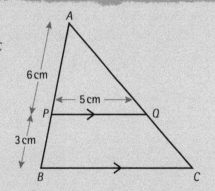

In triangles APQ and ABC

angle BAC = angle PAQ   (a common angle)
angle APQ = angle ABC   (PQ is parallel to BC so these
                              angles are corresponding).

So the third angles of both triangles must also be equal.

Method A

All angles in triangle ABC and triangle APQ are equal, which means
that triangles ABC and APQ are similar so

$$\frac{ABC}{APQ}$$

$$\frac{BC}{PQ} = \frac{AB}{PA}$$

$$\frac{BC}{5} = \frac{9}{6}$$

$$BC = \frac{9 \times 5}{6} = 7.5 \text{ cm}$$

continued ▼

Method B

$\triangle ABC$ is an enlargement of $\triangle APQ$ $\dfrac{ABC}{APQ}$

The scale factor $= \dfrac{AB}{AP} = \dfrac{9}{6} = 1.5$

So $BC = 1.5 \times PQ = 1.5 \times 5 = 7.5$ cm

Always use corresponding sides to work out the scale factor.

 EXERCISE 14B

1 The diagram shows two similar shapes. Find the values of the unknown letters.

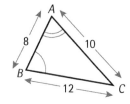 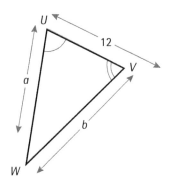

2 The drawing shows a picture frame containing a mount.

Are the two rectangles similar?

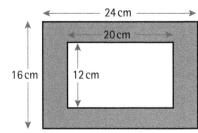

3 In these triangles find the values of c and d.

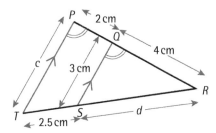

4 Which of the following are True (T) and which are False (F)?
   (a) Any two squares are similar to each other.
   (b) Any two isosceles triangles are similar to each other.
   (c) Any two rhombuses are similar to each other.
   (d) Any two rectangles are similar to each other.
   (e) Any two circles are similar to each other.
   (f) Any two regular hexagons are similar to each other.

5 A mobile phone mast is 22.5 m high and casts a shadow of length 25 m at midday. A tree next to the mast casts a shadow of length 15 m at midday. Find the height of the tree.

6 In the diagram, *ABC* is a right-angled triangle. Find the values of *x* and *y*.

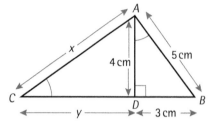

Remember that angle *CAB* = 90°.
There are 3 similar triangles.

7

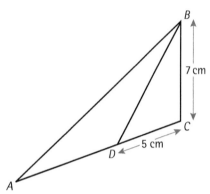

The diagram shows two similar triangles *ABC* and *BDC*.
BC = 7 cm, *DC* = 5 cm and angle *BAD* = angle *CBD*.
Calculate the length of *AD*.

8

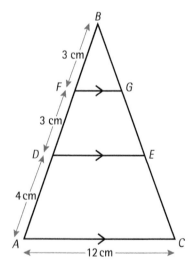

In the triangles above, find the length of
(a) *DE*   (b) *FG*

9

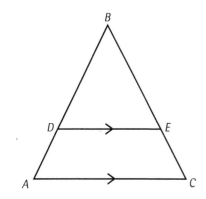

AB = 8cm, AC = 8cm, BC = 8cm and DE = 6cm,

Find the length of **(a)** AD **(b)** BD.

14.3 Areas and volumes of similar shapes

You can work out the area and volume of similar shapes if you know the **linear scale factor.**

The linear scale factor is the scale factor that applies to *lengths* of similar shapes.

Look at the rectangle below, size 1 × 3.
Enlarge it by a linear scale factor of 3.

> Enlargement was covered in Chapter 13.

The original shape   becomes 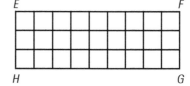

Length $EF = 3 \times$ length $AB = 9$
Length $FG = 3 \times$ length $BC = 3$

Area $ABCD = 1 \times 3 = 3$
Area $EFGH = 9 \times 3 = 27$

Enlarged area $EFGH = 9 \times$ area $ABCD$
                $EFGH = 3^2 \times$ area $ABCD$

This is the (linear scale factor)^2 and leads to the more general result

> When a shape is enlarged by a linear scale factor k the area of the enlarged shape is $k^2 \times$ the area of the original shape.
>
> Enlarged area $= k^2 \times$ original area

> The k^2 factor is called the **area scale factor.**

Now look at a three-dimensional object, size $1 \times 1 \times 3$.
Enlarge this by a linear scale factor 3.

Original shape

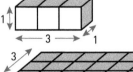

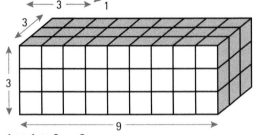

Enlarged shape

The original volume $= 1 \times 1 \times 3 = 3$.

The enlarged volume $= 3 \times 3 \times 9 = 81$.

The enlarged volume $= 27 \times$ the original volume.

$\qquad\qquad\qquad = 3^3 \times$ the original volume.

This is the (linear scale factor)^3 and leads to the more general result

When a shape is enlarged by a linear scale factor k the volume of the enlarged shape is $k^3 \times$ the volume of the original shape.

Enlarged volume $= k^3 \times$ original volume.

The k^3 factor is called the **volume scale factor**.

Area and volume factors can be applied to any 2- or 3-dimensional figures that are mathematically similar. All squares and circles are mathematically similar.

EXAMPLE 4

Two similar cylinders have heights which are in the ratio of $2 : 3$
What is the ratio of

(a) their surface areas

(b) their volumes?

(a) Ratio of surface areas $= 2^2 : 3^2 = 4 : 9$

(b) Ratio of volumes $= 2^3 : 3^3 = 8 : 27$

This means that the large cylinder holds over three times more than the small one ($27 \div 8 = 3.375$).

EXAMPLE 5

The diagram shows a sector of a circle that has been enlarged by a linear scale factor of $\frac{3}{4}$.

(a) What is **(i)** the length of XY **(ii)** the angle ZXY?

(b) If the area of sector $CAB = 16\pi$ cm^2 what is the area of sector ZXY?

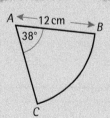

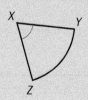

continued ▼

(a) (i) $XY = AB \times$ scale factor

$XY = 12 \times \frac{3}{4} = 9$ cm

(ii) For similar shapes corresponding angles are equal, so angle $ZXY = 38°$.

(b) Area $ZXY = $ (linear scale factor)$^2 \times$ area CAB

Area $ZXY = \frac{9}{16} \times 16\pi = 9\pi$ cm^2

> The scale factor of $\frac{3}{4}$ applies to the radius AB because it is a linear scale factor.

 EXAMPLE 6

The diagram shows two shampoo bottles. The shapes are mathematically similar. The smaller bottle contains 400 ml of shampoo.

Calculate how much shampoo the larger bottle holds. Give your answer to 3 s.f.

15 cm   18 cm

The linear scale factor is $\dfrac{\text{height of large bottle}}{\text{height of small bottle}} = \dfrac{18}{15} = 1.2$

Volume of large bottle $= (1.2)^3 \times 400$

$= 691.2$ ml

$= 691$ ml (to 3 s.f.)

> Volume of large bottle
> = (linear scale factor)^3
> $\times$ volume of small bottle

 EXAMPLE 7

A supermarket sells two sizes of jars of coffee.
The jars are in the shape of cylinders which are mathematically similar.

(a) If the diameter of the large jar is 8.2 cm, calculate the diameter of the small jar.

(b) Calculate the ratio of the areas of circular bases of the two jars.

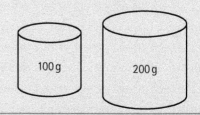

100 g   200 g

(a) Volume scale factor $= \dfrac{\text{amount in large jar}}{\text{amount in small jar}}$

$= \frac{200}{100} = 2$ (this is k^3)

So linear scale factor $(k) = \sqrt[3]{2} = 1.259\,92\ldots$

Diameter of base of small jar $\times k$

$=$ diameter of base of large jar

Diameter of base of small jar $\times 1.25992\ldots = 8.2$ cm

Diameter of base of small jar $= \dfrac{8.2}{1.25992\ldots} = 6.5083\ldots$

$= 6.51$ cm (to 3 s.f.)

> The amount of coffee in the jars represents the **volume** of the jars.

> Do not round 1.25992... Work with this value and only round the final answer.

continued ▼

(b) The ratio of the diameters is $1 : 1.25992...$

The ratio of the areas of the bases of the jars

$$= 1^2 : (1.25992...)^2$$
$$= 1 : 1.58740... \quad (k^2 = 1.58740...)$$
$$= 1 : 1.59$$

EXERCISE 14C

1 The lengths of a photograph are being enlarged by a scale factor 3. If the original area of the print was 24 cm², what is the new area of the photograph?

2 Two similar triangles have areas of 16 cm² and 40 cm². If the base of the smaller triangle is 4 cm, find the base of the larger triangle.

3 In the shape opposite, $BX = 4$ cm, $AB = 6$ cm and the area of triangle $BXY = 10$ cm².

Find **(a)** the area of triangle ABC and
(b) the area of the trapezium $XYCA$.

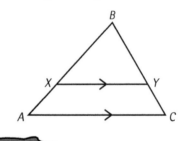

4 The following shape with an area of 12.2 cm² is being enlarged by a length scale factor of 3.4.

What is the area of the enlarged shape?

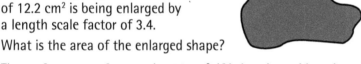

5 The surface area of a cone is 176 cm². If it is enlarged by a length scale factor of $\frac{2}{3}$, what is the surface area of the smaller cone?

6 Garden peas are sold in mathematically similar tins of two different sizes, 300 g and 400 g. If the height of the small tin is 10 cm, calculate the height of the large tin.

7 The radii of two spheres are in the ratio 2 5.

(a) If the volume of the smaller sphere is 8 cm³ calculate the volume of the larger sphere.

(b) What is the ratio of the surface areas of the two spheres?

8 A sheet of A4 paper measures 29.56 cm by 20.9cm. The sheet of paper is cut in half to give two sheets of A5 paper. Show that both sheets of paper are mathematically similar.

9 The height of the great pyramid at Giza, Egypt is 146m. The pyramid at Saqqara is similar but its height is 52.5m. What is the ratio of the volumes of the two pyramids?

10 Two similar cylinders of height 24cm and 40cm are filled with liquid. The smaller one holds 3 litres. How much does the larger contain?

14.4 Increase/decrease in a given ratio

 **EXAMPLE 8**

A family have a wedding photograph which measures 20 cm by 15 cm.
They have it enlarged in the ratio 3 : 2.

(a) What are the dimensions of the new photograph?

(b) What is the ratio of the areas of the two photographs?

An increase in the ratio 3 : 2 is an enlargement scale factor $\frac{3}{2}$.

(a) The new dimensions are $20 \times \frac{3}{2}$ and $15 \times \frac{3}{2}$.
The new photograph measures 30 cm by 22.5 cm.

(b) The area scale factor is $(\frac{3}{2})^2 = \frac{9}{4}$ so the ratio of areas is 4 : 9.

 EXERCISE 14D

1   A company sells boxes of washing powder.
    The large size measures 15cm by 18cm by 12cm.
    The company decides to have a special promotion and increase the
    dimensions of the box in the ratio 7 : 6.

    (a) What are the dimensions of the new box?

    (b) What is the ratio of the volumes of powder in the two boxes
        when they are full?

2   Due to falling demand a factory has to decrease its output in the
    ratio 4 : 5. If the factory used to make 6000 units a week, how
    many units will it now make?

3   A tablecloth has a length of 150 cm and a width of 120 cm.
    The first time that it is washed the length decreases in the
    ratio 29 : 30 and the width decrease in the ratio 19 : 20.

    (a) What are the dimensions of the tablecloth after it has been
        washed?

    (b) What is the ratio of the areas before and after?

4   In a special 25th anniversary event a garage selling cars reduces all
    its prices in the ratio 19 : 20.
    How much will the following cars cost in the promotion?

    (a) Small hatchback $8600

    (b) Family saloon $12 000

    (c) Off road vehicle $16 000

5 A gardener had a small vegetable plot which measures
   10 m by 6 m. He decided to change the size of it to grow fruit
   instead of vegetables.
   He decreased the length in the ratio 4 : 5 and increased the
   width in the ratio 6 : 5.

   (a) Find the new dimensions of the plot.

   (b) Has the area increased or decreased?

   (c) What is the ratio of the areas of the old to new plot?

6 A family take a number of photographs while they are on holiday.
   They have all the photgraphs printed as 30 cm by 20 cm and
   choose the best one to have enlarged in a ratio 12 : 5.

   (a) What are the dimensions of the enlarged photograph?

   (b) What is the ratio of the areas of the two photographs?

EXAMINATION QUESTIONS

1   (a)

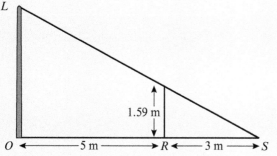

NOT TO SCALE

Robert stands at the point R on level ground, 5 metres from the base of a lamp post OL.
Robert is 1.59m tall and his shadow is 3m long.
Show by calculation that the height of the lamp post OL is 4.24 m.   [2]

(b)

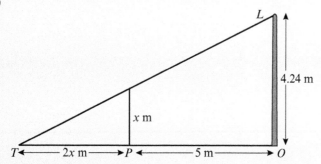

NOT TO SCALE

Pierre stands on level ground at the point P, 5 metres from O.
Pierre is x m tall and his shadow PT is $2x$ metres long.
Find the value of x.   [2]

(CIE Paper 2, Jun 2000)

2   Juan and Pedro each make similar models of the same aeroplane.
Juan uses a scale of 1 : 50.
Pedro uses a scale of 1 : 100.
Find the ratio of the **volumes** of Juan's model : Pedro's model.   [2]

(CIE Paper 2, Jun 2001)

3 (a)

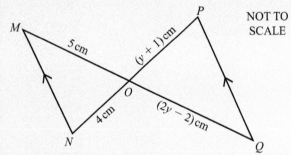

In the diagram, MN and PQ are parallel and MQ and NP meet at O.
(i) Show that triangles MNO and QPO are similar. [2]
(ii) $OM = 5$ cm and $ON = 4$ cm. $OP = (y + 1)$ cm and $OQ = (2y - 2)$ cm.

Explain why $\dfrac{2y - 2}{5} = \dfrac{y + 1}{4}$. [1]

(iii) Solve the equation in part (a)(ii). [3]
(iv) Find the length of NP. [1]

(CIE Paper 4, Nov 2001)

---

4 Mona made a model of a building using a scale of $1 : 20$.
The roof of the building had an area of 300 m^2.
(a) Calculate the area of the roof of the model in square metres. [2]
(b) Write your answer in square centimetres. [1]

(CIE Paper 2, Jun 2002)

5

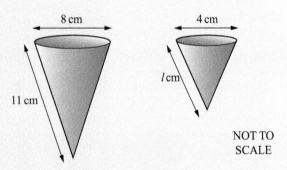

NOT TO
SCALE

(a) Write down the value of l. [1]
(b) When full, the larger cone contains 172 cm^3 of water.
How much water does the smaller cone contain when it is full? [2]

(CIE Paper 2, Nov 2003)

Chapter 15

Averages

This chapter will show you how to

✔ find the 'averages' – mean, median and mode for discrete data

✔ find the range and understand what is meant by the spread of the data

✔ find the mean, median and mode from frequency distributions and grouped frequency distributions for both discrete and continuous data

15.1 Averages – mean, median, mode

An **average** is a value that is representative of a set of data.

Three averages that you need to know are the **mean**, the **mode** and the **median**.

You can also describe how spread out the data is, using the **range**.

The range is found by subtracting the lowest value from the highest value.

⬤ EXAMPLE 1

The list shows the hourly rate received by nine employees.

$12 $7.20 $8.60 $7.50 $10 $7.50 $13.40 $10 $7.50

Find the
(a) mean   (b) mode   (c) median   (d) range for this data.

(a) mean $= \dfrac{12 + 7.20 + 8.60 + 7.50 + 10 + 7.50 + 13.40 + 10 + 7.50}{9}$

$= \dfrac{83.70}{9}$

The mean is $9.30.

> Find the mean hourly rate by adding together all the values and dividing this by the total number of values.
>
> There are 9 values in this example.
>
> This is the mean hourly rate.

continued ▼

(b) The mode is $7.50.

The mode is the value that occurs most often.

(c) 7.20 , 7.50 , 7.50 , 7.50 , 8.60 , 10 , 10 , 12 , 13.40
The median value is $8.60.

The median is the middle value when the values are arranged in order of size.

(d) The range = $13.40 − $7.20 = $6.20.

The lowest hourly rate is $7.20 and the highest is $13.40. The range is the difference between these two amounts. It gives you an idea of how the data is spread out.

Finding the median for an even number of values

If you have an *odd* number of data values then there is *only one middle value* as in Example 1.

If you have an *even* number of data values then there are *two middle values*. The median is the number mid-way between these two values. For example, if a tenth person has an hourly rate of $6.50, then the list in ascending order is

6.50, 7.20, 7.50, 7.50, **7.50, 8.60** , 10, 10, 12, 13.40

and the median value is

$$\text{median value} = \frac{7.50 + 8.60}{2} = \$8.05$$

The addition of this extra value could also affect the mean, range and mode.

These four quantities – mean, mode, median and range – tell you the main features of the data and allow you to make comparisons with other data sets.

 EXAMPLE 2

Jen obtained these scores for the first eight modules of her course.

63   49   51   52   70   67   52   76

(a) Find her mean score.

(b) She needs a mean score of 62 over 9 modules to pass her course. What does she need to score in her ninth module?

(a) mean = $\dfrac{63 + 49 + 51 + 52 + 70 + 67 + 52 + 76}{8} = \dfrac{480}{8}$

   = 60

(b)   New mean = 62

      = $\dfrac{\text{total}}{9}$

So   total = 9 × 62 = 558

   Score needed = 558 − 480 = 78

Total of 9 scores = 9 × 62 = 558.

Subtract sum of 8 scores from sum of 9 scores.

EXERCISE 15A

1 Find the mean, median, mode and range of the following.

(a) 6   3   9   12   1   9   8   8   6   1   3   6

(b) 20.1   20.7   21.4   22.7   29.6   22.6

(c) $\frac{1}{4}$ $\frac{1}{2}$ $\frac{3}{4}$ $\frac{1}{4}$ $\frac{5}{4}$ $\frac{3}{2}$ $\frac{5}{2}$ $\frac{1}{4}$

(d) 151   154   161   179   180   124   162   180   134

2 In a test the following percentage marks were recorded.

75   61   52   82   64   71   90   46   55   57   64   63   67

Find the mean, median and mode for the marks.

3 During a ten-pin bowling game the following scores were recorded.

7   8   4   1   10   8   3   6   5   9

Find the mean score (to the nearest whole number) and the mode.

4 The prices of a new car in a newspaper were

$9 900, $10 200, $9 625, $9 865, $10 150, $9 950

What is the mean price for this new car?

5 Work out the mean of these six amounts.

$150, $75, $62, $87, $46, $102

When a seventh amount is added, the new mean value is $83. What is the amount that has been added?

> Use Example 2 to help you.

6 The mean height of the 13 boys in a class is 162 cm and the mean height for the 12 girls is 153 cm. What is the mean height for the whole class?

> The answer is not 157.5 cm!

7 In a test the following results were recorded.

21, 25, 18, 27, 22, 23, 19, 16, 21, 27
24, 24, 16, 18, 23, 24, 25, 20, 28

Find

(a) the mean score   (b) the median score

(c) the mode   (d) the range.

8 Construct a list of six whole numbers that have range 4, a mode value of 6 and also a mean value of 6. What is the median value for this set of numbers?

Which is the best average to use?

Sometimes when you calculate an average, the answer might not be very representative of the data set.

You must be able to select an appropriate average to use, and give your reasons.

 EXAMPLE 3

A factory's staff consists of a managing director, the works' supervisor and twelve employees.

Their net weekly wages (in dollars) are shown below.

135 135 135 135 150 150 150 164
164 178 193 193 276 957

(a) Find the mean, mode and median wage.

(b) Discuss how representative each of these averages are.

___

(a) Mean $= \dfrac{135 + 135 + \ldots + 276 + 957}{14}$

$= \dfrac{3115}{14} = \$222.50$

Mode $= \$135$

Median $= \dfrac{150 + 164}{2} = \$157$

(b) **The mean wage is \$222.50.**

The only reason why the mean is so high is that the managing director's \$957 is included in the total of \$3115.

The modal wage is \$135.

The mode is not a good average to use because no-one earns less than this and eight of the employees earn quite a lot more.

The median wage is \$157.

All of the twelve employees earn a wage that is not too far away from this figure. The median sits in the middle of the list and is the most sensible answer to use.

> All of the twelve employees earn less than this. Some of them earn nearly \$90 less!

> The value 957 is called an **extreme value.**

> It is important to remember that neither the median nor mode are affected by extreme values, but the mean value will be.

 EXERCISE 15B

1 In a school test, the marks out of 40 for ten students were as follows.

41 38 38 35 34 31 29 28 26 9

Find the mode, median and mean marks and the range for this set of data. Comment on your results.
Which average would best represent the data?

2 The number of cars parked during the day in a city centre car park during a two-week period was recorded as follows

52 45 61 67 48 70 12 56 41 57 53 62 70 9

Find the mode, median and mean number of cars parked. Comment on your results.
Which would be the best average to use?

3 A six-sided dice has numbers 1, 2, 3, 4, 4, 6. What are the mean, mode and median values of these numbers? Why would the mean value be an inappropriate measure of the typical value thrown?

15.2 Frequency distributions

When you have a large amount of data you can place the results into a **frequency table** .

EXAMPLE 4

In a soccer tournament the number of goals scored in each game was as follows.

0 2 5 4 3 2 0 0 3 5 3 4 2 2 2 3 1 1 0 1
6 1 0 0 3 1 0 1 2 2 1 4 3 0 0 1 2 1 2 1
5 0 1 3 2 0 6 3 1 1 1 0 2 0 2 1 0 2 2 0
1 2 3 0 4 2 3 1 5 1 6 1 1 3 2 2 0 0 3 0

Put this data into a frequency table. Find

(a) the mean   (b) the median   (c) the mode   (d) the range

for the goals scored in the tournament.

Number of goals scored (x)	Number of games (f)	Total number of goals (xf)
0	19	0
1	20	20
2	18	36
3	12	36
4	4	16
5	4	20
6	3	18
Totals	80	146

Use x for the data and f for the frequency (the number of times each value occurs).

The column xf records the total number of goals e.g. 12 games resulted in 3 goals, so $12 \times 3 = 36$ goals.

Total number of goals scored.

Total number of games played.

(a) Mean = $\dfrac{\text{total goals scored}}{\text{total games played}}$

= $\dfrac{146}{80}$

= 1.83 goals per game

continued ▼

There are 80 items of data. When they are arranged in order of size, the median will be mid-way between the 40th and 41st values.

Number of goals scored (x)	Number of games (f)	Total number of goals (xf)
0	19	0
1	20	20
2	18	36

20 + 19 = 39 pieces of data in first 2 rows.

40th and 41st items must be in here.

(b) Median = 2 goals per game

(c) Mode = 1 goal per game

The mode is the number of goals with the highest frequency.

(d) Range = 6 − 0 = 6 goals

The range is the difference between the largest and the smallest values.

How to find the median

● See whether the number of data values, n, is odd or even.
● If n is an *odd* number, the median is the $\frac{1}{2}(n + 1)$th value in the ordered list.
● If n is an *even* number, there will be two middle values and the median is the mean of the two middle values in the ordered list.

The two middle values are in the positions given by the integers below and above $\frac{1}{2}(n + 1)$.

 EXERCISE 15C

1 The police recorded the speeds of cars to the nearest 10 km/h on a road.

Speed km/h (x)	Frequency (f)	(xf)
10	0	
20	23	
30	48	
40	16	
50	2	
60	1	
Totals		

$xf = x \times f$

(a) How many cars were recorded?

(b) Copy and complete the table and find the mean, median and mode speeds for this road.

2 In a hockey tournament the following numbers of goals were scored throughout the competition.

Goals scored	x	0	1	2	3	4	5	6	7
Frequency	f	12	14	12	9	4	6	0	3

Use Example 4 to help you.

Find the mean, median and mode of the goals scored in the tournament.

3 The following scores out of ten for a test were recorded for 75 students.

```
5  7  8  2  1   9  3  8  7  4   2  8   4  9   8
2  4  9  5  5   6  6  5  8  9  10  6  10  7   3
8  3  4  2  5   7  3  7  7  8   9  7   8  4  10
6  4  3  8  2   9  9  2  3  8   5  6   6  8  10
5  6  6  2  8  10  5  5  6  7   1  8   7  4   6
```

Put this data into a frequency table and find the mean, median, mode and range of the marks.

4 As part of a Biology field trip, a student measured the height of some plants and recorded these results.

```
18  14  19  13  14  11  15  10  15  10  15  14  15
14  15  19  16  16  11  15  17  13  13  15  16  12
12  17  10  17  18  11  10  12  16  12  15  19  17
```

Construct a frequency table.

Find (a) the mode   (b) the median
      (c) the mean   (d) the range.

5 The number of goals scored in a football league one Saturday was as follows

Number of goals in a match	0	1	2	3	4	5	6	7
Frequency	4	10	5	9	7	5	1	2

Calculate
(a) the mode   (b) the median   (c) the mean.

6 The number of extra hours worked in a week by 60 staff in a factory was as follows

Number of extra hours	1	2	3	4	5	6
Frequency	12	11	7	11	9	10

Calculate
(a) the mode   (b) the median   (c) the mean.

15.3 Dealing with large data sets

When there are a large number of data items it is best to group the data together. This makes it easier to record the information, but individual data values are lost. This means that you can find only estimated values for the mean.

An **estimated mean** is not a guess because it comes from a calculation. It is called an estimate because you do not know the individual values.

When you group your data, the groups are called **classes** or **class intervals** and the frequency table is referred to as a **grouped frequency table**. The class intervals do not have to be the same size but they usually are. The numbers at the start and the end of each class interval are called the **class limits**.

Continuous data that is grouped can also be displayed as a histogram. This was covered in Chapter 6.

In order to calculate the mean from a frequency table, as you learned in Section 15.2, you need to use a single number instead of a class interval.

This single number is called the **mid-interval value** of each of the class intervals. It is found by working out the mean of the two class limits.

So for a class interval 11–15, the mid-interval value is

$$\frac{11 + 15}{2} = \frac{26}{2} = 13$$

Extend your grouped frequency table to include the mid-interval values. These mid-interval values replace the class intervals and so become the 'x values' in your calculation.

For continuous data rounded to the nearest integer, a class interval of 11–15 is strictly 10.5–15.5.

EXAMPLE 5

60 students measure the time it takes them to travel to school (correct to the nearest minute).

Calculate estimates of

(a) the mean

(b) the modal class.

Time (minutes)	Number of students (f)
1–5	6
6–10	12
11–15	8
16–20	11
21–25	14
26–30	4
31–35	3
36–40	2
TOTAL	60

Note that the class intervals must not overlap or have any gaps between them.

continued ▼

Time (minutes)	Number of students (f)	Mid-interval value (x)	Total time (minutes) (fx)
1–5	6	3	18
6–10	12	8	96
11–15	8	13	104
16–20	11	18	198
21–25	14	23	322
26–30	4	28	112
31–35	3	33	99
36–40	2	38	76
TOTAL	60		1025

First calculate the mid-interval values, e.g.
$$x = \frac{(1 + 5)}{2} = \frac{6}{2} = 3$$

Calculate total time by multiplying frequency f by mid-interval value x.

Find the totals of each column.

(a) Estimated mean $= \dfrac{\text{total time taken}}{\text{number of students}}$

$= \dfrac{1025}{60}$

$= 17.1$ (1 d.p.)

The estimated mean journey time is 17.1 minutes.

(b) The highest frequency is 14.

The class interval with this frequency is 21–25 minutes.

The modal class is 21–25 minutes.

You also cannot give an exact value for the mode. The best you can do is to give the modal class interval.

The class with the highest frequency is the modal class.

EXAMPLE 6

The frequency table below shows the heights of students in a Year 11 class.

What is the estimated mean height for boys and for girls?

Height (cm)	Frequency (boys)	Frequency (girls)
$155 \leqslant h < 160$	2	5
$160 \leqslant h <, 165$	6	9
$165 \leqslant h < 170$	14	22
$170 \leqslant h < 175$	19	11
$175 \leqslant h < 180$	8	3
$180 \leqslant h < 185$	1	0

continued ▼

Height (cm)	Frequency (boys)	Mid-point values (x)	(fx)
$155 \leqslant h < 160$	2	157.5	315
$160 \leqslant h <, 165$	6	162.5	975
$165 \leqslant h < 170$	14	167.5	2345
$170 \leqslant h < 175$	19	172.5	3277.5
$175 \leqslant h < 180$	8	177.5	1420
$180 \leqslant h < 185$	1	182.5	182.5
	50		8515

Estimated mean $= \dfrac{\text{total height}}{\text{total frequency}}$

$= \dfrac{8515}{50}$

$= 170$ cm (3 s.f.)

Now work out the estimated mean using the formula.

Boys' heights

To work out the mid-point value for each class interval add together the boundary values and divide by 2 e.g. the mid-point value of $160 \leqslant h < 165$ is given by

$$\dfrac{160 + 165}{2} = 162.5.$$

Extend the table to include the mid-point values. These replace the 'x values' in your calculation.

Height (cm)	Frequency (girls)	Mid-point values (x)	(fx)
$155 \leqslant h < 160$	5	157.5	787.5
$160 \leqslant h <, 165$	9	162.5	1462.5
$165 \leqslant h < 170$	22	167.5	3685
$170 \leqslant h < 175$	11	172.5	1897.5
$175 \leqslant h < 180$	3	177.5	532.5
$180 \leqslant h < 185$	0	182.5	0
	50		8365

Girls' heights

Estimated mean $= \dfrac{\text{total height}}{\text{total frequency}}$

$= \dfrac{8365}{50}$

$= 167$ cm (3 s.f.)

Remember to include the units. Check that your answer is sensible.

The estimated mean height is 3 cm greater for boys than for girls.

EXERCISE 15D

1 The number of telephone calls made from a particular house over a 72-day period was recorded. The results were as follows.

Copy and complete the table and find an estimate of the mean and the class interval for the mode.

Calls made	Frequency (f)	Mid-interval value (x)	fx
0–2	12		
3–5	18		
6–8	31		
9–11	11		
Totals			

2 Some students were asked how many CDs they had in their collection. The results are shown in this grouped frequency table.

Copy the table and extend it to include the mid-interval values.

Use this information to find an estimate for the mean number of CDs and work out the modal class interval.

Number of CDs	Frequency (f)
50–64	12
65–79	0
80–94	11
95–109	9
110–124	15
125–139	33
140–154	28
155–169	41
170–184	16

3 The number of students in a class using the school library was recorded over a term.

Using this data, work out an estimate for the mean number of visits to the library for this class. How does this compare with the modal class interval?

Number of visits	Frequency (f)
0–4	84
5–9	46
10–14	38
15–19	51
20–24	22
25–29	13

4 The frequency table shows the distribution of the mass of fish caught during a local fishing competition. Work out an estimate for the mean mass.

Catch (kg)	Frequency (f)
0.1–0.5	6
0.6–1.0	6
1.1–1.5	9
1.6–2.0	4
2.1–2.5	3
2.6–3.0	4

1   500 eggs were sorted by mass into five different sizes.

	Mass (m grams)	Frequency
Small	$35 \leqslant m < 40$	20
Medium	$40 \leqslant m < 50$	60
Standard	$50 \leqslant m < 60$	200
Large	$60 \leqslant m < 75$	180
Extra large	$75 \leqslant m < 80$	40

Calculate an estimate of the mean mass of the eggs.   [4]

(CIE Paper 4, Jun 2000)

---

2   60 children are asked how many pets they have. The results are shown in the table.

Number of pets	0	1	2	3	4	5	6
Frequency	16	14	3	9	7	6	5

Find
(a) the mode,   [1]
(b) the median,   [2]
(c) the mean.   [2]

(CIE Paper 4, Jun 2001)

---

3   **(a)** The number of people living in 6 houses is

$$3, \quad 8, \quad 4, \quad x, \quad y \text{ and } \quad z$$

The median is $7\frac{1}{2}$, the mode is 8 and the mean is 7.
Find a value for x, y and z.   [5]
(b) The grouped frequency table below shows the amount ($\$A$) spent on travel by a number of students

Cost of travel ($\$A$)	$0 < A \leqslant 10$	$10 < A \leqslant 20$	$20 < A \leqslant 40$
Frequency	15	m	n

(i) Write down an estimate for the total amount in terms of m and n.   [2]
(ii) The calculated estimate of the mean amount is $13 exactly.
Write down an equation in m and n.
Show that it simplifies to $2m + 17n = 120$ [3]

(CIE Paper 4, Jun 2002)

4 For the numbers 8, 3, 5, 8, 7, 8   find
   (a) the mode, [1]
   (b) the median, [1]
   (c) the mean. [1]

(CIE Paper 2, Nov 2002)

5 In a survey, 200 shoppers were asked how much they had just spent at a supermarket. The results are shown in the table.

Amount (x)	$0 < x \leqslant 20$	$20 < x \leqslant 40$	$40 < x \leqslant 60$	$60 < x \leqslant 80$	$80 < x \leqslant 100$	$100 < x \leqslant 140$
Number of shoppers	10	32	48	54	36	20

   (a) **(i)** Write down the modal class. [1]
   (ii) Calculate an estimate of the mean, giving your answer correct to 2 d.p. [4]

(CIE Paper 4, Jun 2003)

6 120 passengers on an aircraft had their baggage weighed. The results are shown in the table.

Mass of baggage (M kg)	$0 < M \leqslant 10$	$10 < M \leqslant 15$	$15 < M \leqslant 20$	$20 < M \leqslant 25$	$25 < M \leqslant 30$
Number of passengers	12	32	28	24	24

   (a) **(i)** Write down the modal class. [1]
   (ii) Calculate an estimate of the mean mass of baggage for the 120 passengers. Show all your working. [4]

(CIE Paper 4, Nov 2003)

Chapter 16

Cumulative frequency

This chapter will show you how to
✔ construct cumulative frequency tables
✔ find quartiles and interquartile ranges
✔ draw box plots
✔ compare and interpret distributions

You will need to know
● how to construct frequency tables

16.1 Cumulative frequency

You can construct a **cumulative frequency table** from a **grouped frequency table** by calculating the running total of the frequency up to the end of each class interval.

You can use the table to plot a **cumulative frequency diagram**.

You can draw cumulative frequency diagrams for both discrete and continuous data sets.

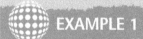 **EXAMPLE 1**

The following grouped frequency distribution shows the time taken for students to solve a puzzle. Using this data, draw a cumulative frequency diagram.

Class intervals (such as $0 < t \leq 5$) were discussed in Chapter 15.

Time taken (seconds)	Frequency
$0 < t \leq 5$	2
$5 < t \leq 10$	9
$10 < t \leq 15$	9
$15 < t \leq 20$	8
$20 < t \leq 25$	3
$25 < t \leq 30$	1

continued ▼

Time taken (seconds)	Cumulative frequency
$0 < t \leqslant 5$	2
$5 < t \leqslant 10$	$2 + 9 = $ **11**
$10 < t \leqslant 15$	$2 + 9 + 9 = $ **20**
$15 < t \leqslant 20$	$2 + 9 + 9 + 8 = $ **28**
$20 < t \leqslant 25$	$2 + 9 + 9 + 8 + 3 = $ **31**
$25 < t \leqslant 30$	$2 + 9 + 9 + 8 + 3 + 1 = $ **32**

Begin by creating a cumulative frequency table. This cumulative frequency column is a running total of the frequency so far.

The figures in bold are the values of the cumulative frequency. The class intervals ($t \leqslant$) are also changed to show the values 'up to and including' i.e. the **upper class boundary** value.

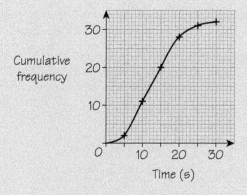

You can now use this data to draw a cumulative frequency diagram by plotting the cumulative frequency against the upper class boundary of each class interval.
Cumulative frequency is always plotted on the vertical axis. The maximum value on the y-axis (the cumulative frequency axis) should be the total number of values in the data set, in this case 32.

Draw a smooth curve through the points (to give a cumulative frequency curve), as shown.

The shape of the cumulative frequency diagram reflects the characteristics of the data and how this data is spread or distributed within the range. This characteristic S shape (called an ogive) appears in nearly all cumulative frequency diagrams.

Cumulative frequency graphs

- Choose a suitable scale for each axis.
- Always plot the cumulative frequencies on the vertical axis (the y-axis).
- Plot the points using the upper class boundary e.g. (5, 2), (10, 11), (15, 20) and so on.
- Draw a smooth curve through the points (points can also be joined with straight lines) and include the origin.
- Check that you have plotted your points correctly.
- Check that your graph is an S-shape.

Estimating values using a cumulative frequency graph

Once you have drawn your cumulative frequency diagram you can use it to estimate values for the data.

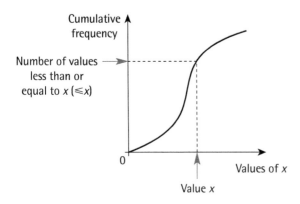

For example, given a value of x you can estimate the number of values less than or greater than x by drawing a straight line that meets the cumulative frequency curve and then drawing a corresponding line to meet the other axis.

EXAMPLE 2

Use the cumulative frequency curve from Example 1 to estimate

(a) how many students solved the puzzle

    (i) within 12 seconds   (ii) in more than 18 seconds

(b) the time by which 28 students had solved the puzzle.

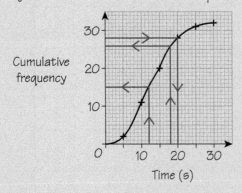

Time (s)

Always draw lines on your graph to show how you obtained your answers. Do not rub them out.

(a) Draw a vertical line for $x = 12$ to intersect the cumulative frequency curve. Now draw a line to meet the cumulative frequency axis. The value obtained is 15.

(b) The line at $x = 18$ seconds gives a value of 26. This means that $32 - 26 = 6$ students took longer than 18 seconds to solve the puzzle.

(c) Draw a line from the cumulative frequency value of 28 to intersect the curve. Now draw a vertical line to meet the x-axis at the point $x = 20$. This is the time by which 28 students solved the puzzle.

(a) (i) 15 students solved the puzzle within 12 seconds.

    (ii) $32 - 26 = 6$

       6 students took longer than 18 seconds.

(b) $x = 20$

    28 students solved the puzzle within 20 seconds.

 **EXERCISE 16A**

1 (a) Copy and complete the cumulative frequency table showing the distribution of test marks for a group of 32 students.

Mark (%)	Number of students		Mark (%)	Cumulative frequency
1–10	1		≤10	1
11–20	2		≤20	3
21–30	4			
31–40	7			
41–50	5			
51–60	8			
61–70	2			
71–80	2			
81–90	1			
91–100	0			

Your *x*-axis (mark) should run from 0 to 100, and your *y*-axis from 0 to 35.

(b) Plot the results in a cumulative frequency graph.

2 The table below shows the frequency distribution of test marks for 120 students.

Mark (%)	Number of students
1–10	1
11–20	6
21–30	8
31–40	15
41–50	17
51–60	24
61–70	22
71–80	15
81–90	9
91–100	3

Construct a cumulative frequency table (taking the first class interval to be ≤10 and the last interval to be ≤100). Draw the corresponding cumulative frequency graph for this distribution.

3 The results for the long jump at a school sports day are shown in the table.

Draw a cumulative frequency diagram for this distribution.

Estimate how many students jumped over 2.35 m.

Distance x (m)	Frequency
1.70 < x ≤ 1.80	2
1.80 < x ≤ 1.90	6
1.90 < x ≤ 2.00	9
2.00 < x ≤ 2.10	7
2.10 < x ≤ 2.20	15
2.20 < x ≤ 2.30	8
2.30 < x ≤ 2.40	8
2.40 < x ≤ 2.50	2

4 The temperature in °C recorded over a 66-day period is shown in the table.

Draw a cumulative frequency diagram and estimate the number of days that the temperature was above 18°C.

Temperature t (°C)	Number of days
0 < t ≤ 3	1
3 < t ≤ 7	7
7 < t ≤ 11	18
11 < t ≤ 15	20
15 < t ≤ 19	17
19 < t ≤ 23	2
23 < t ≤ 27	1

5 The cumulative frequency curve for the amount of time spent on a homework task is shown below.

Construct a cumulative frequency table and use this to estimate the number of students who spent more than 1 hour on the task.

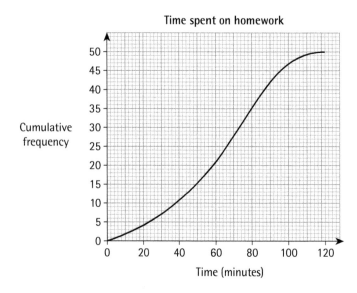

Time spent on homework

Cumulative frequency

Time (minutes)

16.2 The median, quartiles and inter-quartile range

You can obtain important statistical measures from a cumulative frequency graph. These are useful when you want to compare two or more data sets.

- The **median** is the middle value of the distribution. This is at $\frac{1}{2}(n + 1)$ on the cumulative frequency axis.

- The **lower quartile (LQ)** is at $\frac{1}{4}(n+1)$ on the cumulative frequency axis.

- The **upper quartile (UQ)** is at $\frac{3}{4}(n+1)$ on the cumulative frequency axis.

- The **interquartile range (IQR)** gives an improved measure of the spread of the data and is given by
  Inter-quartile range = upper quartile − lower quartile

n is the total frequency.

The answers for the median, the lower quartile and the upper quartile are read off on the *horizontal* axis.
The first step in this process is to locate the appropriate points on the cumulative frequency axis.

The IQR is a measure of spread of the middle 50% of the data, so it excludes extreme values.

EXAMPLE 3

Use the cumulative frequency graph of Example 1 to find an estimate for

(a) the median
(b) the lower quartile
(c) the upper quartile
(d) the interquartile range.

$n = 32$
The middle value is
$\frac{1}{2}(32 + 1) = 16\frac{1}{2}$th value

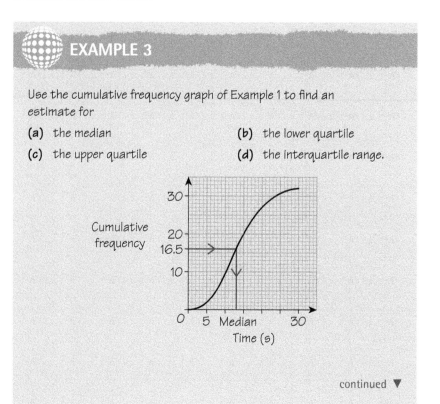

Draw a horizontal line from this point to meet the curve. The median value is where this vertical line meets the x-axis, as shown.

continued ▼

(a) The median = 13 seconds.

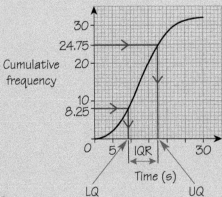

(b) Total = 32

$\frac{1}{4}$ of (32 + 1) = 8.25

LQ = 9.5 seconds

(c) $\frac{3}{4}$ of (32 + 1) = 24.75

UQ = 24.5 seconds

(d) IQR = 17.5 − 9.5 = 8 seconds

(b) To find the lower quartile (LQ), first locate a point at $\frac{1}{4}$(32 + 1) = 8.25 on the frequency axis and draw a horizontal line to intersect the curve. Draw a vertical line to meet the x-axis. This gives the lower quartile.

(c) Find the upper quartile (UQ) in a similar way, but this time use a point at $\frac{3}{4}$(32 + 1) = 24.75 on the cumulative frequency axis.

(d) Remember IQR = UQ − LQ

The cumulative graph can be divided up into other fractions, not just quarters.

Tenths are quite common and these are called **deciles**.

Percentiles divide the cumulative frequency into hundredths.

The 70th percentile will be at $\frac{70}{100}(n + 1)$ on the cumulative frequency (cf) axis.

EXAMPLE 4

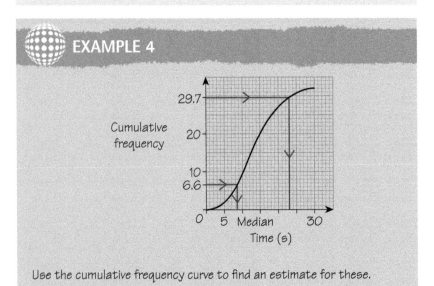

Use the cumulative frequency curve to find an estimate for these.

(a) the 20th percentile   **(b)** the 90th percentile

continued ▼

(a) The 20th percentile will be at $\frac{20}{100}(32 + 1) = 6.6$

Draw a horizontal line at 6.6 to the curve and then a vertical line down to the time axis.

20th percentile = 9 seconds

(b) The 90th percentile will be at $\frac{90}{100}(32 + 1) = 29.7$

Repeat the process of (a) at 29.7

90th percentile = 23 seconds

 EXERCISE 16B

1 The cumulative frequency graph for the distances travelled to school by 50 students is shown below.

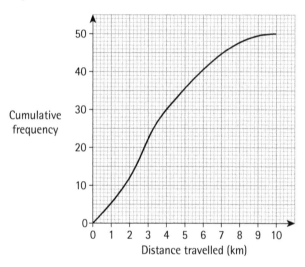

Cumulative frequency

Distance travelled (km)

From the graph, estimate

(a) the median distance   (b) the lower quartile distance

(c) the upper quartile distance   (d) the inter-quartile range.

2 A survey was conducted to find the amount of time students spent on homework each week. The results are shown in the cumulative frequency graph.

From the graph, estimate

(a) the median time

(b) the lower quartile time

(c) the upper quartile time

(d) the IQR.

Give your answers in hours and minutes.

(e) Estimate what percentage of students spent 5 hours or less on homework each week.

Cumulative frequency

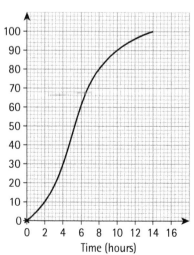

Time (hours)

3 The cumulative frequency diagram shows the marks gained in a geography exam.

Use the graph to find mark estimates for

(a) the median

(b) LQ

(c) UQ

(d) IQR

(e) the 70th percentile.

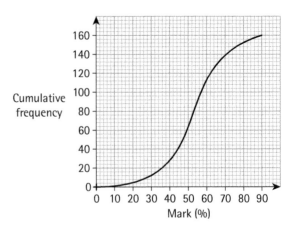

4 A tyre company carried out a survey to find how far cars travel before they need new tyres. The results for 100 cars is shown in the cumulative frequency diagram.

Use the graph to estimate

(a) the median distance travelled

(b) the lower quartile distance travelled

(c) the upper quartile distance travelled

(d) the inter-quartile range.

(e) what percentage of cars travelled a distance of more than 30 000 kilometres before the tyres needed to be changed?

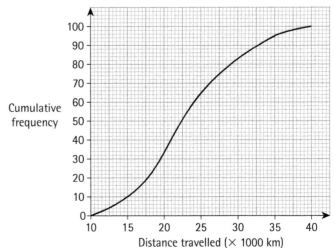

5 During a busy day at a doctor's surgery the amount of waiting time for patients was recorded as shown in the table. The shortest waiting time was $1\frac{1}{2}$ mins. and the longest time was $9\frac{1}{2}$ mins.

(a) Construct a cumulative frequency table.

(b) Draw a cumulative frequency curve.

(c) Give an estimate of the median waiting time.

(d) Find the 60th percentile.

Waiting time, t (minutes)	Frequency (f)
$0 < t \leqslant 1$	0
$1 < t \leqslant 2$	4
$2 < t \leqslant 3$	23
$3 < t \leqslant 4$	43
$4 < t \leqslant 5$	58
$5 < t \leqslant 6$	37
$6 < t \leqslant 7$	11
$7 < t \leqslant 8$	3
$8 < t \leqslant 9$	0
$9 < t \leqslant 10$	1

6 The local sports centre conducted a survey on the age distribution of its 800 members and the results are shown in the table.
The youngest person was 6 years old and the oldest was 78.

Age, a (years)	Frequency (f)
$0 < a \leqslant 10$	41
$10 < a \leqslant 20$	138
$20 < a \leqslant 30$	168
$30 < a \leqslant 40$	192
$40 < a \leqslant 50$	126
$50 < a \leqslant 60$	85
$60 < a \leqslant 70$	39
$70 < a \leqslant 80$	11

(a) Construct a cumulative frequency table for this data.

(b) Draw a cumulative frequency graph.

(c) Use the curve to estimate the median age of the leisure centre members.

(d) Find an estimate of the lower and upper quartiles.

(e) Find the 95th percentile.

1 500 eggs were sorted by mass into five different sizes.

	Mass (m grams)	Frequency
Small	$35 \leqslant m < 40$	20
Medium	$40 \leqslant m < 50$	60
Standard	$50 \leqslant m < 60$	200
Large	$60 \leqslant m < 75$	180
Extra large	$75 \leqslant m < 80$	40

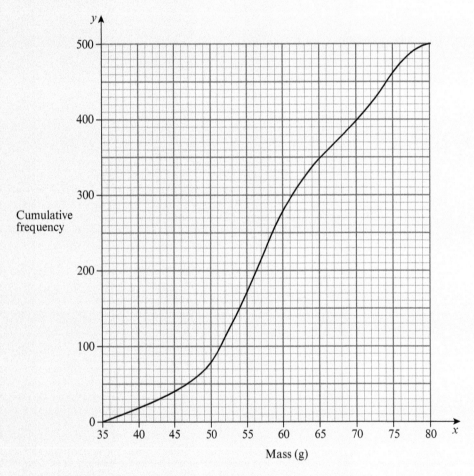

Mass (g)

This cumulative frequency curve has been drawn using the information in the table above.

(a) Explain why the point (60, 280) is on the curve. [2]

(b) Estimate the median mass of the eggs. [1]

(c) Estimate the inter-quartile range of the masses of the eggs. [2]

(CIE Paper 4, Jun 2000)

2

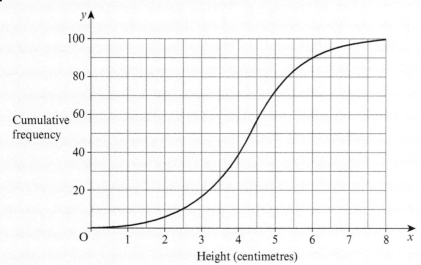

Height (centimetres)

The cumulative frequency diagram shows the heights of plants measured in an experiment.
From the diagram, estimate

(a) (i)   the lower quartile,   [1]
     (ii) the inter-quartile range.   [1]
(b) the number of plants with a height greater than 25cm.   [1]

(CIE Paper 2, Nov 2000)

---

3   In a survey, 200 shoppers were asked how much they had just spent at a supermarket.
The results are shown in the table.

Amount (x)	$0 < x \leqslant 20$	$20 < x \leqslant 40$	$40 < x \leqslant 60$	$60 < x \leqslant 80$	$80 < x \leqslant 100$	$100 < x \leqslant 140$
Number of shoppers	10	32	48	54	36	20

(a) (i)   Make a cumulative frequency table for these 200 shoppers.   [2]
     (ii) Using a scale of 2 cm to represent $20 on the horizontal axis and 2 cm to
          represent 20 shoppers on the vertical axis, draw a cumulative frequency diagram
          for this data.   [4]
(b) Use your cumulative frequency diagram to find
     (i)   the median amount,   [1]
     (ii) the upper quartile,   [1]
     (iii) the inter-quartile range,   [1]
     (iv) how many shoppers spent at least $75.   [2]

(CIE Paper 4, Jun 2003)

4   The depth, d centimetres, of a river was recorded each day during a period of one year (365 days). The results are shown by the cumulative frequency curve.

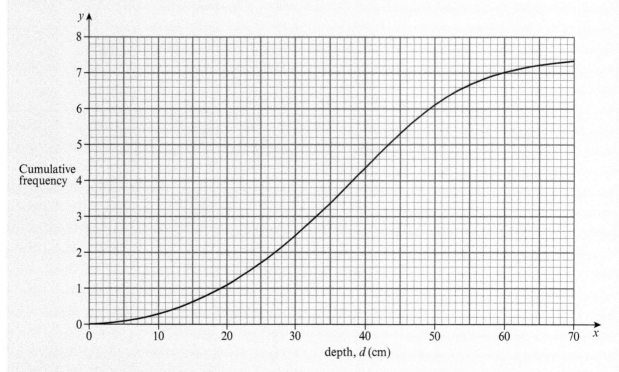

(a) Use the cumulative frequency curve to find
   (i)   the median depth,   [1]
   (ii) the inter-quartile range,   [2]
   (iii) the depth at the 40th percentile,   [2]
   (iv) the number of days when the depth of the river was **at least** 25 cm. [2]

(b)

d	$0 < d \leqslant 10$	$10 < d \leqslant 20$	$20 < d \leqslant 30$	$30 < d \leqslant 40$	$40 < d \leqslant 50$	$50 < d \leqslant 60$	$60 < d \leqslant 70$
Number of days	17	41	62	98	85	p	q

Show that $p = 47$ and $q = 15$.   [2]

(CIE Paper 4, Jun 2004)

Chapter 17

Pythagoras' theorem and trigonometry

This chapter will show you how to
- ✔ apply Pythagoras' theorem to right-angled triangles
- ✔ find the distance between two co-ordinate points
- ✔ use the basic trigonometric functions sine, cosine and tangent
- ✔ solve problems in three dimensions

The theorem of Pythagoras and trigonometry are connected as they both involve right-angled triangles. This chapter shows how they can be used to solve a number of problems in both two and three dimensions.

17.1 Pythagoras' theorem

Pythagoras' theorem involves only **right-angled triangles** – those containing a 90° angle.

You can use Pythagoras' theorem to find the longest side of a triangle (called the **hypotenuse**) or to find the length of one of the shorter sides.

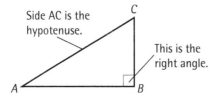

The hypotenuse is always opposite the right angle.

For a right-angled triangle with sides of lengths a, b and c, where c is the hypotenuse, Pythagoras' theorem states that $c^2 = a^2 + b^2$

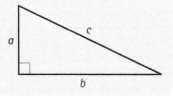

Applying Pythagoras' theorem allows you to find the length of any side of a right-angled triangle.

EXAMPLE 1

Work out the length
of the hypotenuse
(the side marked x) in
this right-angled triangle.

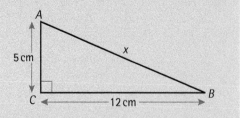

$x^2 = 5^2 + 12^2$

$x^2 = 25 + 144$

$x^2 = 169$

$x = \sqrt{169}$

$x = 13$ cm

Any set of three positive whole numbers a, b, c that satisfies
Pythagoras' theorem is called a **Pythagorean triple**.

A right-angled triangle with sides 3, 4 and 5 is one example (the
easiest) of a Pythagorean triple. Another triple is 5, 12 and 13.

These two basic Pythagorean triples
are worth remembering.

All triangles whose sides are multiples of these sets of lengths must be
mathematically similar, and so have identical angles. For example, the
triangle (6, 8, 10) is mathematically similar to triangle (3, 4, 5).

Most Pythagoras questions do not involve integer quantities,
particularly those in 'real' situations, so the answers must be rounded
to 3 s.f.

EXAMPLE 2

In the triangle PQR, angle $Q = 90°$,
$QP = 4$ cm and $QR = 7$ cm.
Calculate the length of PR.

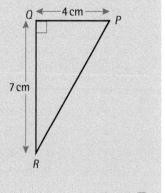

continued ▼

$PR^2 = 4^2 + 7^2$

$PR^2 = 16 + 49$

$PR^2 = 65$

$PR = \sqrt{65}$

$PR = 8.06$ cm (to 3 s.f.)

PR is the hypotenuse, because it is opposite the right angle.

Use your calculator to find the square root.

Always put the units in your answer.

 EXAMPLE 3

Calculate the length *a* (to 1 d.p.) in this triangle, where *b* = 4 cm and *c* = 7 cm.

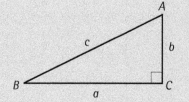

c is the longest side (the hypotenuse) since it is opposite the right angle.

$a^2 + 4^2 = 7^2$

$a^2 + 16 = 49$

$a^2 = 33$

$a = \sqrt{33} = 5.744$

$a \approx 5.74$ cm (3 s.f.)

 EXERCISE 17A

1 Calculate the lengths marked with letters in each of the following triangles.

(a)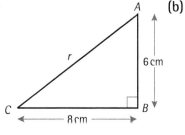

(b)

(c)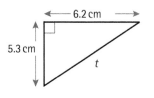

(d)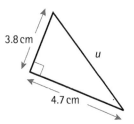

2 A gate measures 3.5 m long by 1.5 m high. Work out the length of the piece of wood that is needed to make the diagonal.

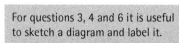

3 Fiona is flying her kite in a strong breeze and standing on level ground. If the kite is flying at a height of 18 m and is 20 m away horizontally from Fiona how long is the piece of string that is attached to the kite?

For questions 3, 4 and 6 it is useful to sketch a diagram and label it.

4 A boat sails due east for 24 km. However, the current takes the boat 10 km due south. How far does the boat actually travel?

5 Calculate the lengths
(a) XY and **(b)** QR.

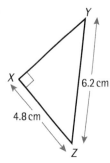
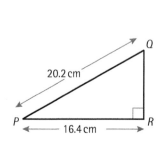

6 A children's slide is 3.6 m long. The vertical height of the slide above the ground is 2.1 m. Work out the horizontal distance between each end of the slide.

7 Work out the lengths of c and d.

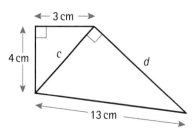

8 A section through a bicycle shed is shown opposite. Work out the width of the bicycle shed, giving your answer correct to 2 d.p.

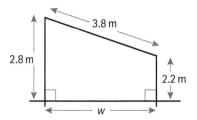

9 Find the perimeter of this kite.

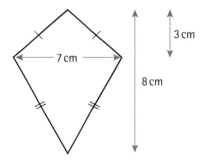

17.2 Finding the distance between two co-ordinate points

Pythagoras' theorem can also be used to find the straight line distance between two **co-ordinate points** on a graph. Example 4 has positive co-ordinate values (points contained within the first **quadrant**) and Example 5 shows how to calculate the distance if one or more of the co-ordinates are negative.

EXAMPLE 4

Two points on a graph have co-ordinates $P(6, 4)$ and $Q(2, 1)$. Find the length of PQ.

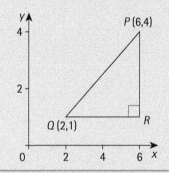

A sketch will help you. Complete the diagram by drawing the triangle PQR where the angle at R is 90°.

Use the x co-ordinates to calculate horizontal distances and the y co-ordinates to calculate vertical distances.

The length $QR = 6 - 2 = 4$ and the length $PR = 4 - 1 = 3$.

$PQ^2 = QR^2 + PR^2$

$PQ^2 = 4^2 + 3^2$

$PQ^2 = 16 + 9 = 25$

$PQ = \sqrt{25}$

$PQ = 5$

R has the same y co-ordinate as Q and the same x co-ordinate as P, so the co-ordinate of R is (6, 1).

Apply Pythagoras' theorem to triangle PQR.

EXAMPLE 5

Find the length of line MN where M is point $(-2, 3)$ and N is point $(3, -5)$.

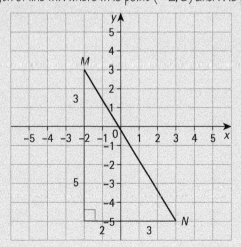

Draw a sketch, labelling the ends of the line, and construct a right-angled triangle.

continued ▼

$$MN^2 = (3 + 5)^2 + (2 + 3)^2$$
$$= 8^2 + 5^2$$

$$MN = \sqrt{8^2 + 5^2}$$
$$= \sqrt{89}$$
$$= 9.43$$

Apply Pythagoras.

 EXERCISE 17B

1 Two points have co-ordinates $A(15, 9)$ and $B(3, 4)$. Find the length of AB.

2 The co-ordinates of two points on a graph have co-ordinates $X(9, 12)$ and $Y(5, 6)$. Find the length of XY to 1 d.p.

3 Find the distance between the following two points that have co-ordinates.

(a) $G(1, 8)$ $H(7, 5)$ (b) $C(-3, 7)$ $D(5, 4)$

(c) $W(9, 4)$ $V(1, -6)$ (d) $F(2, -2)$ $E(-4, -6)$

(e) $X(-4, -7)$ $Y(2, 3)$ (f) $A(4, 0)$ $B(0, 4)$

(g) $R(-1, 3)$ $S(4, -1)$ (h) $M(-7, -6)$ $N(-8, -9)$

If in doubt always sketch a diagram and label the points. Draw a right-angled triangle and use Pythagoras' theorem.

17.3 Trigonometry – the ratios of sine, cosine and tangent

Trigonometry is concerned with calculating sides and angles in triangles and involves three ratios called **sine**, **cosine** and **tangent**.

A more detailed introduction to trigonometry can be found in the Core textbook.

Consider the right-angled triangle ABC shown below.

The side opposite the angle x is called the **opposite**.

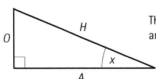

The side opposite the right angle is the **hypotenuse**.

The side next to the angle x is called the **adjacent**.

Questions on trigonometry are always on the examination paper, so it is well worth learning the basics.

The hypotenuse is always the same side but the adjacent and opposite sides change depending on which angle you are using.

 EXERCISE 17C

Copy these triangles and label the sides A, O and H, where x is the angle to be used.

1   2 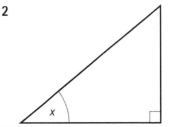   3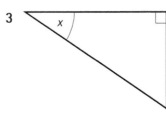

4 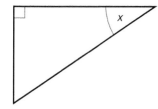   5 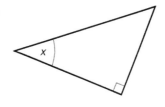   6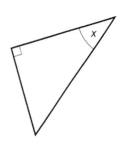

Tangent

This ratio uses the opposite and adjacent sides.

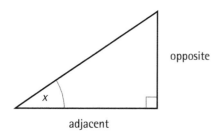

We can write $\tan x = \dfrac{\text{opposite}}{\text{adjacent}}$

We are now going to use this idea to find unknown angles and lengths.

 EXAMPLE 6

In the triangle work out the size of angle x.

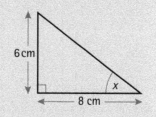

$\tan x = \dfrac{\text{opposite}}{\text{adjacent}} = \dfrac{6}{8} = 0.75$

$x = \tan^{-1} 0.75$

$\quad = 36.9°$ (1 d.p.)

Give angle answers to 1 d.p.

EXAMPLE 7

In the triangle work out the length of the side labelled y.

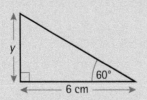

Use your calculator to find tan 60°. Always work to 4 s.f. or use your calculator value.
Give the final answer to 3 s.f.

$$\tan 60 = \frac{\text{opposite}}{\text{adjacent}} = \frac{y}{6}$$
$$y = 6 \times 1.732$$
$$= 10.392\ldots = 10.4 \text{ cm (3 s.f.)}$$

EXERCISE 17D

Find the angles marked with a letter.

1
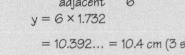

2
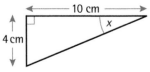

3
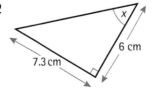

4

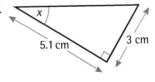

5
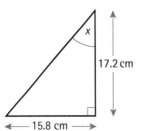

6
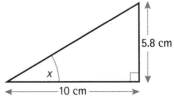

Find the lengths marked with a letter.

7
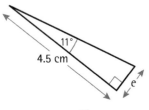

8
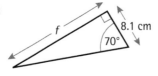

9
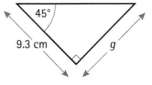

10
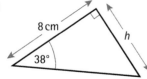

11
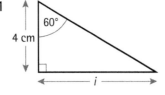

Sine

This ratio uses the opposite side and the hypotenuse but otherwise it works in the same way as the tangent did.

We can write

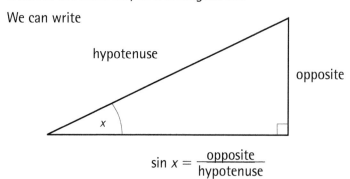

$$\sin x = \frac{\text{opposite}}{\text{hypotenuse}}$$

EXAMPLE 8

In the triangle work out the size of angle x.

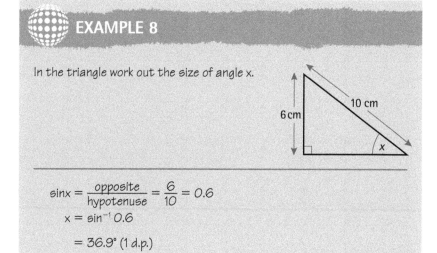

$$\sin x = \frac{\text{opposite}}{\text{hypotenuse}} = \frac{6}{10} = 0.6$$
$$x = \sin^{-1} 0.6$$
$$= 36.9° \ (1 \text{ d.p.})$$

EXAMPLE 9

In the triangle work out the length of the side labelled y.

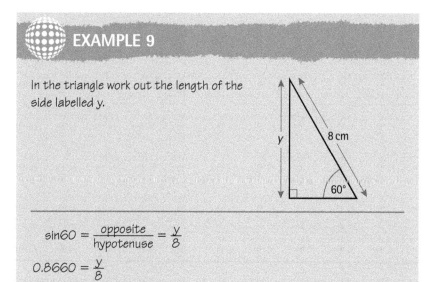

$$\sin 60 = \frac{\text{opposite}}{\text{hypotenuse}} = \frac{y}{8}$$

$$0.8660 = \frac{y}{8}$$

$$y = 8 \times 0.8660$$
$$- 6.928... = 6.93 \text{ cm} \ (3 \text{ s.f.})$$

Use your calculator to find sin 60°. Always work to 4 s.f. or use your calculator value.

1 Find the angles marked with a letter.

(a)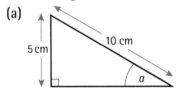

(b)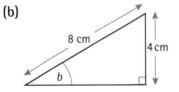

(c)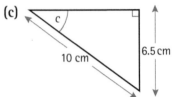

(d)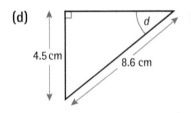

(e)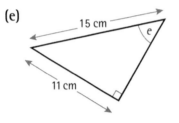

(f)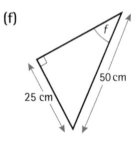

2 Find the lengths marked with a letter.

(a)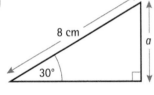

(b)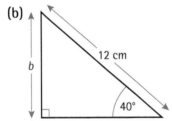

(c)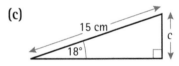

(d)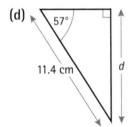

(e)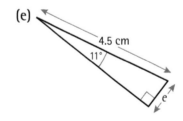

(f)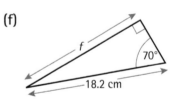

Cosine

Finally we have the cosine of x which uses the sides adjacent and hypotenuse.

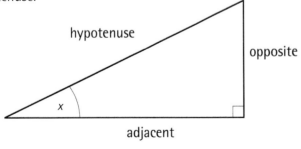

$$\cos x = \frac{\text{adjacent}}{\text{hypotenuse}}$$

EXAMPLE 10

In the triangle work out the size of angle x.

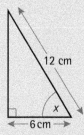

12 cm

x

6 cm

$$\cos x = \frac{adjacent}{hypotenuse} = \frac{6}{12} = 0.5$$

$$x = \cos^{-1} 0.5$$

$$= 60°$$

 EXAMPLE 11

In the triangle work out the length of the side labelled *a*.

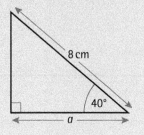

8 cm

40°

a

$$\cos 40 = \frac{adjacent}{hypotenuse} = \frac{a}{8}$$

$$0.7660 = \frac{a}{8}$$

$$a = 8 \times 0.7660$$

$$= 6.128... = 6.13 \text{ cm (3 s.f.)}$$

Use your calculator to find cos 40°.
Always work to 4 s.f. or use your
calculator value.

EXERCISE 17F

1 Find the angles marked with a letter.

(a)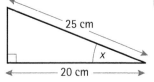

25 cm

x

20 cm

(b)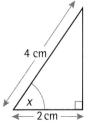

4 cm

x

2 cm

(c)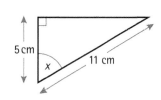

5 cm

x

11 cm

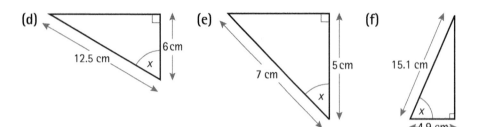

2 Find the lengths marked with a letter.

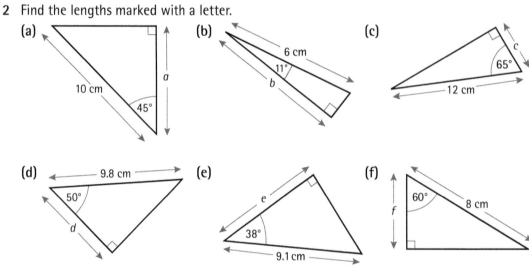

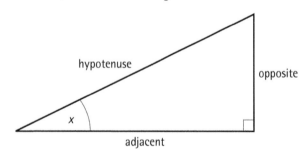

To summarise, we have three trigonometric ratios.

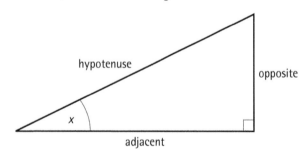

$$\sin x = \frac{\text{opposite}}{\text{hypoteneuse}} \qquad \cos x = \frac{\text{adjacent}}{\text{hypoteneuse}} \qquad \tan x = \frac{\text{opposite}}{\text{adjacent}}$$

This is sometimes written as

$$\text{Sin } x = \frac{O}{H} \qquad\qquad \text{Cos } x = \frac{A}{H} \qquad\qquad \text{Tan } x = \frac{O}{A}$$

to make the memory aid SOHCAHTOA

Problem solving

We can now begin to use trigonometry to solve problems.

EXAMPLE 12

In the triangle PQR, $QR = 15$ cm, angle $RPQ = 90°$ and angle $PRQ = 50°$. Calculate the length of PR.

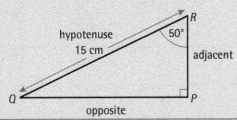

Start by labelling the sides in order of hypotenuse, opposite and then adjacent.

You can then see that the two sides in this problem are the hypotenuse (15 cm) and adjacent (PR).

This means that the ratio required is cosine.

$\cos 50° = \dfrac{PR}{15}$

$PR = 15 \times \cos 50°$

$PR = 9.6418\ldots$ cm

$= 9.64$ cm (3 s.f.)

EXERCISE 17G

1 Calculate the unknown length marked on each diagram (all lengths are in cm).

(a)
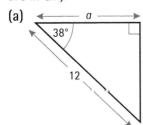

(b)
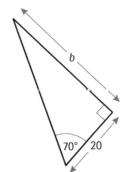

(c)
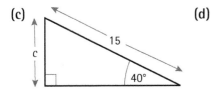

(d)
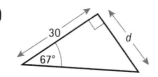

(e)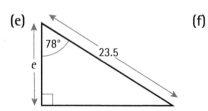

(f)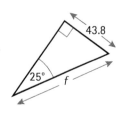

(g)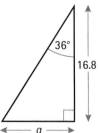

(h)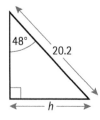

 EXAMPLE 13

Sometimes the questions are a little harder to solve.

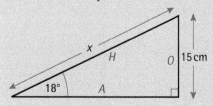

We can see from the red labels that this is a sine problem

$$\sin 18° = \frac{15}{x}$$

$$0.3090 = \frac{15}{x}$$

$$0.3090x = 15$$

$$x = \frac{15}{0.3090}$$

$$= 48.54... \text{ cm}$$

$$= 48.5 \text{ cm (3 s.f.)}$$

Notice that the x is in the denominator.

You would expect the answer to be larger than 15 as you are finding the hypotenuse.

 EXERCISE 17H

Calculate the lengths marked with a letter.

1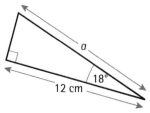

2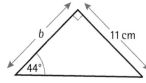

3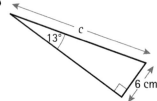

4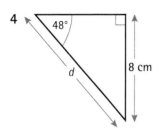

5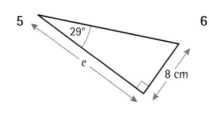

6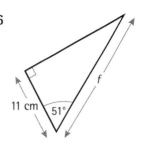

 EXERCISE 17I

1 In the following diagram, find the length marked *x*.

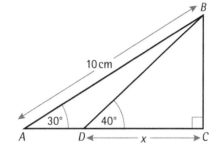

2 Triangle *ABC* is a right-angled triangle. The line *BD* meets the side *AC* at right angles.

If *AD* = 5 cm calculate the length *DC* (marked as *y*).

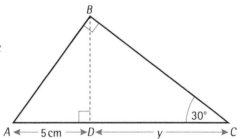

3 In this shape work out the length marked *b*.

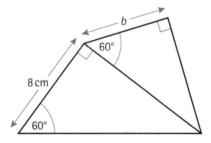

4 The diagram shows two right-angled triangles.
(a) Given that cos *x* = $\frac{2}{3}$, calculate the length *BD*.
(b) Find the value of sin *y*.

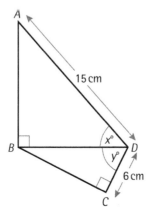

5

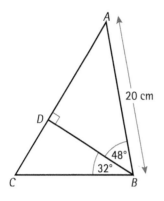

Calculate
(a) *BD*   (b) *BC*   (c) *AC.*

6

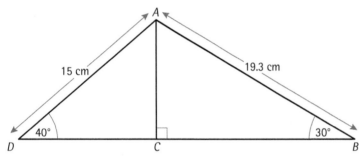

Calculate the length of
(a) *AC*   (b) *BC*   (c) *BD.*

7

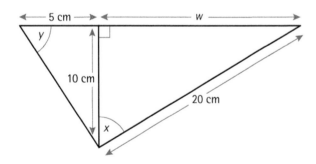

Calculate
(a) cos *x*   (b) *x*   (c) tan *y*   (d) *y*   (e) *w.*

17.4 Applications of trigonometry

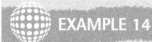 **EXAMPLE 14**

A yacht sails from a harbour X at 11.00 am.
The current makes the yacht drift south so that after 2 hours it is
12 km east of the harbour and on a bearing of 146°. How far south has
the yacht travelled? If it maintains its initial speed and direction, how
far south will the yacht be at 5 pm?

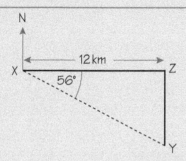

This is a sketch. It is not drawn to scale. Note that a bearing of 146° means an angle of 56° between *XZ* and *XY* since bearings are measured from the North.

$$\tan 56° = \frac{O}{A} = \frac{ZY}{12}$$

$$ZY = 12 \tan 56°$$

$$ZY = 12 \times 1.4826$$

$$ZY = 17.79 \text{ km (2 d.p.)}$$

After 6 hours it will be 3× further

$$3 \times 17.79 \text{ km} = 53.37 \text{ km}.$$

Combining topics in this way is usual when asking questions on trigonometry and Pythagoras.

EXERCISE 17J

1 A flagpole is kept vertical by two guy ropes attached
   to the top of the pole and the ground which is level.

   If *FM* = 6 m, *AM* = 4.5 m and angle *MCF* = 42°, calculate
   (a) the length *FC*
   (b) the length *FA*
   (c) the distance between *A* and *C*.

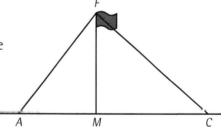

2 A rocket lifts off vertically and travels to a height of 5000 m.
   The second stage cuts in and takes the rocket at an angle of 25°
   to the vertical, covering a further distance of 2000 m. Calculate the
   height of the rocket above the ground.

3 A kite flying in a strong wind makes an angle of 35° with the
   ground. If the horizontal distance between the kite and the
   end of the string is 28 m, find the height of the kite above
   the ground.

4 An aeroplane is approaching an airport at a height of 1000 m.
If the aeroplane is 8 km from the airport, work out the angle of
approach.

5 $A(3, 0)$, $B(9, 0)$ and $C(9,8)$ form a triangle ABC
Calculate the angle BAC.

6 $ABCD$ is a rectangle with sides $AB = 26$ cm and $BC = 30$ cm.
Calculate

(a) the angle between the diagonal AC and the side AB

(b) the length of AC.

7 The diagram represents part of a cable car system.

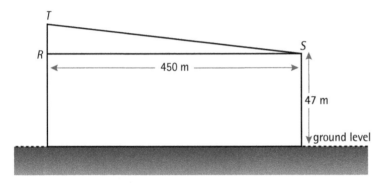

ST is the cable between two points S and T.
The point T is 88 metres above the ground.
The point S is 47 metres above the ground.
Calculate

(a) the angle RST,   (b) the length of the cable ST.

Angles of elevation and depression

When solving problems using Pythagoras or
trigonometry, you might meet
the following terms.

The **angle of elevation** is the angle
measured upward from the horizontal.

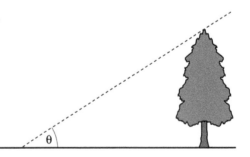

The **angle of depression** is the angle
measured downward from the horizontal.

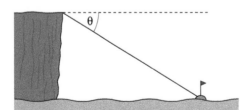

EXERCISE 17K

1   The angle of elevation of a church steeple, measured at a distance
    of 45 m from the base of the steeple, is 65°. If it is measured from a
    point 2 m above ground level, what is the height of the steeple?
    Another measurement is taken giving an angle of 25°. How far
    from the base of the church was this measurement taken?

2   A surveyor stands 150 m away from the centre of a church tower.
    The angle of elevation to the top of the tower is 38°. The angle of
    elevation to the tip of the flagpole on top of the tower is 41°. Work
    out the height of the flagpole.

3   An aeroplane is flying at a constant altitude of 10 000 m.
    An observer measures the angle of elevation to the plane as 25°
    and 15 seconds later as 22.6°.

    (a) Work out the horizontal distance the plane has covered in
        this time.

    (b) What is the speed of the aeroplane in km/h?

4   From the top of a sea cliff 35 m above the water the angles of
    depression of two boats A and B at sea are 19° and 4° respectively.

    Calculate the distance between the two boats.

5   The angle of elevation of the top of the Eiffel Tower, from a
    point on the ground 800 m away is 20.5°. Calculate the height
    of the tower.

6   A boat C is 200 m from the foot B of a vertical cliff which is
    40 m high. What is the angle of depression of the boat from
    the top of the cliff.

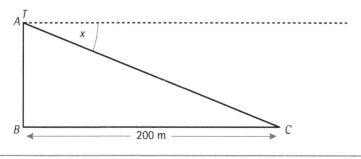

17.5 Problems in three dimensions

You can use Pythagoras' theorem and trigonometry to solve
problems in **three dimensions (3-D)**.

A reminder about 3-D shapes can
be found in Chapter 5.

You need to be able to identify and draw the correct right-angled
triangles that contain the length or angle to be found.

EXAMPLE 15

This cuboid has $a = 8$ cm, $b = 4$ cm and $c = 5$ cm.

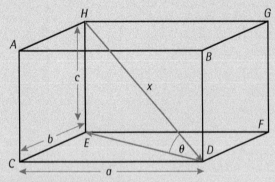

Work out

(a) the length of the longest diagonal HD (marked x) to 1 d.p.

(b) the angle between HD and DE (marked θ).

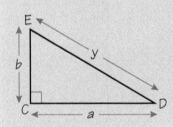

$y^2 = a^2 + b^2$

$y^2 = 8^2 + 4^2$

$y^2 = 64 + 16 = 80$

$y = \sqrt{80}$

You need to find the length ED first (label this with the letter y). Draw the right-angled triangle that contains the length ED.

Apply Pythagoras' theorem to the right-angled triangle ECD.

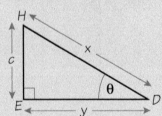

$x^2 = c^2 + y^2$

$x^2 = 5^2 + 80$

$x^2 = 25 + 80 = 105$

$x = \sqrt{105}$

$x = HD = 10.24$ cm ≈ 10.2 cm (3 s.f.)

To find x, use Pythagoras' theorem a second time on the right-angled triangle HED.

You must use the value of y you found in your previous calculation, not the rounded value. In fact it is best to use y^2 directly in the calculation.

Angle between a line and a plane

EXAMPLE 16

$ABCDE$ is a pyramid with a rectangular base, $ABCD$. $AB = 10$ cm and $BC = 5$ cm.

The vertex of the pyramid, E, is vertically above the centre of the base, O. $EO = 8$ cm.

Find the angle between EA and the plane $ABCD$.

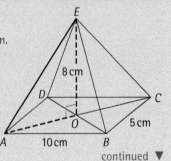

When the vertex of the pyramid is above the centre of the base, the pyramid is called a **right pyramid**.

continued ▼

$AC^2 = AB^2 + BC^2$

$AC^2 = 10^2 + 5^2$

$AC^2 = 125$

$AC^2 = \sqrt{125} = 11.1803\ldots$

$AO = \dfrac{11.1803\ldots}{2} = 5.59016\ldots$

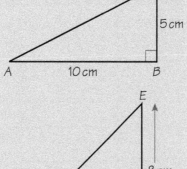

$\tan x = \dfrac{O}{A} = \dfrac{8}{5.59016\ldots}$

$x = 55.055\ldots$

$x = 55.1 \ (1 \ d.p.)$

The angle between EA and
the plane ABCD is 55.1° (1 d.p.)

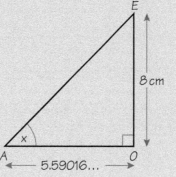

Drop a perpendicular from E onto
the base. This line meets the base at
O. Join O to A and use triangle EAO
to calculate the angle EAO, the
angle between EA and the base,
ABCD.

First find AC by using Pythagoras'
theorem on the base triangle ABC,
then divide it by 2 to find AO.

ABCD is a rectangle so angle
B = 90°

Draw the right-angled triangle EAO.
Label the angle x.

It is important to draw the correct
right-angled triangle that contains
the length or angle you require.

 EXERCISE 17L

1   A cuboid has side lengths $a = 3$ cm, $b = 4$ cm and $c = 12$ cm.
    Work out the length of the longest diagonal of the cuboid.

2   A square-based pyramid ABCDE has
    a base of side 4 cm and vertical height
    EO = 6 cm.

    Find

    (a) the length of EC

    (b) the angle between EC and AC.

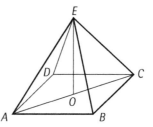

3   A vertical pole, CP, stands at one corner
    of a horizontal rectangular field ABCD.

    AB = 25 m and BC = 18 m

    The angle of elevation of P from D is 27°

    Calculate

    (a) the height of the pole

    (b) the angle of elevation of P from B

    (c) the length AC

    (d) the angle of elevation of P from A.

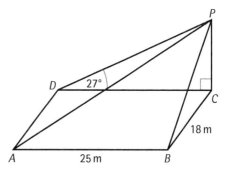

1

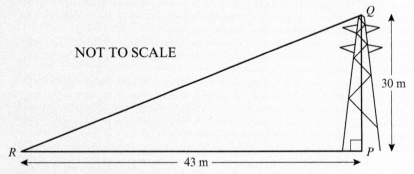

NOT TO SCALE

30 m

R

43 m

A pylon PQ is 30 metres high and it stands on level ground.
Its base P is 43 metres from a point R.
Find the angle of elevation of the top of the pylon from R. [2]

(CIE Paper 2, Jun 2001))

---

2 **(a)** Write down the value of sin 30° as a fraction. [1]

(b)

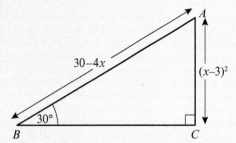

In triangle ABC, angle $ACB = 90°$ and angle $ABC = 30°$.
$AC = (x - 3)^2$ and $AB = (30 - 4x)$.
Use your answer to part (a) to write down an equation in x.
Show that it simplifies to $x^2 - 4x - 6 = 0$. [3]

(c) Solve the equation $x^2 - 4x - 6 = 0$.
Show all your working and give your answers correct to 2 decimal places. [4]

(d) Find the length of AB when AC is greater than 10. [2]

(CIE Paper 4, Nov 2001)

3

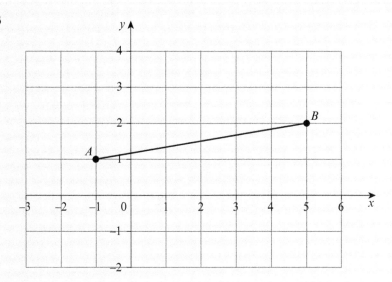

(a) Find the gradient of the line AB. [1]
(b) Calculate the angle that AB makes with the x-axis. [2]

(CIE Paper 2, Jun 2003)

4

NOT TO SCALE

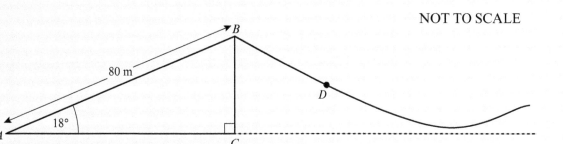

The diagram shows the start of a roller-coaster ride at a fairground.
A car rises from A to B along a straight track.
(a) $AB = 80$ metres and angle $BAC = 18°$.
Calculate the vertical height of B above A. [2]
(b) The car runs down the slope from B to D, a distance of s metres.
Use the formula $s = t(p + qt)$ to find values of s,
given that $p = 4$, $t = 3$ and $q = 3.8$. [2]

(CIE Paper 2, Jun 2003)

5

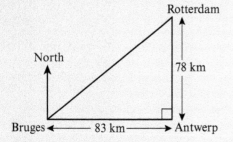

Antwerp is 78 km due south of Rotterdam and 83 km due east of Bruges, as shown in the diagram.

Calculate

(a) the distance between Bruges and Rotterdam. [2]

(b) the bearing of Rotterdam from Bruges, correct to the nearest degree. [3]

(CIE Paper 2, Jun 2004)

---

6 A mountain railway AB is of length 864 m and rises at an angle of 12° to the horizontal.
A train is 586 m above sea level when it is at A.
Calculate the height above sea level when it reaches B. [3]

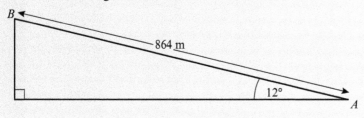

(CIE Paper 2, Nov 2004)

7

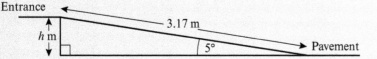

A shop has a wheelchair ramp to its entrance from the pavement.
The ramp is 3.17 metres long and is inclined at 5° to the horizontal.
Calculate the height, h metres, of the entrance above the pavement.
Show all your working. [2]

(CIE Paper 2, Jun 2005)

Chapter 18

Circle theorems

This chapter will show you how to
✔ apply your knowledge of circle properties to solving problems
✔ prove important circle theorems
✔ apply the circle theorems to a variety of problems
✔ set out your solutions in a clear and logical way
✔ write out reasons for your answers

18.1 Symmetry properties of the circle

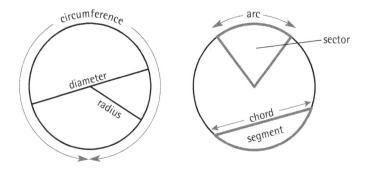

The diagrams above show some of the terms you will use when solving problems involving circles. A **chord** is a straight line joining two points on the circumference. A **segment** is the region between a chord and the circumference.

Arcs were introduced in Chapter 5.

A **tangent** to a circle is a line that just touches the circumference at only one point of contact.

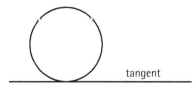

In this section we start with four important circle properties.

1 The perpendicular from the centre of a circle to a chord bisects the chord.

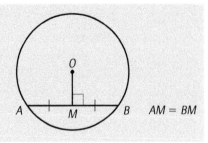

$AM = BM$

2 Equal chords are equidistant from the centre.

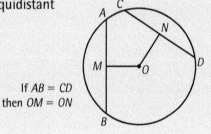

If $AB = CD$
then $OM = ON$

3 Tangents drawn to a circle from an external point are equal in length.

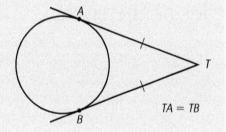

$TA = TB$

4 The angle between a tangent and a radius is 90°.

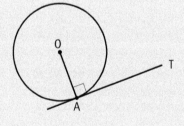

You need to remember these results because they are often needed for examination questions.

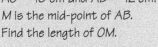

In the diagram, O is the centre of the circle and AB is a chord.
$AO = 10$ cm and $AB = 12$ cm.
M is the mid-point of AB.
Find the length of OM.

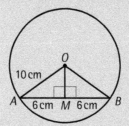

Using Pythagoras' theorem in $\triangle AOM$

$$OM^2 + 6^2 = 10^2$$
$$OM^2 = 10^2 - 6^2$$
$$= 64$$
$$OM = 8$$

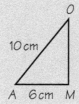

M is the mid-point of chord AB so angle $OMA = 90°$

EXAMPLE 2

In the diagram, O is the centre of the circle and AB is a chord.
T is an external point and tangents from T to the circle touch the circle at points A and B.
If angle $ATB = 40°$, find the size of angles
(a) TAB and **(b)** AOB.

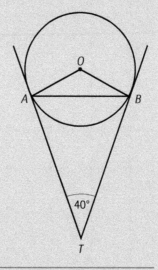

(a) Tangents from an external point are equal in length,
so $TA = TB$ which means that $\triangle TAB$ is isosceles.
Angle $TAB = 70° =$ angle TBA (base angles of isosceles $\triangle TAB$)

(b) TA is perpendicular to AO (tangent & radius meet at 90°).
So, angle $OAB = 90° - 70° = 20°$
In the same way, angle $OBA = 20°$
so, angle $AOB = 180° - 20° - 20° = 140°$

EXERCISE 18A

1

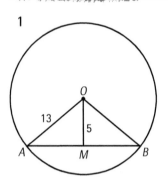

Find the length of *AM*.

2

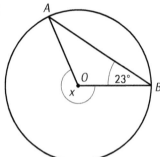

Find angle *x*.

3

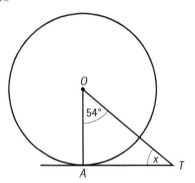

Find angle *x*.

4

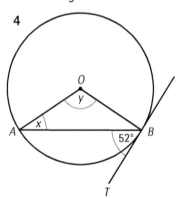

Find angles *x* and *y*.

5

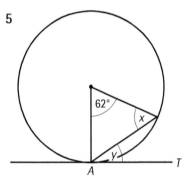

Find angles *x* and *y*.

6

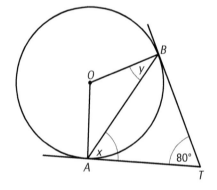

Find angles *x* and *y*.

18.2 Circle theorems

In this section you are going to see some important results about the relationship between angles in circles.

You are not required to prove any of the following results but it helps to remember them if you can see how they work.

Property 1

The angle at the centre is twice the angle at the circumference.

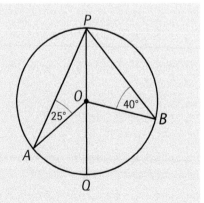

Let angle $OAP = 25°$

You could choose any value.

Then   Angle $OPA = 25°$ (isosceles triangle)
        Angle $AOP = 130°$ (angles in a triangle)
        Angle $AOQ = 50°$ (angles on a line)

Similarly if you start with $OBP = 40°$
you will find that angle $BOQ = 80°$

You could choose any value.

Angle at the centre $AOB = 50° + 80° = 130°$
Angle at the circumference $= 25° + 40° = 65°$

If you want to prove the result for all angles just start with x and y.

The diagram used above can appear in many different forms.
The result is true no matter which of these forms it takes.
Here are the ones you are likely to meet.

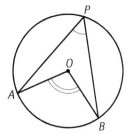 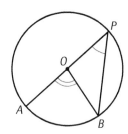 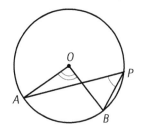 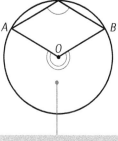

In all of these diagrams, angle $AOB = 2 \times$ angle APB

Notice that it is reflex angle AOB here.

Property 2

The angle in a semi-circle is a right angle.

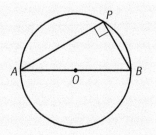

Note that AB is a diameter.

Angle $AOB = 180°$
so angle $APB = 90°$

 EXAMPLE 3

In the diagram, O is the centre of the circle.
Calculate the size of the angle marked x, giving reasons for your answer.

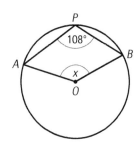

reflex angle $AOB = 216°$ (angle at centre = twice
                              angle at circumference)

$x = 360° - 216°$ (angles at a point)

$x = 144°$

EXAMPLE 4

In the diagram, O is the centre of the circle and AB is a diameter. Calculate the value of x, giving reasons for your answer.

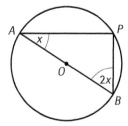

angle $APB = 90°$ (angle in a semi-circle)

$x + 2x + 90° = 180°$ (angle sum of triangle = 180°)

$$3x = 90°$$
$$x = 30°$$

EXAMPLE 5

In the diagram, O is the centre of the circle and TA and TB are tangents to the circle from T. Angle $ATB = 46°$.

Calculate the size of

(a) angle AOB **(b)** angle ACB

giving reasons for your answers.

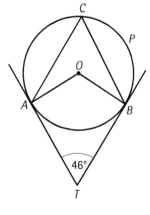

(a)   angle $TAO = 90°$ (tangent & radius meet at 90°)

           angle $TBO = 90°$ (tangent & radius meet at 90°)

           angle $AOB = 360° - 90° - 90° - 46°$

                    (angle sum of quadrilateral = 360°)

    so   angle $AOB = 134°$

(b)   angle $AOB = 2 \times$ angle ACB

                  (angle at centre = twice angle at circumference)

    so   angle $ACB = 134° \div 2$

               $= 67°$

EXERCISE 18B

1

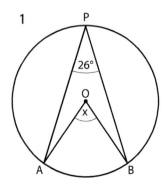

Find angle x.

2

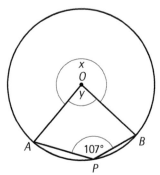

Find angle x.

3

Find angles x and y.

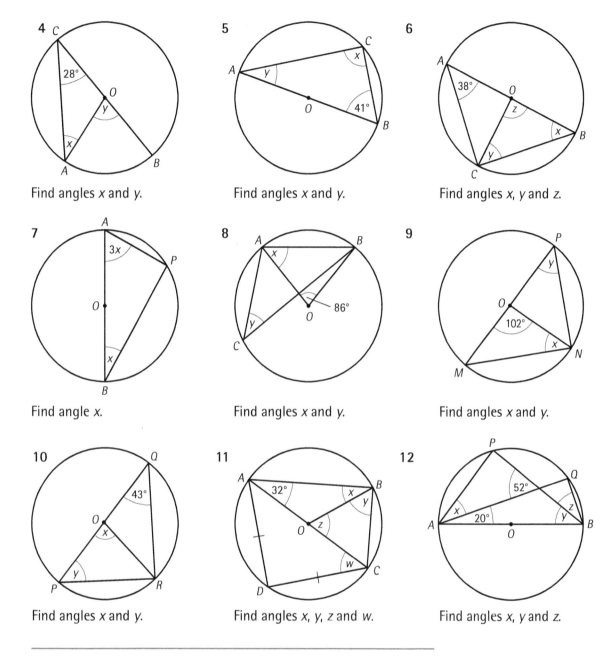

4 Find angles x and y.

5 Find angles x and y.

6 Find angles x, y and z.

7 Find angle x.

8 Find angles x and y.

9 Find angles x and y.

10 Find angles x and y.

11 Find angles x, y, z and w.

12 Find angles x, y and z.

In the two circle properties you have just met, the centre was important. The first result involved the angle at the centre of the circle and the second one involved a diameter.

The next two circle properties do not depend on the centre of the circle.

Remember that a segment is a part of a circle cut off by a chord. There is always a major segment and a minor segment.

This next property concerns angles in the *same* segment, which means that they must both lie on the same side of the chord.

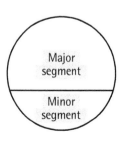

Major segment

Minor segment

Property 3

Angles in the same segment are equal.

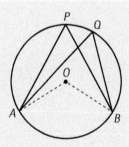

angle $AOB = 2 \times$ angle APB (angle at centre = twice angle at circumference)

angle $AOB = 2 \times$ angle AQB (angle at centre = twice angle at circumference)

angle $APB =$ angle AQB

The next property involves two words you may not know.
A **cyclic** quadrilateral is a quadrilateral whose four vertices (corners) lie on the circumference of a circle. Angles that are **supplementary** add up to 180°.

Notice that the chord does not need to be drawn. You can imagine where it would be and you can see that both angles APB and AQB are in the same segment.

A similar word to this is **complementary**, which means that angles add up to 90°.

Property 4

Opposite angles of a cyclic quadrilateral are supplementary.

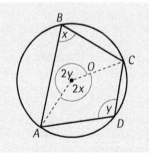

Let angle $ABC = x$ and angle $ADC = y$

angle $AOC = 2 \times$ angle ABC
(angle at centre = twice angle at circumference)

so angle $AOC = 2x$

reflex angle $AOC = 2 \times$ angle ADC
(angle at centre = twice angle at circumference)

so reflex angle $AOC = 2y$

but angle AOC and reflex angle AOC make up a complete circle (360°)

so $\qquad\qquad\qquad 2x + 2y = 360°$
which means that $\qquad\qquad x + y = 180°$

$\qquad$ angle $ABC +$ angle $ADC = 180°$

It is also true that the other opposite pair are supplementary, namely angle $BAD +$ angle $BCD = 180°$.

Notice that, as before, you are using results already proved to work out new results. You will see this many times.

Property 4 has a useful 'extra' result. Look at this diagram.

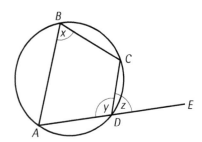

$x + y = 180°$ (shown above)
$y + z = 180°$ (angles on a straight line)
so $x = z$

Angle *CDE* is an *exterior* angle of the cyclic quadrilateral because it is formed by extending one of the sides. Angle *ABC* is the interior angle *opposite* to angle *CDE*, so …

An exterior angle of a cyclic quadrilateral is equal to the opposite interior angle.

Examples 6 and 7 use the four properties that you have seen above.

EXAMPLE 6

In the diagram angle QRT = 78° and angle PTS = 25°.

Calculate the size of

(a) angle PQS   (b) angle QPT,

giving reasons for your answers.

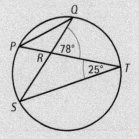

_____

(a)   angle PQS = 25° (angles in the same segment)

(b) angle QPT + angle PQS = 78° (exterior angle property △QPR)

    so   angle QPT = 53°

EXAMPLE 7

ABCD is a cyclic quadrilateral. Angle ADC = 100° and angle ACD = 33°.

Calculate the size of

(a) angle ABD   (b) angle DBC,

giving reasons for your answers.

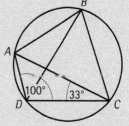

_____

(a)   angle ABD = angle ACD   (angles in the same segment)

    so   angle ABD = 33°

(b) angle ABC + angle ADC = 180° (opposite angles of cyclic quadrilateral)

    so   angle ABC = 80°

        angle DBC = angle ABC − angle ABD = 80° − 33°

    so   angle DBC = 47°

1

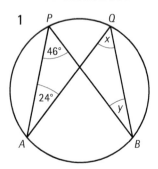

Find angles x and y.

2

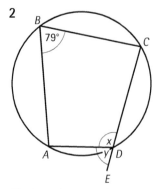

Find angles x and y.

3

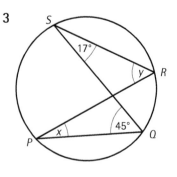

Find angles x and y.

4

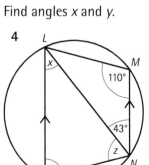

Find angles x, y and z.

5

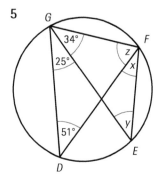

Find angles x, y and z.

6

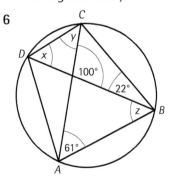

Find angles x, y and z.

7

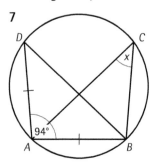

Find angle x.

8

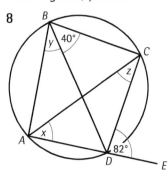

Find angles x, y and z.

9

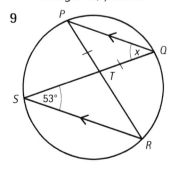

Find angle x.

10

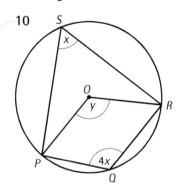

Find angles x and y.

11

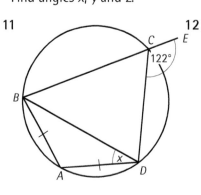

Find angle x.

12

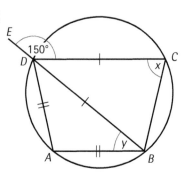

Find angles x and y.

Examples 8, 9 and 10 use all the theorems that you have learned so far.

 EXAMPLE 8

ABCD is a cyclic quadrilateral and O is the centre of the circle.
Angle AOC = 82°.

Calculate the size of

(a) angle ABC   (b) angle ADC,

giving reasons for your answers.

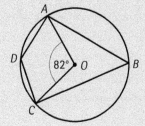

(a)   angle ABC = 41°   (angle at centre = twice angle at circumference)
(b)   angle ADC + angle ABC = 180°   (opposite angles of cyclic quadrilateral)
        so   angle ADC = 139°

 EXAMPLE 9

PQRS is a cyclic quadrilateral with exterior angle QPM = 112°.
The diagonals of the cyclic quadrilateral intersect at L.
Angle PSQ = 44° and angle QSR = 37°.

Calculate the size of

(a) angle QRS   (b) angle SQR   (c) angle PLS,

giving reasons for your answers.

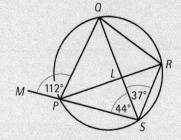

(a)   angle QRS = 112°   (exterior angle of cyclic quadrilateral = interior opposite angle)
(b)   angle SQR = 180° − 112° − 37°   (angle sum of △QRS)
      so angle SQR = 31°
(c)   angle LPS = angle SQR   (angles in the same segment)
      so angle LPS = 31°
              angle PLS = 180° − 31° − 44° (angle sum of △PLS)
      so angle PLS = 105°

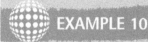
EXAMPLE 10

In the diagram, O is the centre of the circle, triangle DEG is isosceles with $DE = EG$ and angle $GEF = 18°$.

Calculate the sizes of the angles marked x, y and z, giving reasons for your answers.

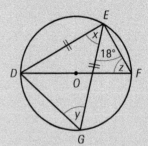

O is the centre of the circle so DF is a diameter,

so   angle $DEF = 90°$ (angle in a semi-circle)

which means that $x = 90° - 18° = 72°$

y is one of the base angles of isosceles triangle DEG

since $x = 72°$ then $y = (180° - 72°) \div 2 = 54°$

                 $z = y$ (angles in the same segment)

so $z = 54°$

Notice how, in all of these examples, each step follows logically from the previous step(s).

You can see that it is sometimes necessary to find angles other than those you are asked for ... they often form an important link in the thought process.

Always write a reason for each statement you make.

The next exercise uses all of the circle theorems you have learnt so far.

EXERCISE 18D

1

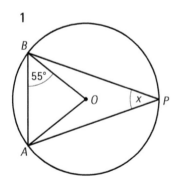

Find angle x.

2

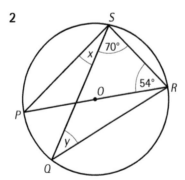

Find angles x and y.

3

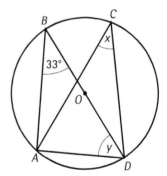

Find angles x and y.

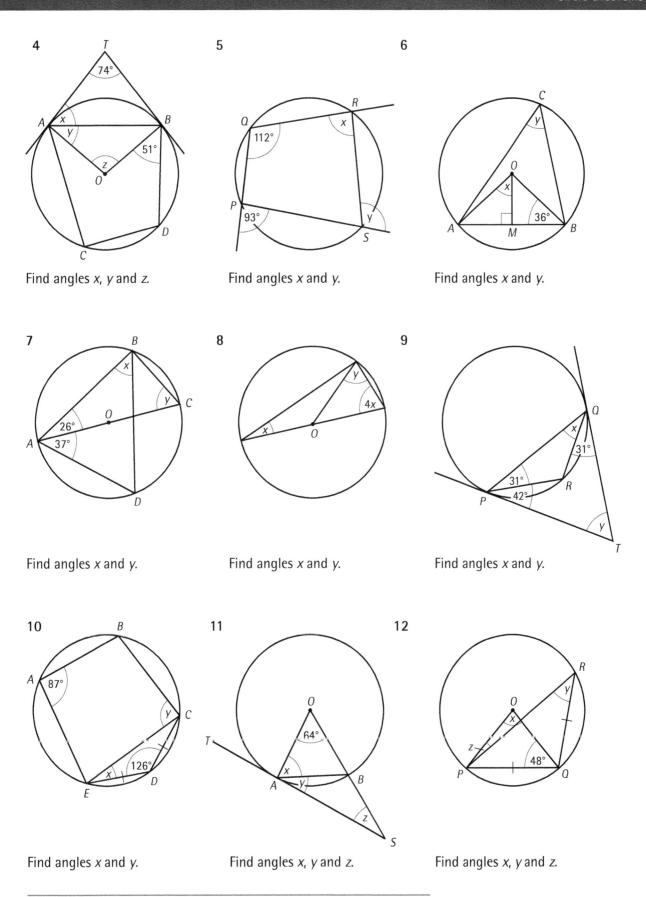

4

Find angles x, y and z.

5

Find angles x and y.

6

Find angles x and y.

7

Find angles x and y.

8

Find angles x and y.

9

Find angles x and y.

10

Find angles x and y.

11

Find angles x, y and z.

12

Find angles x, y and z.

18.3 Using circle properties and theorems

The next three examples revise all of the work in this chapter. The exercise that follows them tests your knowledge of all the circle properties and theorems.

EXAMPLE 11

In the diagram, O is the centre of the circle, TB is a tangent to the circle at B and angle $TBA = 58°$.

Calculate the size of angle AOB, giving reasons for your answer.

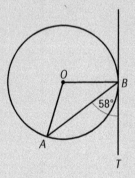

angle $OBA = 90° - 58° = 32°$
            (tangent & radius meet at 90°)

$OA = OB$ (radii) so $\triangle OAB$ is isosceles

so   angle $OAB = 32°$ (base angles of isosceles $\triangle OAB$)

angle $AOB = 180° - 32° - 32° = 116°$
            (angle sum of $\triangle OAB$)

EXAMPLE 12

In the diagram, O is the centre of the circle, reflex angle $ROQ = 206°$ and angle $PRO = 45°$.

Calculate the size of

(a) angle RPQ **(b)** angle OQP,

giving reasons for your answers.

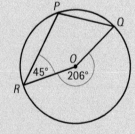

(a)   angle $RPQ = 103°$ (angle at centre = twice angle at circumference)

(b)   angle $ROQ = 360° - 206° = 154°$ (angles round a point)

angle $OQP = 360° - 154° - 45° - 103°$ (angles sum of quadrilateral = 360°)

so angle $OQP = 58°$

EXAMPLE 13

In the diagram, O is the centre of the circle and points A, B, C and D lie on the circumference. AC is a diameter and angle CAD = 71°.

Calculate the size of angle ABD, giving reasons for your answer.

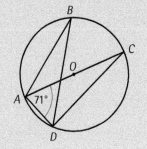

AC is a diameter so angle ADC = 90° (angle in a semi-circle)

angle ACD = 180° − 90° − 71° (angle sum of △ACD)

so   angle ACD = 19°

angle ABD = angle ACD = 19° (angles in the same segment)

 EXERCISE 18E

1

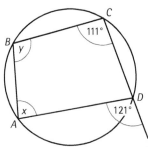

Find angles x and y.

2

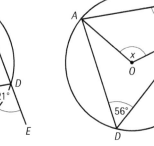

Find angles x and y.

3

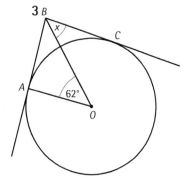

Find angle x.

4

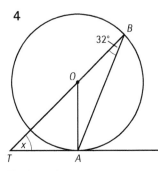

Find angle x.

5

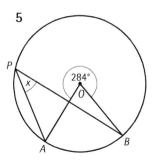

Find angle x.

6

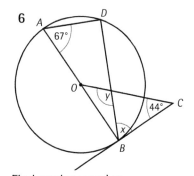

Find angles x and y.

7

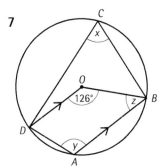

Find angles x, y and z.

1

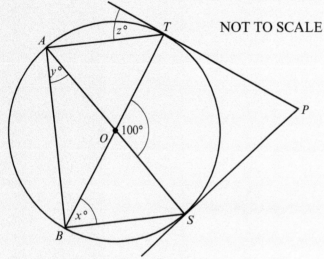

NOT TO SCALE

PT and *PS* are tangents to a circle centre *O*. *TOB* and *AOS* are diameters and angle *TOS* = 100°.

(a) Find the values of *x*, *y* and *z*. [3]

(b) Is *AS* parallel to *TP*? Give a reason for your answer. [1]

(CIE Paper 2, Jun 2000)

2

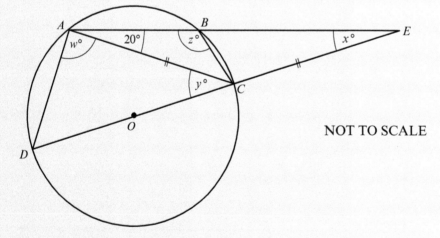

NOT TO SCALE

The centre of the circle *ABCD* is *O*.
ABE and *DOCE* are straight lines.
AC = *CE* and angle *BAC* = 20°.
Find the values of *w*, *x*, *y* and *z*. [4]

(CIE Paper 2, Jun 2001)

3

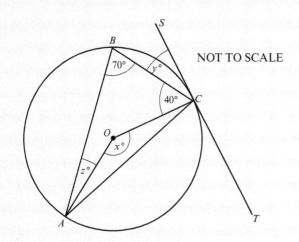

NOT TO SCALE

Circle *ABC* has centre *O*. The line *SCT* is a tangent.
Angle *ABC* = 70° and angle *OCB* = 40°.
Find *x*, *y* and *z*. [3]

(CIE Paper 2, Nov 2001)

4

NOT TO SCALE

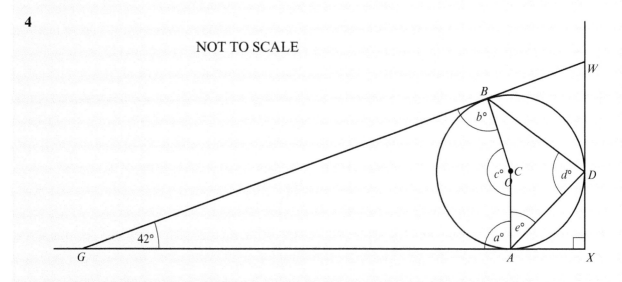

A sphere, centre *C*, rests on horizontal ground at *A* and touches a vertical wall at *D*.
A straight plank of wood, *GBW*, touches the sphere at *B*, rests on the ground
at *G* and against the wall at *W*.
Angle *WGX* = 42°.
Find *a*, *b*, *c*, *d*, and *e* marked on the diagram. [5]

(CIE Paper 4, Jun 2002)

5

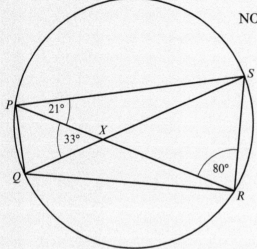

NOT TO SCALE

PQRS is a cyclic quadrilateral. The diagonals *PR* and *QS* intersect at *X*.
Angle *SPR* = 21°, angle *PRS* = 80° and angle *PXQ* = 33°.
Calculate
(a) angle *PQS*, [1]
(b) angle *QPR*, [1]
(c) angle *PSQ*. [1]

(CIE Paper 2, Nov 2002)

6

NOT TO SCALE

A, *B*, *C*, *D* and *E* lie on a circle, centre *O*. *AOC* is a diameter.
Find the value of
(a) *p*, [2]
(b) *q*. [2]

(CIE Paper 2, Jun 2003)

Chapter 19

Quadratic expressions and equations

This chapter will show you how to
- ✔ factorise quadratic expressions
- ✔ solve quadratic equations
- ✔ use the quadratic formula
- ✔ complete the square
- ✔ solve problems using quadratic equations

19.1 Factorising quadratic expressions

An expression of the form $ax^2 + bx + c$ where a, b and c are numbers, and $a \neq 0$, is called a **quadratic** expression in x.

> Remember that $\neq$ means 'is not equal to'.

For example

$$x^2 + 3x - 4, \qquad 3x^2 - 12, \qquad 2x^2 + 10x,$$

are all quadratics in x.

Difference of two squares

EXAMPLE 1

Expand **(a)** $(x + 9)(x - 9)$ **(b)** $(5n + 4)(5n - 4)$

(a) $(x + 9)(x - 9) = x^2 - 81 + 9x - 9x$

$\qquad\qquad\qquad\quad = x^2 - 81$

(b) $(5n + 4)(5n - 4) = 25n^2 - 16 + 20n - 20n$

$\qquad\qquad\qquad\qquad\quad = 25n^2 - 16$

> You could use
> F first
> O outside
> I inside
> L last
> You first met this in Chapter 7.

In general $\qquad (x + a)(x - a) = x^2 - a^2$

> This result is known as 'the difference of two squares'.

This means that any expression of the form $x^2 - a^2$ can be factorised into two factors that differ only in that the sign in one bracket is $+$ and in the other is $-$.

> Multiply out the brackets $(x + a)(x - a)$ to check.

EXAMPLE 2

Factorise these.
(a) $x^2 - 49$ (b) $9t^2 - y^2$

(a) $x^2 - 49 = x^2 - 7^2$
$$= (x + 7)(x - 7)$$
(b) $9t^2 - y^2 = (3t)^2 - y^2$
$$= (3t + y)(3t - y)$$

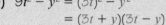

EXERCISE 19A

Factorise these.

(a) $x^2 - 4$ (b) $x^2 - 25$ (c) $x^2 - 64$

(d) $y^2 - 36$ (e) $n^2 - 100$ (f) $t^2 - 1$

(g) $a^2 - 121$ (h) $49 - x^2$ (i) $81 - x^2$

(j) $x^2 - y^2$ (k) $a^2 - b^2$ (l) $4x^2 - 81$

(m) $9x^2 - 16$ (n) $25x^2 - 4$ (o) $9x^2 - y^2$

(p) $16a^2 - b^2$ (q) $9x^2 - 25y^2$ (r) $36n^2 - 4m^2$

(s) $20p^2 - 45q^2$ (t) $75t^2 - 48w^2$

> Questions **(s)** and **(t)** need an extra step ... can you see what it is?

Factorising quadratics of the form $x^2 + bx + c$

To factorise a quadratic you need to write it as the product of two expressions.

> Factorising is the opposite process to expanding two brackets.

For example,
To factorise $x^2 + 6x + 8$ you are trying to find the two linear expressions which multiply together to give $x^2 + 6x + 8$.

$x \times x = x^2$ so the first term in each bracket is x
So $x^2 + 6x + 8 = (x + ?)(x + ?)$

×	x	?
x	x^2	?
?	?	8

Now you need to find the two numbers which multiply together to give 8 and which add together to give 6 (the two numbers with a product of 8 and a sum of 6).

$1 \times 8 = 8$, but $1 + 8 = 9$, so the two numbers are *not* 1 and 8.
$2 \times 4 = 8$, *and* $2 + 4 = 6$, so the two numbers are 2 and 4.
Check,

Check the factor pairs of 8.

×	x	2
x	x^2	$2x$
4	$4x$	8

$$(x + 4)(x + 2) = x^2 + 2x + 4x + 8$$
$$= x^2 + 6x + 8$$

So $x^2 + 6x + 8$ factorises to $(x + 4)(x + 2)$

EXAMPLE 3

Factorise these.

(a) $x^2 + 10x + 9$ (b) $a^2 + 4a - 5$ (c) $t^2 - 8t + 12$

(a) $x^2 + 10x + 9$

Remember you can use a grid to help.

$x \times x = x^2$ so the first term in each bracket is x

$(x + ?)(x + ?)$

×	x	?
x	x^2	?
?	?	9

$1 \times 9 = 9$ and $1 + 9 = 10$

Find two numbers that multiply to give 9 and add together to give 10. In this example all the terms in the quadratic are positive so both numbers you are looking for will be positive.

Check $(x + 1)(x + 9) = x^2 + 9x + x + 9$
$$= x^2 + 10x + 9 \checkmark$$

So the two numbers are 1 and 9.

$x^2 + 10x + 9 = (x + 1)(x + 9)$

(b) $a^2 + 4a - 5 = (a + ?)(a + ?)$

×	a	?
a	a^2	?
?	?	-5

$-1 \times 5 = -5$ and $-1 + 5 = 4$

$a^2 + 4a - 5 = (a - 1)(a + 5)$

Find two numbers that multiply to give -5 and add together to give 4. In this example the numbers you are looking for must multiply to give -5, so one will be negative and the other positive. They could be -1 and 5 or they could be 1 and -5. $-1 + 5 = 4$, so the two numbers are -1 and 5.

Check by multiplying out the brackets.

(c) $t^2 - 8t + 12$

×	t	?
t	t^2	?
?	?	12

$-2 \times -6 = 12$ and $-2 + -6 = -8$

so $t^2 - 8t + 12 = (t - 2)(t - 6)$

$-ve \times -ve = +ve$ so in this example the two numbers are both negative because they must multiply to give $+12$ but add together to give -8.

Check by multiplying out the brackets.

EXERCISE 19B

Factorise these.

1. (a) $a^2 + 10a + 9$ (b) $x^2 + 4x + 3$ (c) $n^2 + 8n + 7$
   (d) $x^2 + 8x + 15$ (e) $y^2 + 6y + 8$ (f) $p^2 + 7p + 12$

2. (a) $x^2 + 4x - 5$ (b) $k^2 + 2k - 3$ (c) $r^2 + 7r - 8$
   (d) $z^2 + 4z - 12$ (e) $d^2 + 3d - 10$ (f) $x^2 + x - 6$

3. (a) $b^2 - 4b - 5$ (b) $x^2 - 6x - 7$ (c) $g^2 - 9g - 10$
   (d) $m^2 - 3m - 10$ (e) $t^2 - 2t - 8$ (f) $f^2 - f - 12$

4. (a) $q^2 - 7q + 12$ (b) $y^2 - 8y + 15$ (c) $x^2 - 11x + 24$
   (d) $a^2 - 12a + 11$ (e) $x^2 - 10x + 16$ (f) $h^2 - 6h + 9$

5. (a) $t^2 + 5t - 14$ (b) $z^2 - 7z - 18$ (c) $p^2 + 9p + 20$
   (d) $d^2 - 5d - 36$ (e) $n^2 + 23n - 24$ (f) $x^2 - x - 20$

Factorising quadratics of the form $ax^2 + bx + c$

In the expression $ax^2 + bx + c$, a is known as the **coefficient** of x^2, b is the coefficient of x, and c is the constant term.

> To factorise an expression like this, first consider the factors of the coefficient of x^2.

For example,
Factorise $2x^2 + 7x + 6$.
The coefficient of x^2 is 2 and the factors of 2 are 2 and 1, so the first terms in the brackets are $2x$ and x, because $2x \times x = 2x^2$.

2 is a prime number so only has factors of 2 and 1.

Remember $x = 1x$.

×	x	?
$2x$	$2x^2$	?
?	?	6

Now you need to find the two numbers with a product of 6 which you can combine with $2x$ and $1x$ to give $7x$.

$1 \times 6 = 6$, but $1 \times 2x + 6 \times 1x = 10x$, and $6 \times 2x + 1x \times 1 = 13x$
         so the numbers are *not* 1 and 6.

$2 \times 3 = 6$, and $2 \times 2x + 3 \times x = 7x$ which is correct.

List the factors of 6 first and try them in different ways to see which combination gives $+7x$.

Check,

×	x	2
$2x$	$2x^2$	$4x$
3	$3x$	6

$(2x + 3)(x + 2) = 2x^2 + 4x + 3x + 6$
$ = 2x^2 + 7x + 6$

So $2x^2 + 7x + 6$ factorises to $(2x + 3)(x + 2)$.

The questions in the next example show you what to do when the number of possible combinations increases. The method is the same as in the example above but there is more work to do to arrive at the correct combination.

 **EXAMPLE 4**

Factorise these.

(a) $3x^2 - 2x - 8$ **(b)** $6x^2 + 11x + 4$ **(c)** $10x^2 + 34x - 24$

(a) $3x^2 - 2x - 8$

The coefficient of x^2 is 3 (which is prime).

×	x	?
$3x$	$3x^2$	?
?	?	-8

$3x^2 - 2x - 8 = (3x + ?)(x + ?)$
$1 \times 8 = 8$ or $2 \times 4 = 8$

$3x \times 1 + 1x \times -8 = -5x$
$3x \times -8 + 1x \times 1 = -23x$

$3x \times -1 + 1x \times 8 = +5x$
$3x \times 8 + 1x \times -1 = +23x$

$3x \times 2 + 1x \times -4 = +2x$
$3x \times -4 + 1x \times 2 = -10x$

$3x \times -2 + 1x \times 4 = -2x$
$3x \times 4 + 1x \times -2 = +10x$

×	x	-2
$3x$	$3x^2$	$-6x$
$+4$	$+4x$	-8

So $3x^2 - 2x - 8 = (3x + 4)(x - 2)$

(b) $6x^2 + 11x + 4$

The coefficient of x^2 is 6. $6 \times 1 = 6$ and $3 \times 2 = 6$

×	x	?
$6x$	$6x^2$	?
?	?	4

or

×	$2x$	?
$3x$	$6x^2$	?
?	?	4

$(6x + ?)(x + ?)$ or $(3x + ?)(2x + ?)$

$1 \times 4 = 4$ and $2 \times 2 = 4$

$3x \times 1 + 2x \times 4 = 11x$ ✓

×	$2x$	1
$3x$	$6x^2$	$3x$
4	$8x$	4

So $6x^2 + 11x + 4 = (3x + 4)(2x + 1)$

continued ▼

$3 \times 1 = 3$

The number term is negative so one of the numbers you are looking for will be positive and the other will be negative.

Try different combinations until you find which will give $-2x$.

You can see that there are quite a lot of combinations but notice that swapping the signs round in any one only changes the sign of the answer, not the amount of x's.

Check by expanding the brackets.

In this example all the terms in the quadratic are positive so both numbers you are looking for will be positive.

At this stage you cannot tell which of these is correct.

You need to find which of 1 and 4 or 2 and 2 combines with either $6x$ and $1x$, or $3x$ and $2x$, to give $11x$. You will get better at this the more you practise!

You should always check by multiplying out the brackets.

(c) $10x^2 + 34x - 24 = 2(5x^2 + 17x - 12)$

The coefficient of x^2 is 5, which is prime,

so $5x^2 + 17x - 12 = (5x + ?)(x + ?)$

The number term is 12 so possible products are

$1 \times 12 = 12 \quad 2 \times 6 = 12 \quad 3 \times 4 = 12$

Some possibilities are

$5x \times -1 + 1x \times 12 = 7x$ not correct

$5x \times 2 + 1x \times -6 = 4x$ not correct

$5x \times -3 + 1x \times 4 = -11x$ not correct

... and so on ...

$5x \times 4 + 1x \times -3 = 17x$ ✓

×	x	4
$5x$	$5x^2$	$20x$
-3	$-3x$	-12

So $5x^2 + 17x - 12 = (5x - 3)(x + 4)$

So $10x^2 + 34x - 24 = 2(5x^2 + 17x - 12) = 2(5x - 3)(x + 4)$

Notice that the **first** step is to remove a common factor. Always look for this, it makes factorising easier. Now factorise $5x^2 + 17x - 12$

You need to find which of 1 and 12, 2 and 6, or 3 and 4, combine with 5 and 1 to give $+17$, the x coefficient.

Remember that the number term is negative so one of the numbers you are looking for will be positive and the other will be negative.

Remember to check by expanding the brackets.

Don't forget the factor of 2 at the beginning of the final answer.

Look at Example 3(a) again

$3x^2 - 2x - 8 = (3x + 4)(x - 2)$

The	First terms in each bracket	multiply to give $3x^2$,
the	Outside pair of terms	multiply to give $-6x$,
the	Inside pair of terms	multiply to give $+4x$,
the	Last terms in each bracket	multiply to give -8

You can use FOIL to check that your factorising is correct. It acts in the same way as putting the terms into a grid because it generates all four terms of the expansion.

EXERCISE 19C

Factorise these.

(a) $2x^2 + 5x + 3$ (b) $3x^2 + 16x + 5$ (c) $2x^2 + 3x + 1$

(d) $3t^2 + 5t + 2$ (e) $4y^2 + 8y + 3$ (f) $4x^2 + 23x + 15$

(g) $4x^2 + 17x + 15$ (h) $6a^2 + 25a + 4$ (i) $2x^2 + 5x - 3$

(j) $3x^2 + x - 2$ (k) $2x^2 - 9x - 5$ (l) $4x^2 - 4x - 3$

(m) $2x^2 - 3x + 1$ (n) $3x^2 - 11x + 10$ (o) $8x^2 - 18x + 9$

(p) $4x^2 - 26x - 14$ (q) $6x^2 + 21x - 90$ (r) $6x^2 + 32x - 24$

(s) $12x^2 - 34x + 24$ (t) $24x^2 - 30x - 21$

19.2 Solving quadratic equations

When a quadratic expression forms part of an equation, the equation is called a **quadratic equation**.

Here are three examples of quadratic equations.

$$x^2 + 3x - 4 = 0 \qquad 3x^2 = 12 \qquad x^2 + 5x = 0$$

You can use different methods to solve, or find the **roots** of, quadratic equations.

Solving quadratic equations by rearranging

Some quadratic equations can be solved by rearranging the terms.

A quadratic equation may have 0, 1 or 2 solutions.

EXAMPLE 5

Solve these equations.

(a) $3x^2 = 12$

(b) $2t^2 - 72 = 0$

(c) $2(x - 3)^2 - 50 = 0$

(a) $3x^2 = 12$

$x^2 = 4$

$x = \pm\sqrt{4}$

$x = \pm2$

You must remember the negative square root as well as the positive one. Read ±2 as 'positive or negative 2', or 'plus or minus 2'.

(b) $2t^2 - 72 = 0$

$2t^2 = 72$

$t^2 = 36$

$t = \pm6$

Or you could divide throughout by the common factor of 2 as a first step.

(c) $2(x - 3)^2 - 50 = 0$

$2(x - 3)^2 = 50$

$(x - 3)^2 = 25$

$x - 3 = \pm5$

$x = 3 \pm 5$

$x = 3 + 5 \quad \text{or} \quad x = 3 - 5$

$= 8 \qquad\qquad = -2$

so the two solutions are $x = 8$ or $x = -2$

Solutions are sometimes referred to as roots ... you can use either word.

1 Solve these equations.
   (a) $t^2 = 9$ (b) $3x^2 = 75$
   (c) $5y^2 = 80$ (d) $z^2 - 49 = 0$
   (e) $2a^2 - 32 = 0$ (f) $4x^2 - 16 = 0$
   (g) $(x - 2)^2 = 25$ (h) $(y - 1)^2 = 36$
   (i) $2(x + 2)^2 = 18$ (j) $3(x - 5)^2 - 48 = 0$
   (k) $2(t + 3)^2 - 50 = 0$

2 Solve these quadratic equations, giving your answers to 2 d.p.
   (a) $2(x - 1)^2 = 6$ (b) $3(x - 4)^2 = 15$
   (c) $5(x + 1)^2 - 10 = 0$ (d) $4(x + 3)^2 - 32 = 0$

3 What problem arises if you try to solve $3(x - 2)^2 + 27 = 0$?

> This is an example of a quadratic equation that has no solutions. You will meet these again later.

Solving quadratic equations by factorising

Some quadratic equations can be solved by factorising.
First rearrange the equation so that all the terms are on one side and are equated to zero.

Then, factorise the quadratic expression using the methods in Section 19.1

Before looking at an example, consider this

   If $A \times B = 0$ then either $A = 0$ or $B = 0$

> The product of two terms can only be zero if either one or the other (or both) of the terms is zero.

This is a key statement in the solution of quadratic equations.
Examples 6, 7 and 8 all use this fact and show you how to set out your work when solving quadratic equations.

 EXAMPLE 6

Solve these equations.
(a) $x^2 + 5x = 0$ (b) $x^2 = 7x$

(a) $x^2 + 5x = 0$
   $x(x + 5) = 0$
   $x = 0$ or $x + 5 = 0$
                      $x = -5$

The equation has two solutions
   $x = 0$ or $x = -5$

> Don't divide both terms by x because x could be 0 and you would lose the $x = 0$ solution.

> If the product of two numbers is 0 then one of the numbers must be 0.
> So if $x \times (x + 5) = 0$ then either $x = 0$ or $x + 5 = 0$.

continued ▼

(b) $\qquad x^2 = 7x$

$x^2 - 7x = 0$ ————————————— First rearrange the equation so that all the terms are on one side.

$x(x - 7) = 0$ ————————————— Now factorise.

$\qquad x = 0 \quad \text{or} \quad x - 7 = 0$

$\qquad\qquad\qquad\qquad x = 7$

The two solutions are $x = 0$ or $x = 7$

 EXAMPLE 7

Solve these equations.

(a) $x^2 + 10x + 9 = 0$ **(b)** $x^2 - 6x + 9 = 0$ **(c)** $x^2 = 4x + 21$

(a) $x^2 + 10x + 9 = 0$ ————————————— All the terms are on one side of the equation already, so factorise this side.
If the product of two numbers is 0 then one of the numbers must be 0.

$(x + 1)(x + 9) = 0$

$\qquad x + 1 = 0 \quad \text{or} \quad x + 9 = 0$

$\qquad\qquad x = -1 \quad \text{or} \quad x = -9$

The two solutions are $x = -1$ or $x = -9$

(b) $\quad x^2 - 6x + 9 = 0$

$(x - 3)(x - 3) = 0$ ————————————— This equation has only one solution, $x = 3$.
This is sometimes called a repeated solution or a repeated root.

$\qquad x - 3 = 0 \quad \text{or} \quad x - 3 = 0$

$\qquad\qquad x = 3 \qquad\qquad x = 3$

(c) $\qquad\qquad x^2 = 4x + 21$

$x^2 - 4x - 21 = 0$ ————————————— First rearrange the equation so that all the terms are on one side. Then factorise.

$(x + 3)(x - 7) = 0$

$\qquad x + 3 = 0 \quad \text{or} \quad x - 7 = 0$

$\qquad\qquad x = -3 \qquad\qquad x = 7$

The two solutions are $x = -3$ or $x = 7$

Remember, always set out your work as in these examples.

The steps are   **1**   Rearrange (equation = 0).

                 2   Factorise the quadratic expression.

                 3   Use 'either/or' to find the two solutions.

 EXERCISE 19E

Solve these quadratic equations.

1   **(a)** $t^2 + 5t = 0$ **(b)** $x^2 + 6x = 0$ **(c)** $n^2 - 9n = 0$

    (d) $x^2 - 8x = 0$ **(e)** $z^2 = 2z$ **(f)** $a^2 - 10a = 0$

    (g) $b^2 = 7b$ **(h)** $y^2 + y = 0$ **(i)** $x^2 = x$

2 (a) $b^2 + 10b + 9 = 0$ (b) $x^2 + 5x + 4 = 0$

  (c) $m^2 + m - 2 = 0$ (d) $t^2 - 8t + 12 = 0$

  (e) $x^2 + 2x - 15 = 0$ (f) $y^2 - 12y + 36 = 0$

  (g) $z^2 - 2z - 24 = 0$ (h) $a^2 - 5a - 14 = 0$

  (i) $x^2 + 11x + 30 = 0$ (j) $x^2 + 14x + 49 = 0$

3 (a) $x^2 = 5x + 6$ (b) $x^2 - 12 = x$ (c) $x^2 + 4 = 4x$

  (d) $x^2 + 3x = 10$ (e) $x^2 = 5x - 6$ (f) $18x = x^2 + 81$

  (g) $30 - x = x^2$ (h) $x^2 = 24 - 5x$ (i) $15x - 54 = x^2$

> Remember to rearrange the equations so that all the terms are on one side.

All of the questions in Exercise 19E have a squared term whose coefficient is 1. This means that factorising the quadratic expression is usually straightforward.

The next examples (and almost all of the questions in Exercise 19F) have a squared term whose coefficient is not 1. This means that the factorising is more difficult.

> Look back at Example 3 if you need help with factorising expressions of the form $ax^2 + bx + c$.

EXAMPLE 8

Solve the equations.

(a) $3x^2 - x = 0$ (b) $2x^2 + x - 6 = 0$

(a) $3x^2 - x = 0$

     $x(3x - 1) = 0$

         $x = 0$ or $3x - 1 = 0$

                     $3x = 1$

                     $x = \frac{1}{3}$

The two solutions are $x = 0$ or $x = \frac{1}{3}$

> These two terms have a common factor of x.

(b) $2x^2 + x - 6 = 0$

     $(2x - 3)(x + 2) = 0$

         $2x - 3 = 0$ or $x + 2 = 0$

            $2x = 3$ $x = -2$

            $x = \frac{3}{2}$

The two solutions are $x = \frac{3}{2}$ $(1\frac{1}{2})$ or $x = -2$

EXERCISE 19F

Solve these quadratic equations.

1 (a) $2t^2 - t = 0$ (b) $3x^2 + 2x = 0$ (c) $2y^2 - 5y = 0$

  (d) $3n^2 = n$ (e) $3z^2 = 5z$ (f) $5a^2 + 3a = 0$

2 (a) $2x^2 + 7x + 3 = 0$ (b) $2x^2 + 3x - 2 = 0$

   (c) $3x^2 - 8x - 3 = 0$ (d) $3a^2 + 10a - 8 = 0$

   (e) $2y^2 - y - 10 = 0$ (f) $4k^2 + 8k + 3 = 0$

   (g) $4z^2 + 7z - 2 = 0$ (h) $3d^2 - 14d + 8 = 0$

   (i) $6r^2 + 7r - 3 = 0$ (j) $4p^2 + 4p + 1 = 0$

3 (a) $3x^2 + 5x = 2$ (b) $3x^2 = 10x - 3$

   (c) $2x^2 = 3 - 5x$ (d) $(x + 1)(x - 2) = 10$

   (e) $(2x - 3)^2 = 8 - 8x$ (f) $2x = 35 - x^2$

   (g) $2 - x - 6x^2 = 0$ (h) $12x^2 = 16x + 3$

> Remember to rearrange the equations so that all the terms are on one side.

Using the quadratic formula

You can solve a quadratic equation by factorisation if it has simple factors. For many quadratics this is not the case.

For example
$x^2 + 2x - 5$ does not have simple factors (try factorising it!).
So you cannot solve the equation $x^2 + 2x - 5 = 0$ by factorisation.

One way to solve a quadratic equation that does have solutions is to use the **quadratic formula**.

> The solutions of the quadratic equation $ax^2 + bx + c = 0$, where $a \neq 0$, are given by the formula
> $$x = \frac{-b \pm \sqrt{b^2 - 4ac}}{2a}$$

> This formula can always be used to solve a quadratic equation, even when the quadratic factorises. You need to remember the formula (it will not be given on your exam paper).

 EXAMPLE 9

Solve the equation $x^2 + 2x - 5 = 0$
Give your solutions to 2 d.p.

$x^2 + 2x - 5 = 0$

$a = 1, \quad b = 2, \quad c = -5$

$x = \dfrac{-b \pm \sqrt{b^2 - 4ac}}{2a}$

$= \dfrac{-2 \pm \sqrt{2^2 - 4 \times 1 \times (-5)}}{2a}$

$= \dfrac{-2 \pm \sqrt{4 - -20}}{2}$

$= \dfrac{-2 \pm \sqrt{4 + 20}}{2}$

$= \dfrac{-2 \pm \sqrt{24}}{2}$

$x = \dfrac{-2 + \sqrt{24}}{2}$ or $x = \dfrac{-2 - \sqrt{24}}{2}$

$x = 1.45$ or $x = -3.45$ (2 d.p.)

> It is a good idea to start by writing down the values of a, b, and c.

> Substitute the values of a, b, and c into the quadratic formula.

EXERCISE 19G

1 Use the quadratic formula to solve the following equations. Give your answers to 2 d.p.

(a) $x^2 + 3x + 1 = 0$

(b) $x^2 + 5x + 2 = 0$

(c) $x^2 + 4x - 3 = 0$

(d) $d^2 - 2d - 5 = 0$

(e) $y^2 - y - 8 = 0$

(f) $k^2 - 8k + 6 = 0$

(g) $2x^2 + 7x - 3 = 0$

(h) $2x^2 - 9x + 8 = 0$

(i) $3x^2 + 5x - 1 = 0$

(j) $4p^2 + 7p - 5 = 0$

(k) $5y^2 - 2y - 5 = 0$

(l) $4t^2 + 9t + 1 = 0$

(m) $3z^2 + 5z - 1 = 0$

(n) $6p^2 - 7p - 2 = 0$

> If an exam question asks for the solutions to a quadratic equation to a certain number of decimal places or significant figures it is no use trying to factorise ... it will be impossible to do so.

2 (a) Solve the equation $6p^2 + 7p - 3 = 0$, using the quadratic formula.

(b) How can you tell from your working and answers that you did not need to use the quadratic formula?

3 (a) Try to solve the equation $3x^2 + 5x + 4 = 0$, using the quadratic formula.

(b) What prevents you from being able to find the solutions?

The discriminant

The part of the quadratic formula underneath the square root sign is called the **discriminant**.

- If $b^2 - 4ac$ is a square number then the quadratic will factorise.

- If $b^2 - 4ac > 0$ there are two distinct solutions of the quadratic equation.

- If $b^2 - 4ac = 0$ there is one solution (it is a repeated root as in Example 7(b)).

- If $b^2 - 4ac < 0$ there are no solutions because you cannot find the square root of a negative number.

Graphically the last three cases can be shown as

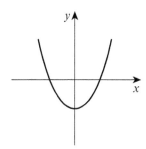

$b^2 - 4ac > 0$
Two solutions, so two points where the quadratic graph crosses the x-axis.

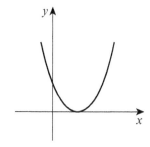

$b^2 - 4ac = 0$
One solution, so the quadratic graph touches the x-axis.

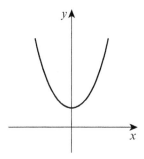

$b^2 - 4ac < 0$
No solutions, so the quadratic graph never crosses the x-axis.

EXERCISE 19H

State whether these quadratic equations will have two, one, or zero solutions.

Consider the discriminant.

(a) $x^2 - 5x + 6 = 0$

(b) $x^2 + 3x - 7 = 0$

(c) $x^2 + 2x + 4 = 0$

(d) $x^2 - 6x + 9 = 0$

(e) $2x^2 + x - 3 = 0$

(f) $3x^2 - 2x + 1 = 0$

(g) $4x^2 - 3x - 4 = 0$

(h) $6x^2 + 5 = 10x$

(i) $2x^2 = 7x - 5$

(j) $4x = 12 - \dfrac{9}{x}$

You need to rewrite questions (h), (i) and (j).

Completing the square

There is another way to solve quadratic equations that cannot be factorised easily. You rewrite the equation in a way that is known as **completing the square**.

In the examination you will be able to choose whether to use the formula or complete the square.

When you complete the square on a quadratic you are going to change it into the form $(x + p)^2 + q$ where p and q are numbers.

To carry out this method, we are going to make use of the fact that

$$(x + b)^2 \equiv x^2 + 2bx + b^2$$

$\equiv$ means 'is identical to'.

It follows that

$$(x + b)^2 - b^2 \equiv x^2 + 2bx$$

Subtract b^2 from both sides.

Then

$$(x + b)^2 - b^2 + c \equiv x^2 + 2bx + c$$

Add c to both sides.

In reverse this reads $x^2 + 2bx + c \equiv (x + b)^2 - b^2 + c$

So if we have

$$x^2 + 8x + 6 \equiv x^2 + 2bx + c$$

$$x^2 + 8x + 6 \equiv (x + 4)^2 - 4^2 + 6 \equiv (x + 4)^2 - 10$$

Note the $+$ sign remains.

Half of the x coefficient.

Always **subtract** the square of the number in the bracket.

we will have completed the square.

The same method will work for $x^2 - 2bx + c$

This will become $(x - b)^2 - b^2 + c$

so that

$$x^2 - 6x + 1 \equiv (x - 3)^2 - 3^2 + 1 \equiv (x - 3)^2 - 8$$

Note the $-$ sign remains.

Half of the x coefficient.

Always **subtract** the square of the number in the bracket.

EXAMPLE 10

Write the expression $x^2 + 8x + 10$ in completed square form.

Half the coefficient of x

Subtract 4^2

$$x^2 + 8x + 10 = (x + 4)^2 - 4^2 + 10$$

Put in the original number term.

$$= (x + 4)^2 - 16 + 10$$

$$= (x + 4)^2 - 6$$

EXAMPLE 11

Find the values of p and q such that $x^2 - 6x + 2 = (x - p)^2 + q$

Half the coefficient of x

Subtract 3^2

$$x^2 - 6x + 2 = (x - 3)^2 - 3^2 + 2$$

Put in the original number term.

$$= (x - 3)^2 - 9 + 2$$

$$= (x - 3)^2 - 7$$

So $p = 3, q = -7$

Some quadratics can be a little more difficult but the process always works, if the coefficient of x^2 is 1.

 EXAMPLE 12

Write the expression $x^2 + 5x - 4$ in completed square form.

$x^2 + 5x - 4 \equiv (x + 2.5)^2 - 2.5^2 - 4 \equiv (x + 2.5)^2 - 10.25$

 EXERCISE 19I

1 Complete the square for the following quadratics.
   (a) $x^2 + 10x + 5$ (b) $x^2 + 4x - 2$
   (c) $x^2 - 12x + 20$ (d) $y^2 + 2y + 9$
   (e) $x^2 - 3x - 1$ (f) $y^2 + 5y + 7$
   (g) $x^2 - x - 3$ (h) $x^2 - x + 3$
   (i) $x^2 + 12x$ (j) $x^2 - 5x$

2 Write each of the following expressions in the form $(x + p)^2 + q$
   (a) $x^2 + 10x + 5$ (b) $x^2 + 5x - 3$
   (c) $x^2 + 16x - 7$ (d) $x^2 - 3x + 2$

You can now start to solve equations with this method.

 EXAMPLE 13

Solve the equation $x^2 + 10x + 11 = 0$ by completing the square. Give your answers correct to 2 decimal places.

(a) $x^2 + 10x + 11 = 0$

$(x + 5)^2 - 25 + 11 = 0$

$(x + 5)^2 - 14 = 0$

$(x + 5)^2 = 14$

$x + 5 = \pm\sqrt{14}$

$x = -5 \pm \sqrt{14}$

so $x = -5 + \sqrt{14}$ or $x = -5 - \sqrt{14}$

$x = -1.26$ $x = -8.74$ (to 2 d.p.)

Start by completing the square on the left hand side.

Now solve the equation by rearranging.

Don't forget both the positive and negative square root.

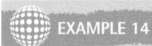 **EXAMPLE 14**

Solve $2x^2 + 6x - 5 = 0$

Equation becomes

$x^2 + 3x - 2.5 = 0$

completing the square

$(x + 1.5)^2 - 1.5^2 - 2.5 = 0$

$(x + 1.5)^2 - 4.75 = 0$

$(x + 1.5)^2 = 4.75$

$x + 1.5 = \pm\sqrt{4.75}$

$x = -1.5 \pm\sqrt{4.75}$

$x = 3.68 \text{ or } 0.679 \text{ (3 s.f.)}$

If the coefficient of x^2 is not 1, you must divide through your equation so that it becomes 1.

EXERCISE 19J

1 Solve these equations by completing the square.
   Give your answers correct to 2 decimal places.
   (a) $x^2 + 8x + 5 = 0$ (b) $x^2 - 10x + 3 = 0$
   (c) $y^2 + 12y - 3 = 0$ (d) $x^2 - 4x - 2 = 0$
   (e) $x^2 - 16x - 4 = 0$ (f) $z^2 + 6z + 7 = 0$
   (g) $y^2 - 5y + 2 = 0$ (h) $x^2 + 3x - 5 = 0$

2 Solve these equations by completing the square.
   (a) $x^2 + 4x + 1 = 0$ (b) $x^2 - 12x + 16 = 0$
   (c) $x^2 - 8x - 6 = 0$ (d) $x^2 + 6x - 1 = 0$
   (e) $x^2 - 2x - 4 = 0$ (f) $x^2 + 8x + 2 = 0$

When no accuracy is specified you must use 3 s.f.

3 Solve these equations by completing the square.
   Give your answers correct to 2 decimal places.
   (a) $x^2 + 4 = 6x$ (b) $x^2 = 10x - 5$
   (c) $x^2 + 10x = 2x - 6$ (d) $8x = 2 - x^2$
   (e) $2x^2 - 3 = x^2 + 6x$ (f) $2x^2 + 4x = x^2 + x + 1$

Remember to rearrange the equations so that all the terms are on one side.

19.3 Applications of quadratic equations

The theory of quadratic equations can be applied to problems.

These questions are typical of questions you can expect on your exam paper.

 EXAMPLE 15

I think of a number, square it then subtract four times the number. The answer is 77. Find the two possible values of the original number, showing all your working.

Let the original number be x.

Squaring gives x^2,

then subtract four times the number to give a final expression of $x^2 - 4x$

So
$$x^2 - 4x = 77$$
$$x^2 - 4x - 77 = 0$$
$$(x + 7)(x - 11) = 0$$

Either $\quad x + 7 = 0$, giving $x = -7$

or $\quad x - 11 = 0$, giving $x = 11$

So the two possible values of the original number are -7 and 11.

> Set up the quadratic equation, reading the question carefully.

> Solve the quadratic equation by rearranging and factorising.

> Remember to state the answer to the question you were asked.

 EXAMPLE 16

The diagram shows a right-angled triangle with sides of lengths $(2x - 1)$ cm, $(x + 4)$ cm and 15 cm.

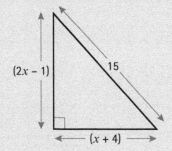

Calculate the lengths of the sides of the triangle.
Give your answers correct to 2 decimal places.

continued ▼

Using Pythagoras' theorem

$$(x + 4)^2 + (2x - 1)^2 = 15^2$$

$$x^2 + 8x + 16 + 4x^2 - 4x + 1 = 225$$

$$5x^2 + 4x - 208 = 0$$

$$x = \frac{-b \pm \sqrt{b^2 - 4ac}}{2a}$$

$a = 5, b = 4$ and $c = -208$

$$x = \frac{-4 \pm \sqrt{4^2 - 4 \times 5 \times (208)}}{2 \times 5}$$

$$x = \frac{-4 \pm \sqrt{16 - -4160}}{10}$$

$$x = \frac{-4 \pm \sqrt{16 + 4160}}{10}$$

$$x = \frac{-4 \pm \sqrt{4176}}{10}$$

$$x = \frac{-4 + \sqrt{4176}}{10} \text{ or } x = \frac{-4 - \sqrt{4176}}{10}$$

giving $x = 6.062$ and $x = -6.862$ (4 s.f.)

x cannot be -6.862 as this would give negative lengths.

So $x = 6.06$ and the lengths of the sides of the triangle are 10.1 cm, 11.1 cm and 15 cm.

Using Pythagoras to set up the equation is straightforward, as long as you remember to expand the brackets correctly.

Simplify.

Since the question asked for answers correct to 2 d.p. you know the formula will be needed. Take care when substituting the values of a, b and c.

Explain why the negative solution is discounted.

Always answer the question you were asked with a final statement.

 EXAMPLE 17

Find the points of intersection of the quadratic graph $y = 3x^2 - x - 4$ and the straight line $y = 6 - 2x$.

Points of intersection are given by the equation

$$3x^2 - x - 4 = 6 - 2x$$

$$3x^2 + x - 10 = 0$$

$$(3x - 5)(x + 2) = 0$$

Either $\quad 3x - 5 = 0 \rightarrow 3x = 5 \rightarrow x = \frac{5}{3} = 1\frac{2}{3}$

or $\quad\quad x + 2 = 0 \rightarrow x = -2$

When $\quad x = 1\frac{2}{3}, y = 6 - 2(1\frac{2}{3}) = 2\frac{2}{3}$

and when $\quad\quad x = -2, y = 6 - 2(-2) = 10$

So the points of intersection are $(1\frac{2}{3}, 2\frac{2}{3})$ and $(-2, 10)$.

The graphs will intersect when the expression $3x^2 - x - 4$ and the expression $6 - 2x$ both give the same value of y, so equate the two expressions.

Simplify.

You only need to substitute the x values into one equation (the linear one is the easiest) to find the y values.

If you are asked for the points of intersection, you **must** work out the y values as well as the x values. Sometimes you are only asked for the x values.

EXERCISE 19K

1 The sum of the square of a number and six times the number is 91. Find the two possible values of the number.

2 The length of a rectangular garden is 5 m longer than the width. If the area of the lawn is 176 m² find the dimensions of the garden.

> Let the width be x.

3 Two positive numbers have a difference of 3 and their squares have a sum of 317. Let one of the numbers be x. Write down an equation in x based on this information and solve it to find the two numbers.

4 The sum of a positive number and three times its reciprocal is 5. Find two possible values of the number to 3 s.f.

> The reciprocal of n is $\frac{1}{n}$.

5 Find the lengths of the sides of the right-angled triangle shown in the diagram. Give your answer to 2 d.p.

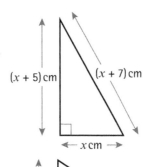

6 The area of this triangle is 13 cm².

Calculate the value of x.

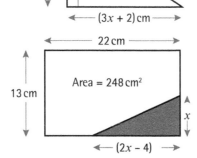

7 The rectangle in this diagram has a length of 22 cm and a width of 13 cm.
A triangle of base $(2x - 4)$ cm and height x cm is cut off and the area of the remaining shape is 248 cm².

Calculate the value of x giving your answer to 3 s.f.

8 Find the points of intersection of the curve $y = 2x^2 + 3x - 5$ and the straight line $y = 2x + 10$.

9 Find the x-coordinates of the points of intersection of the curve $y = x^2 - 7x + 12$ and the straight line $y = 9 - 2x$. Give your answers correct to 2 d.p.

10 Find the x-values of the points of intersection of the circle $x^2 + y^2 = 16$ and the straight line $y = 3 - x$. Give your answers correct to 2 d.p.

1   (a) Factorise $t^2 - 4$.   [1]
    (b) Factorise completely $at^2 - 4a + 2t^2 - 8$.   [2]

(CIE Paper 2, Nov 2000)

---

2   Monica received x marks in a test. Sandra received 4 marks more than Monica.
    (a) Write down Sandra's mark in terms of x.   [1]
    (b) When Monica subtracts 7 from her mark and squares the result, her answer
        is 1 more than Sandra's mark.
        (i) Write down an equation in x and show that it simplifies to

                $x^2 - 15x + 44 = 0$.   [3]

        (ii) Solve the equation $x^2 - 15x + 44 = 0$.   [3]
    (c) The test was marked out of 10. Write down the mark received by each girl.   [1]

(CIE Paper 4, Jun 2001)

---

3   (a) (i) Expand $(x^2 - 1)(x^2 + 1)$.   [1]
        (ii) Factorise $x^2 - 1$.   [1]
    (b) $9999 = 10^4 - 1$. Write 9999 as a product of prime factors.   [2]

(CIE Paper 2, Jun 2001)

---

4   (a) Factorise **completely** $6x^2 + 6x$.   [1]
    (b) Factorise $6x^2 + 5x + 1$.   [2]

(CIE Paper 2, Nov 2001)

---

5   (a) Factorise
        (i) $x^2 - 5x$,   [1]
        (ii) $2x^2 - 11x + 5$.   [2]
    (b) Simplify $\dfrac{x^2 - 5x}{2x^2 - 11x + 5}$.   [2]

(CIE Paper 2, Jun 2002)

6   Factorise
   (a) $x^2 - 16,$ [1]
   (b) $x^2 - 16x,$ [1]
   (c) $x^2 - 9x + 8.$ [2]

(CIE Paper 4, Nov 2003)

7   Maria walks 10 kilometres to a waterfall at an average speed of x kilometres per hour.
   (a) Write down, in terms of x, the time taken in hours. [1]
   (b) Maria returns from the waterfall but this time she walks the 10 kilometres at
        an average speed of $(x + 1)$ kilometres per hour. The time of the return journey
        is 30 minutes less than the time of the first journey.
        Write down an equation in x and solve it. [4]
   (c) Solve the equation $x^2 + x - 20 = 0.$ [2]
   (d) Find the time Maria takes to walk to the waterfall. [2]

(CIE Paper 4, Jun 2004)

8   Solve the equation $x^2 + 4x - 22 = 0.$
   Give your answer correct to 2 decimal places.
   Show all your working. [4]

(CIE Paper 2, Nov 2004)

Chapter 20

Further graphs

This chapter will show you how to
✔ recognise linear, quadratic and cubic graphs by inspection
✔ recognise reciprocal and exponential graphs and use their associated properties
✔ solve simultaneous equations graphically
✔ solve quadratic equations graphically
✔ apply graphs to solving realistic problems

20.1 Non-linear equations

A straight line graph is called a **linear graph**. It represents a **linear equation** in which the highest power of x is x^1.

> Linear functions have equations of the form $y = mx + c$ and give straight line graphs.

Graphs that have highest powers of x larger than 1 are called **non-linear graphs** – they do not form a straight line. Several non-linear graphs have easily recognisable features.

Straight line or linear graphs and equations were dealt with in Chapter 11.

20.2 Graphs of quadratic functions

> An algebraic expression in which the highest power of x is x^2 is called a **quadratic function**.

You met quadratic functions in Chapter 19.

Examples of quadratic functions include $y = x^2 - 3$, $y = 3x^2 + 4x - 7$, $y = 4x^2 - x$, $y = -2x^2 + 3x - 4$ and $y = -7x^2$.

> The graph of a quadratic function is a parabola ($\vee$-shaped) curve that is symmetrical about a line parallel to the y-axis.

All quadratic graphs are parabolas, or $\vee$-shaped. The $\vee$ shape can be this way up or upside down.

The path of a ball after it has been thrown is an example of a parabola.

This is the graph of the quadratic function $y = x^2$. It is symmetrical about the y-axis and touches the x-axis at only one point $(0, 0)$.

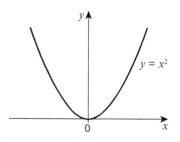

> The general form of a quadratic function is given by
>
> $$y = ax^2 + bx + c$$

where the **coefficients** a, b and c are constants (numbers) with $a \neq 0$.

You will find it useful to remember the following basic shapes.

$\neq$ means 'not equal to'.

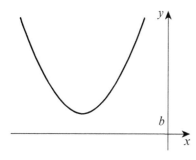

$$y = ax^2 + b$$
$$a > 0, \quad b > 0$$

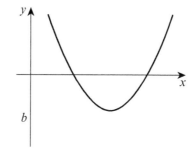

$$y = ax^2 + b$$
$$a > 0, \quad b < 0$$

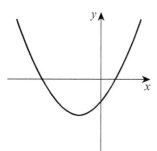

$$y = ax^2 + bx + c$$
$$a > 0$$

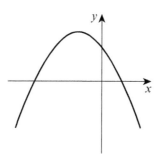

$$y = ax^2 + bx + c$$
$$a < 0$$

When the coefficient of x^2 is negative, the parabola is inverted.

When plotting the graph of a quadratic function, construct a table of values to calculate y for a given range of values of x.

EXAMPLE 1

(a) Plot the graph of $y = 2x^2 - 5x - 3$ between x values of -2 and 4.

(b) Use your graph to find solutions to the equation $2x^2 - 5x - 3 = 0$.

continued ▼

x	−2	−1	0	1	2	3	4
$2x^2$	8	2	0	2	8	18	32
$-5x$	10	5	0	−5	−10	−15	−20
−3	−3	−3	−3	−3	−3	−3	−3
y	15	4	−3	−6	−5	0	9

Each row calculates one term in the equation of the graph you are plotting.

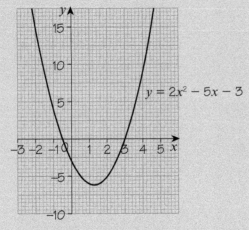

$y = 2x^2 - 5x - 3$

When working out the values of $2x^2$, do not forget that this means $2 \times x^2$; square first then multiply by 2. More care is needed with negative numbers.

Plot the (x, y) points from your table of values and join them up with a *smooth* curve.

Do *not* join the points with straight lines. Marks will be lost in the examination if you do!

It takes practice to draw a smooth curve. Remember your curve should look symmetrical. It is important always to label your axes and label the curve with the equation.

(b) The curve crosses the x-axis at two points $x = -\frac{1}{2}$ and $x = 3$. These are the solutions to the equation
$2x^2 - 5x - 3 = 0$.

This quadratic equation can also be factorised to give $(2x + 1)(x - 3) = 0$ with solutions $x = -\frac{1}{2}$ and $x = 3$. Look at Chapter 19 on factorising quadratics.

Some quadratic curves do not cross the x-axis at all. They still have a line of symmetry but do not have any solutions for $y = 0$.

In these cases, the quadratic expression cannot be factorised.

Guidelines to help you plot non-linear graphs

● Look at the range of values of x for which the graph is to be drawn.

● Put these integer values into the equation and work out the corresponding values for y.

● Place the results into a table.

● From the results identify the extreme values for x and y in the table and draw a co-ordinate grid using these values.

● Plot the points from the table.

● Draw a smooth curve through all the points.

● Label the graph with the equation.

EXERCISE 20A

1 Draw the graph of $y = 3x^2$ by completing the table of values given.

   What is the equation of the line of symmetry?

x	-4	-3	-2	-1	0	1	2	3	4
y	48			3	0		12		

2 Draw a graph of the function $y = -2x^2$ between the x-values -4 and $+4$, by constructing a table of results.
   What effect does the minus sign have on the graph?

3 Draw the graph of $y = x^2 - 12$ between $x = -4$ and $x = 4$.

4 For each of the following graphs make a table of values and draw the graph for the given range of values of x. State the line of symmetry of each graph.
   (a) $y = x^2 + x - 2$ for values of x from -3 to $+2$
   (b) $y = x^2 + 3x + 1$ for values of x from -5 to $+2$
   (c) $y = 2x^2 - 2x + 3$ for values of x from -3 to $+4$
   (d) $y = 2x^2 - 4x - 9$ for values of x from -2 to $+4$

5 Draw the graph of $y = x^2 - x - 12$. What are the solutions to the equation $x^2 - x - 12 = 0$?

Look at Example 1(b).

6 For x-values between -3 and $+4$ construct a table of values for the function $y = 3x^2 - 7x - 6$. What are the co-ordinates of the points of intersection of the curve and the x-axis?

Remember the x-axis is the line $y = 0$.

20.3 Graphs of cubic functions

A **cubic function** is one in which the highest power of x is x^3.

Typical examples of cubic functions include $x^3 - 4x + 2$, $-x^3 + 4$, $3x^3 + 5x^2 - 6x - 2$, $-8x^3$.

This is the graph of the cubic function $y = x^3$.

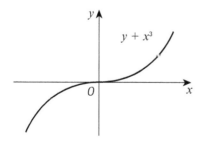

This curve goes through the origin (0, 0).
The graph of $y = x^3$ has rotational symmetry of order 2 about the origin.

The general form of a cubic function is given by

$$y = ax^3 + bx^2 + cx + d$$

where a, b, c and d are constants with $a \neq 0$.

Some shapes to remember include

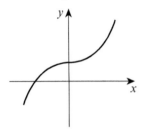

$y = ax^3 + b$
$a > 0, \quad b > 0$

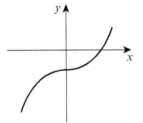

$y = ax^3 + b$
$a > 0, \quad b < 0$

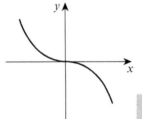

$y = -ax^3$
$a > 0$

When the coefficient of x^3 is negative the graph is reflected in the x-axis.

 EXAMPLE 2

Draw the graph of $y = x^3 + 3x^2$ for $-4 \leq x \leq 2$.
Use the graph to find solutions to the equation $x^3 + 3x^2 = 0$.

Complete a table of values to find values of y.

x	-4	-3	-2	-1	0	1	2
x^3	-64	-27	-8	-1	0	1	8
$3x^2$	48	27	12	3	0	3	12
y	-16	0	4	2	0	4	20

Draw axes with x-values between -4 and 2 and y-values between -20 and 25. Plot the points and join them up with a *smooth* curve.

At $x = -\frac{1}{2}$
$y = -\frac{1}{8} - 2 \times \frac{1}{4} - 3x - \frac{1}{2}$
$= \frac{7}{8}$

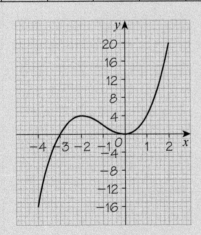

The curve crosses the x-axis at two points $(-3, 0)$ and $(0, 0)$. The solutions of the equation $x^3 + 3x^2 = 0$ are $x = -3$ or 0.

EXERCISE 20B

1   Draw the graph of $y = -x^3$ taking values of x between -3 and $+3$.

2   Copy and complete the table for the cubic function
    $y = x^3 - 3x^2 - 5x$.

x	-2	-1	0	1	2	3
x^3						
$-3x^2$						
$-5x$						
y	-10		0			-15

Draw the graph of this function for $-2 \leqslant x \leqslant 3$, and find the values for x when the curve crosses the x-axis.

3   Plot the graph of $y = x^3 - 3x - 2$ between $-3 \leqslant x \leqslant 3$ by constructing a table of values. Use your graph to estimate the value of x when $y = 0$.

4   Draw the graph of $y = x^3 - 2x^2 - 3x$ for x between -2 and $+4$. Use your graph to estimate the solutions to the equation $x^3 - 2x^2 - 3x = 0$.

5   Draw the graphs of the following cubic functions for $-3 \leqslant x \leqslant 3$ by constructing a table of x- and y-values.

(a) $y = \frac{1}{2}x^3 + 2$ (b) $y = (x - 1)^3$ (c) $y = x^3 + x^2 + x$

20.4 Graphs of reciprocal functions

A function in which the power of x is of the form x^{-1} or $\frac{1}{x}$ is called a **reciprocal function**.

Typical examples of reciprocal functions include
$$y = \frac{1}{x}, \quad y = -\frac{3}{x}, \quad y = \frac{2}{x} - 3.$$
The key features of reciprocal graphs are that they tend towards certain values but never reach them.

These features are called **asymptotes**.

You met reciprocals in Chapter 9.

The word asymptotes will not be used on the examination papers.

The graph of the simplest reciprocal function, $y = \dfrac{1}{x}$ (or $y = x^{-1}$) is

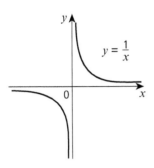

It is well worth remembering this shape.

When x tends to very large (positive or negative) values, y tends to $\dfrac{1}{\text{very large}}$ = very small values. In fact y tends to 0 but never reaches it. The x-axis is an asymptote.

Asymptotes are usually denoted by a dashed line, but a dashed line on the axis would not show up.

When x tends to very small (positive or negative) values, y tends to $\dfrac{1}{\text{very small}}$ = very large values. In fact y tends to infinity but never reaches it. The y-axis is another asymptote.

The general expression for a reciprocal function is $y = \dfrac{a}{x}$, where a is a positive or negative constant.

Examples of graphs of reciprocal functions are

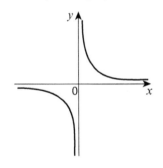

$$y = \frac{a}{x}$$

$$y = -\frac{a}{x}$$

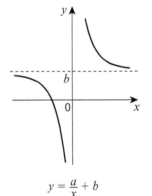

$$y = \frac{a}{x} + b$$

$y = b$ is an asymptote on the graph of
$y = \dfrac{a}{x} + b.$

$a > 0$ in these 3 sketch graphs.

 **EXAMPLE 3**

Draw the graph of the function $y = 2 - \dfrac{3}{x}$ for x-values between -3 and $+3$.

x	-3	-2	-1	-0.5	-0.2	0.2	0.5	1	2	3
2	2	2	2	2	2	2	2	2	2	2
$-\dfrac{3}{x}$	1	1.5	3	6	15	-15	-6	-3	-1.5	-1
y	3	3.5	5	8	17	-13	-4	-1	0.5	1

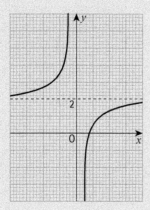

Begin by tabulating the results between these values. It is important to include smaller x-values close to zero but not zero itself, which is undefined.

x-values of -0.5, -0.2, 0.2 and 0.5 are typically used between -1 and $+1$.

The maximum and minimum values for y are 17 and -13.

The y-axis should be between -15 and $+20$.

The dashed line at $y = 2$ shows the horizontal asymptote. As x becomes large, $\dfrac{a}{x}$ tends to zero, so the value of y must approach 2.

The y-axis itself is the second (vertical) asymptote with equation $x = 0$.

EXERCISE 20C

1 For each of these graphs make a table of values and draw the graph for values of x from -3 to $+3$. Choose a sensible scale for each axis.

(a) $y = -\dfrac{2}{x}$ (b) $y = -\dfrac{5}{x}$ (c) $y = -\dfrac{3}{x} + 4$

(d) $y = -6 - \dfrac{4}{x}$ (e) $y = \dfrac{6}{x}$ (f) $xy = 4$

2 Copy and complete the table of values for the function $y = -\dfrac{3}{x}$.

x	-3	-2	-1	-0.5	-0.2	0.2	0.5	1	2	3
y	1		3	6		-15		-3	-1.5	

Draw the graph over this x range. What are the equations of the two asymptotes?

3 Draw the graph of the function $y = \dfrac{3}{x} + 2$ over the range of x values between -3 and 3. How does the graph compare with that drawn in question 2?

4 Draw the graph $y = 4 - \dfrac{1}{x}$ between the x-values 0 and 5.
What are the equations of the two asymptotes?

20.5 Graphs of exponential functions

An exponential function is a function of the form $y = a^x$ where a is a positive number.

Because the function power is x itself the graph is sometimes called the **power curve**. Exponential functions describe a very rapid increase in the values of y for small changes in the x value. Typical examples of exponential functions include $y = 2^x$, $y = 4^{3x}$, $y = (3)^{-x}$ and $y = 10^x$.

The basic shape of the curve is the same for all exponential functions.

All exponential functions are positive, that is they lie above the x-axis. All exponential functions pass through $(0, 1)$, because $y = a^0 = 1$ for all a.

The inverse function $y = a^{-x}$, illustrating exponential decrease, is simply a reflection in the y-axis of the function $y = a^x$, as shown in the diagram.

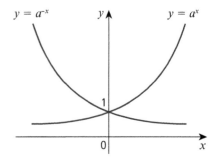

EXAMPLE 4

Draw the graph of the exponential function $y = 2^x$ for x-values between -2 and 4. Give the values to 2 d.p. where necessary.

x	-2	-1	0	1	2	3	4
y	0.25	0.5	1	2	4	8	16

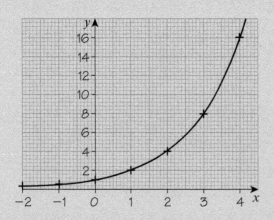

Begin by constructing a table of values between $x = -2$ and $x = +4$.

Decide on a sensible scale for each axis. Here the minimum and maximum values for y are 0.25 and 8. The y-axis should be between 0 and 12.

Plot these points and join them up with a *smooth* curve.
The smooth curve crosses the y-axis at $y = 1$ as expected. Do *not* join the points with straight lines.

EXERCISE 20D

1   Draw the graph of $y = 3^x$ for x-values between -2 and $+2$ (give your values to 1 d.p.).

First construct a table.

2   Copy and complete the table below, and draw the graph of the exponential function $y = 10^{2x}$ for the x-values shown in the table.

x	-0.5	-0.2	-0.1	0	0.1	0.2	0.5
y	0.1		0.6	1			10

3   Copy and complete the table of values for the function $y = 4^x$ for x-values between -3 and $+2$, giving your answers to 1 d.p.

x	-3	-2	-1	0	1	2
y			0.25	1		

Draw the graph of this function for $-3 \leqslant x \leqslant 2$.

20.6 Combined non–linear graphs

These are functions that are a combination of those functions described in the previous sections.

Combined functions involve linear, quadratic, cubic and/or reciprocal terms.

EXAMPLE 5

Make a table of values for $y = \dfrac{1}{x} + x$ between $x = 0$ and $x = 5$.

Extend the table to negative values of x between 0 and -5. Draw the graph of this function for $-5 \leqslant x \leqslant 5$.

x	0.1	0.2	0.5	1	2	3	4	5
$\dfrac{1}{x}$	10	5	2	1	0.5	0.3	0.25	0.2
y	10.1	5.2	2.5	2	2.5	3.3	4.3	5.2

continued ▼

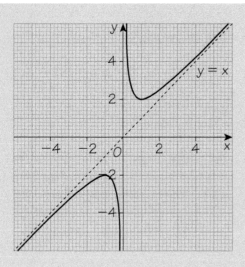

Do not include $x = 0$ as $\frac{3}{0}$ is undefined (infinite).

As in the case of reciprocal graphs include x-values close to zero.

Give the y-values to 1 d.p.

For the corresponding negative x-values the y-values will also be negative but the same numerical value.

Note the rotational symmetry of the curve.

There are also two asymptotes at $x = 0$ (the y-axis) and along the line $y = x$.

As x gets larger (positive or negative) the $\frac{1}{x}$ term tends to zero so the graph is approximately $y = x$.

 EXERCISE 20E

1 Copy and complete the table for the function $y = \dfrac{1}{x} - x$ between the x-values $x = 0$ and $x = 5$.

x	0.1	0.2	0.5	1	2	3	4	5
$\dfrac{1}{x}$								
y	9.9		1.5	0			-3.8	

Draw the graph of this function.

2 Draw the graph of the function $y = \dfrac{4}{x} - 3x$ between x-values 0.1 and 5 (as in Example 5) by completing a table of results.

3 Draw the graph of $y = x^2 - \dfrac{1}{x} + 2$ for x between -3 and 3.

Remember to include x-values close to zero but do not include zero itself.

20.7 Graphs that intersect

Linear graphs

In Chapter 11, you used linear graphs to find solutions to simultaneous equations. You can use the same method to find solutions to linear and non-linear functions.

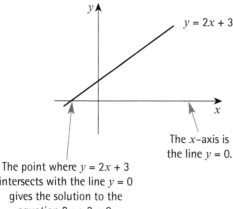

The point where $y = 2x + 3$ intersects with the line $y = 0$ gives the solution to the equation $2x + 3 = 0$.

The x-axis is the line $y = 0$.

Solutions to other equations, for example $y = 3$, can also be found by plotting the graph and finding the **points of intersection** with the particular line.

EXAMPLE 6

Draw the graph of $y = x + 1$. From the graph find the x-value when $x + 1 = 0$ and when $x + 1 = 3$.

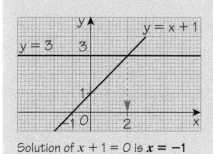

You can sketch this linear graph quickly by noting where the line crosses the x- and y-axes. When $x = 0$, $y = 1$. When $y = 0$, $x = -1$.

This is a quick and easy method for any straight line that is not parallel to the axes.

You need accurate drawings to obtain accurate solutions.

Solution of $x + 1 = 0$ is $x = -1$

The line crosses the x-axis at $x = -1$.

Solution of $x + 1 = 3$ is $x = 2$

You can solve $x + 1 = 3$ by finding where the graph crosses the line $y = 3$. This is called the point of intersection of the graph with the line $y = 3$. You can see that the solution is $x = 2$.

EXAMPLE 7

Plot the graph of $y = 3x - 2$. Find the co-ordinates of the point of intersection where this line meets the line $y = 3$.

x	-1	0	1
$3x$	-3	0	3
-2	-2	-2	-2
y	-5	-2	1

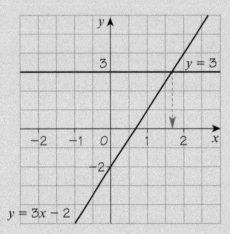

The co-ordinates are $(1.6, 3)$.

Begin by constructing a table using x-values of -1, 0 and 1.

Plot the graph and the straight line $y = 3$.

Always draw your graphs as accurately as possible. In this example, the value of the point of intersection is not a whole number.

The exact co-ordinates are $(1\frac{2}{3}, 3)$ but examiners always allow for small errors.

Quadratic graphs

When quadratic functions are plotted the curve may do one of the following

- it may cross the x-axis at two points
- it may just touch the x-axis
- it may never cross or touch the x-axis.

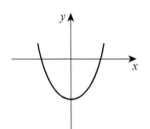

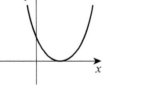

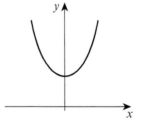

There are two solutions to $y = 0$.

There is one solution to $y = 0$.

There are no solutions to $y = 0$.

Quadratic curves may also intersect other lines of the form $y = k$ (where k is any number). The method for finding solutions is to plot the line and look for points of intersection.

EXAMPLE 8

On a co-ordinate grid with x-values between -3 and $+3$ and y-values between -5 and 10, draw the curve $y = x^2 - 2$.

(a) What are the solutions of the equation $x^2 - 2 = 0$?

(b) Draw the straight line $y = 3$. Write down the co-ordinates of both points where the curve and line intersect.

x	-3	-2	-1	0	1	2	3
x^2	9	4	1	0	1	4	9
-2	-2	-2	-2	-2	-2	-2	-2
y	7	2	-1	-2	-1	2	7

Begin by constructing a table of values between $x = 3$ and $x = -3$ and then plotting the curve.

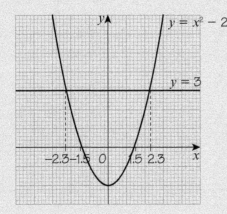

The curve crosses the x-axis at points $x = -1.5$ and $x = 1.5$.

Draw the line $y = 3$ on the graph. At the points of intersection draw two vertical dashed lines to the x-axis.

(a) Solutions to $x^2 - 2 = 0$ are $x = \pm 1.4$.

(b) The curve and the line $y = 3$ intersect at $(-2.3, 3)$ and $(2.3, 3)$.

Finding the solution of the point of intersection between $y = x^2 - 2$ and $y = 3$ is the same as solving the equation $x^2 - 2 = 3$. This rearranges to $x^2 = 5$.

EXAMPLE 9

Draw the graph of the quadratic function $y = x^2 - 2x - 4$ for values of x between $x = -2$ and $x = +4$.

(a) Use your graph to solve the equation $x^2 - 2x - 4 = 0$ from the graph.

(b) Use your graph to solve the equation $x^2 - 2x - 4 = 2x - 5$.

(c) Use your graph to find the positive solution of the equation $x^2 - x - 2 = 0$.

continued ▼

x	-2	-1	0	1	2	3	4
x^2	4	1	0	1	4	9	16
$-2x$	4	2	0	-2	-4	-6	-8
-4	-4	-4	-4	-4	-4	-4	-4
y	4	-1	-4	-5	-4	-1	4

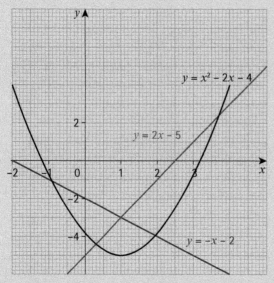

$y = x^2 - 2x - 4$

$y = 2x - 5$

$y = -x - 2$

Points of intersection with the x-axis.

In part (b) draw the straight line $y = 2x - 5$. Where this line and the quadratic curve intersect gives the solution to the equation $x^2 - 2x - 4 = 2x - 5$.

You are solving

'curve' = 'line'.

(a) From the graph the solutions of the equation
$x^2 - 2x - 4 = 0$ are $x = -1.2$ and $x = 3.2$.

(b) From the graph, $x^2 - 2x - 4 = 2x - 5$ when $x = 0.3$ or 3.7

To solve $x^2 - x - 2 = 0$, rearrange the equation so that it has the quadratic expression of the graph you have drawn on one side of the equation. The expression on the other side of the equation indicates the graph you need to draw.

(c) $x^2 - x - 2 = 0$

$x^2 - 2x - 4 + x + 2 = 0$

$x^2 - 2x - 4 = -x - 2$

The points of intersection occur when $x = -1$ or 2

Draw the line $y = -x - 2$ and find the point of intersection with the original quadratic curve. The line $y = -x - 2$ is shown on the graph.

EXERCISE 20F

1 Draw the graph $y = 2x + 5$. It intersects the line $y = 3$ at a point P. What are the co-ordinates of P?

2 The line $y = 7$ intersects another line $y = 4x + 9$ at a point Q. What are the co-ordinates of Q? Where does the line $y = 4x + 9$ cross the x-axis?

3 Copy and complete the table for the equation $y = x^2 + 1$.

x	-2	-1	0	1	2
y	5				

Draw this curve with x-values from -2 to 2 and y-values from 0 to 6. Draw the line $y = 3$ on the same graph.
What are the co-ordinates of the points of intersection of the two graphs?

4 Draw the graph of $y = x^2 + 4x + 2$ for values of x from -5 to $+1$. Use a scale of 1 cm for 1 unit on each axis.

(a) On the same axes draw the graph of the line $y = 5$.

(b) Write down the x-values of the points of intersection of the curve and the line $y = 5$.

(c) What equation is solved by these x-values?

(d) Use your graph to solve the equation $x^2 + 4x + 2 = 0$.

5 For each of the following, solve graphically the quadratic equations which are written alongside them. Give your answers correct to 1 d.p.

Each solution will be given by the points of intersection of a quadratic graph and a straight line graph (which may be the x-axis).

	Graph	Solve these equations	
(a)	$y = x^2 + x - 2$	$x^2 + x - 2 = 0$	$x^2 + x - 2 = 2$
(b)	$y = x^2 + 4x - 1$	$x^2 + 4x - 1 = 0$	$x^2 + 4x - 1 = -3$
(c)	$y = 2x^2 - 2x + 3$	$2x^2 - 2x + 3 = 0$	$2x^2 - 2x + 3 = 20$
(d)	$y = 2x^2 + 4x - 5$	$2x^2 + 4x - 5 = 0$	$2x^2 + 4x - 5 = 5$

6 Draw the graph of the function $y = x^2 - 2x - 4$ for x-values between -3 and 4. Using the graph, find the solutions of $x^2 - 2x - 4 = 0$ giving your answers to 1 d.p.
By drawing an appropriate linear graph on the same axes, solve the equation $x^2 - x - 6 = 0$.

Look at Example 9(c).

7 (a) Copy and complete the table of values for $y = x^2 - 4x + 3$.

x	-1	0	1	2	3	4	5
y	8	3		-1			

(b) Draw the graph of this function between -1 and 5 with y-values between -3 and 10.

(c) Write down the solutions of $x^2 - 4x + 3 = 0$.

(d) By drawing an appropriate linear graph on the same axes, solve the equation $x^2 - 5x + 5 = 0$.

20.8 Gradient of a graph

As you walk over Sydney Harbour Bridge from point **5** to **6** to **7** you will find that the climb starts very steeply and becomes less and less steep until you arrive at the top **7** when the walkway is level.

You can see that it is uphill from **5** to **6** to **7** and then downhill from **7** to the other side of the water.

This shows that the graph of a curve does not have a single gradient as a straight line does.

The gradient of a curve **at a point** can be found by drawing a tangent to the curve at the point.

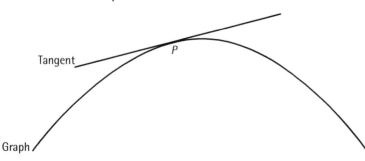

| Uphill | positive gradient |
| Downhill | negative gradient |

The tangent must only **touch** the curve at the point P.

Once you have drawn the tangent you can find the gradient of it in the usual way.

You should try to angle your ruler so that it makes equal angles with the curve.

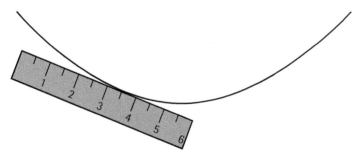

The value of the gradient by this method is not exact.

A range of answers will be allowed in the examination.

EXAMPLE 10

Draw the graph of $y = x^2 - 2x - 3$ for values of x between $x = -2$ and $x = +4$.

Draw a tangent to the graph at the point P(2, -3).

Find the gradient of the graph at the point P.

x	-2	-1	0	1	2	3	4
x^2	4	1	0	1	4	9	16
$-2x$	4	2	0	-2	-4	-6	-8
-3	-3	-3	-3	-3	-3	-3	-3
y	5	0	-3	-4	-3	0	5

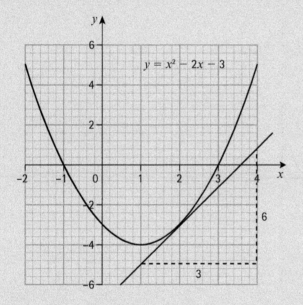

The gradient of the graph at P is $\dfrac{6}{3} = 2$

The larger the triangle the closer the gradient will be to the exact value.

EXERCISE 20G

1   Draw the graph of $y = x^2$ for values of x from -4 to $+4$.
Use a scale of 2 cm to 1 unit on the x-axis and 1 cm to 2 units on the y-axis.

Find the gradient of the curve at the points where

(a) $x = 2$ (b) $x = 0$ (c) $x = -3$

2 Use the table in Example 1 to make an accurate drawing of the graph of $y = 2x^2 - 5x - 3$.
   Use a scale 2 cm to 1 unit on the x-axis and 1 cm to 2 units on the y-axis.
   Find the gradient of the curve at $x = 3$.

3 Use the table in Example 2 to make an accurate drawing of the curve $y = x^3 + 3x^2$.
   Use a scale of 2 cm to 1 unit on the x-axis and 1 cm to 2 units on the y-axis.
   Find the gradient of the curve at

   (a) $x = 2$ (b) $x = 1$ (c) $x = -1$

4 Use the table in Example 4 to make an accurate drawing of the graph of $y = 2^x$.
   Use a scale 2 cm to 1 unit on each axis.
   Find the gradient of the curve at $x = 2$.

20.9 Recognising non-linear graphs

You need to be able to recognise linear and **non-linear graphs** and use them to describe real-life situations.

EXAMPLE 11

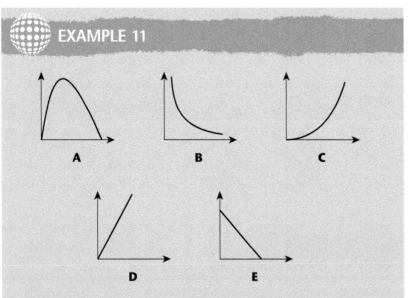

Which graph best matches the relationships below?
Describe the type of function used in each case.

(a) The circumference of a circle plotted against its diameter.

(b) The area of a circle as a function of its radius.

(c) The length of a rectangle of fixed area plotted against its width.

continued ▼

(a) $C = \pi d$ This is linear, so of the form $y = mx + c$.
As d increases so does C. The graph must
pass through $(0, 0)$.   Graph D

(b) $A = \pi r^2$ This is quadratic, so of the form $y = ax^2$.
As r increases so does A. The graph must
pass through $(0, 0)$.   Graph C

(c) $l = \dfrac{A}{w}$ This is reciprocal, so of the form $y = \dfrac{a}{x}$.
As l increases w decreases.   Graph B

 EXERCISE 20H

1 Look at the following functions. Describe the graph of the function as either linear (L), quadratic (Q), cubic (Cu), reciprocal (R), exponential (E) or a combination (Co).

(a) $y = 2x^2 - 3$ (b) $y = 5 + x^3$ (c) $y = -\dfrac{3}{x}$

(d) $y = 5x^3 - 2x - 1$ (e) $y = 12a^x$ (f) $y = 4 - 3x$

(g) $y = \dfrac{1}{x} + x$ (h) $y = x + 2 - 2x^2$ (i) $y = x - 3 + \dfrac{2}{x}$

2 Match each equation to one of the graphs **A–E** below.

(a) $y = \dfrac{3}{x}$ (b) $y = 4x^3$ (c) $y = 4x + 3$

(d) $y = 3x^2 + 4$ (e) $y = 3^{4x}$

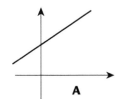 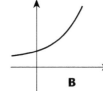 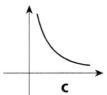

A   B   C

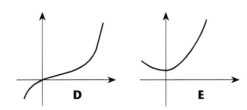

D   E

3 What type of graphs could be drawn from the following functions? Label them linear (L), quadratic (Q), cubic (Cu), reciprocal (R), exponential (E) or a combination (Co).

(a) $xy = -6$ (b) $3x + 2y = 4$ (c) $\dfrac{y}{3} = 2^x$

(d) $3x^2 + y = 2x - 4$ (e) $y = \dfrac{x^3 - 3x^2}{x}$ (f) $3x = xy - 2$

(g) $9x^3 = 4x^2 + y - 7$ (h) $xy = 2 + 4x^2$ (i) $x = \dfrac{y}{5}$

1 $$f(x) = 2^x$$

(a) Fill in the values of $f(x) = 2^x$. in the table below.

x	-1	-0.5	0	1	2	3
$f(x)$						

[2]

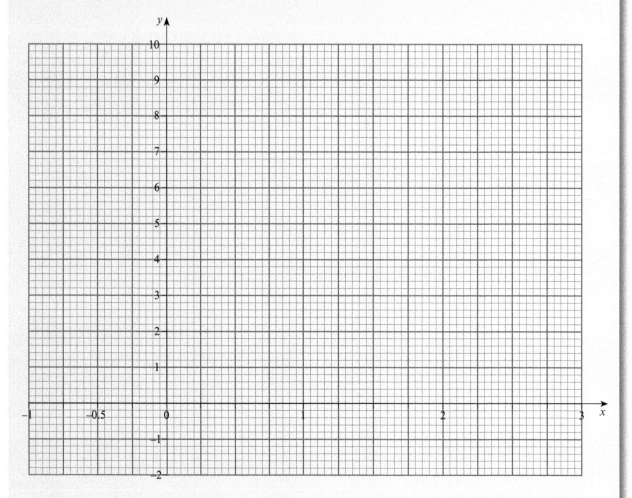

(b) Copy the grid above and draw the graph of $y = f(x)$ for $-1 \leqslant x \leqslant 3$. [2]

(c) Use your graph to find the value of x when

(i) $2^x = 3$, [1]

(ii) $2^x = -x$. [2]

(CIE Paper 2, Jun 2001)

2 **Answer the whole of this question on a sheet of graph paper.**

  (a) The table gives the values of $f(x) = \dfrac{24}{x^2} + x^2$ for $0.8 \leqslant x \leqslant 6$.

x	0.8	1	1.5	2	2.5	3	3.5	4	4.5	5	5.5	6
$f(x)$	38.1	25	12.9	10	10.1	11.7	l	m	n	26	31	36.7

  Calculate, correct to 1 decimal place, the values of l, m and n.   [3]

  (b) Using a scale of 2 cm to represent 1 unit on the x-axis and 2 cm to represent 5 units on the y-axis, draw an x-axis for $0 \leqslant x \leqslant 6$ and a y-axis for $0 \leqslant x \leqslant 40$.

  Draw the graph of $y = f(x)$ for $0.8 \leqslant x \leqslant 6$.   [6]

  (c) Draw the tangent to your graph at $x = 1.5$ and use it to calculate an estimate of the gradient of the curve at this point.   [4]

  (d) (i) Draw a straight line joining the points (0, 20) and (6, 32).   [1]
  (ii) Write down the equation of this line in the form $y = mx + c$.   [2]
  (iii) Use your graph to write down the x-values of the points of intersection of this line and the curve.   [2]
  (iv) Draw the tangent to the curve that has the same gradient as your line in part (d)(i).   [1]
  (v) Write down the equation for tangent in part (d)(iv).   [2]

(CIE Paper 4, Nov 2002)

Chapter 21

Further trigonometry

This chapter will show you how to
- ✔ draw graphs of sine, cosine and tangent
- ✔ solve trigonometric equations using the symmetry properties of the trigonometric graphs
- ✔ find areas of triangles using the trigonometrical formula for area
- ✔ find lengths and angles in triangles using the sine and cosine rules
- ✔ work out areas of segments of circles

21.1 Graphs of $y = \cos x°$ and $y = \sin x°$

Drawing the graph of $y = \cos x°$

You can draw a graph of $y = \cos x°$ by using your calculator to compile a table of values. Values of x from 0° to 360° in intervals of 30° will give a good graph.

$x°$	0	30	60	90	120	150	180	210	240	270	300	330	360
$\cos x°$	1	0.87	0.5	0	−0.5	−0.87	−1	−0.87	−0.5	0	0.5	0.87	1

This table shows how the value of $\cos x°$ gradually decreases from 1 to 0 then to −1 then increases again to 0 and back to 1.

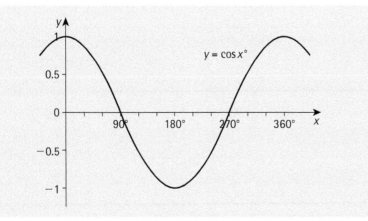

$y = \cos x°$

Notice that the graph has a maximum value of +1 and a minimum value of −1.

The syllabus only requires this to be plotted up to 180° but a complete cycle is shown here.

You can see that the graph has symmetrical properties.
A vertical line through $x = 180°$ is an axis of symmetry.

If you drew the graph for negative values of x you would find that the y-axis is a line of symmetry.

The graph has a **period** of 360° (it repeats itself every 360°).

Drawing the graph of $y = \sin x$

You can also draw a graph of $y = \sin x$ by using your calculator to make a table of values and then plot the points.

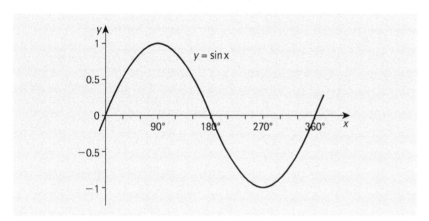

Notice that the graph has a maximum value of $+1$ and a minimum value of -1.

You are only required to work to 180°.

This graph also has symmetrical properties.
Some of the more obvious ones are

$$\sin x = \sin(180° - x)$$
$$\sin(90° - x) = \sin(90° + x)$$

The graph has a period of 360° (it repeats itself every 360°).

21.2 Solving trigonometric equations

A **trigonometric equation** is an equation involving a trigonometric function.

Because sine and cosine have a period of 360° and all the graphs continue *ad infinitum*, there will be an infinite number of solutions to any trigonometric equation.

Ad infinitum means forever or infinity.

You need to look at the range of values required for the solution and make sure you state answers in the correct range.

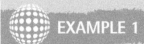

EXAMPLE 1

You are given that sin 34° = 0.5592.
For values of x in the range 0° ≤ x ≤ 180°, use the symmetry of the
sine curve to do this exercise.
Find another solution of the equation sin x = 0.5592.

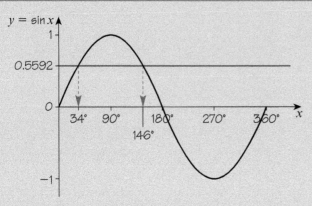

Notice how the given value of 34° is
really important in finding other
solutions.
The symmetry properties of the curve
are the key to finding the correct
solutions.

Another solution of sin x = 0.5592 is x = 180° − 34° = 146°

EXAMPLE 2

Solve the equation cos x = 0.3090 for 0° ≤ x ≤ 180°.
Give your answers correct to the nearest degree.

One solution of cos x = 0.3090 is x = cos⁻¹(0.3090) which gives
x = 72°

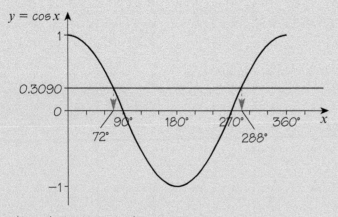

Use the inverse cos function on
your calculator to find one solution.
cos⁻¹(0.3090) = 72.001 02... rounds
to 72°

Remember to check that your
calculator is set to **degree** mode.

Sketch the graph of y = cos x.

The other solution is not in the range given.

EXAMPLE 3

Find the solution to the equation $3 \sin x = 1$ in the range
$0° \leqslant x \leqslant 180°$.

$3 \sin x = 1$

$\sin x = \frac{1}{3}$

$x = \sin^{-1}\left(\frac{1}{3}\right)$

$x = 19.4712°... = 19.5°$

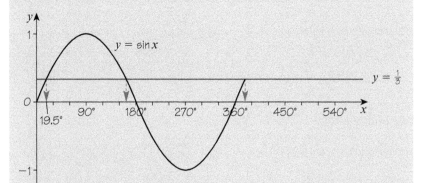

From the symmetry of the graph, $x = 19.5°$, $(180° - 19.5°)$

so the solutions are $x = 19.5°, 160.5°$

Begin by rearranging the equation
to make $\sin x$ the subject.
Use your calculator to work out the
inverse function to find one
solution.
Other solutions can be found by
using the symmetry of the sine
graph.

The next solution is outside the
range of angle required.

EXERCISE 21A

1 Find angles in the range $0° \leqslant x \leqslant 180°$ that satisfy each of the
   following equations. Give your answers to 1 d.p.
   (a) $\sin x = 0.8$ (b) $\cos x = 0.45$
   (c) $\sin x = -0.24$ (d) $\cos x = -0.866$

2 Find all solutions of the equation $\sin x = \frac{2}{3}$ for $0° \leqslant x \leqslant 180°$.
   Give your answers correct to 1 d.p.

3 Find all the solutions to the equation $\cos x = 0.5$ in the range
   $0° \leqslant x \leqslant 180°$.

4 You are given that $\cos 38° = 0.7880$ for $0° \leqslant x \leqslant 180°$.
   (a) Find all values of x in this range that satisfy the equation
       $\cos x = -0.7880$.
   (b) Find all solutions of the equation $\sin x = 0.7880$ in this range.

21.3 The area of a triangle using trigonometry

The area of a triangle is given by the expression $\frac{1}{2}bh$ where b is the base length and h is the perpendicular height. However, you can also work out the area of a triangle if you know the lengths of any two sides *and* the size of the angle between them.

The diagram below shows a general triangle *ABC* with side lengths given by a, b and c.

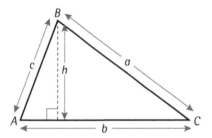

The area of the triangle is $\frac{1}{2} \times base \times height = \frac{1}{2}bh$

The height h is given by the trigonometric function $\sin C = \dfrac{h}{a}$

giving $h = a \sin C$.

Substituting this value of h into the original expression gives
Area $= \frac{1}{2}b \times a \sin C$, which we can write as

Area $ABC = \frac{1}{2}ab \sin C$.

> Notice how to label the sides of the triangle.
> a is the side opposite angle A, b is opposite angle B and c is opposite angle C.

> Notice that the two sides involved are a and b and the angle in between is C.

> When the triangle is right-angled use the simple area formula
> Area $= \frac{1}{2} \times b \times h$

⊕ EXAMPLE 4

Find the area of the triangle PQR.

From the diagram $p = 14$ cm and $q = 8$ cm.

Area $PQR = \frac{1}{2}pq \sin R$

$\quad = \frac{1}{2} \times 14 \times 8 \times \sin 60°$

$\quad = 56 \times 0.8660$

$\quad = 48.4974$

$\quad = 48.5$

Area $PQR = 48.5$ cm^2

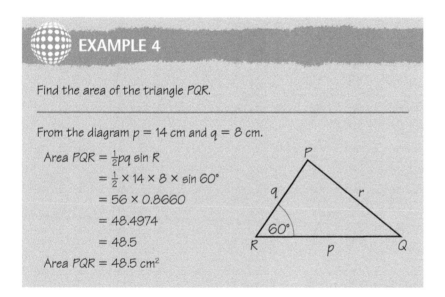

 **EXAMPLE 5**

The area of a triangle XYZ is 90 cm². If $XY = 15$ cm and $XZ = 21.5$ cm work out angle X to 1 d.p.

Begin by sketching the triangle.

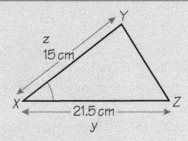

Area $XYZ = \frac{1}{2} yz \sin X$

$\quad\quad 90 = \frac{1}{2} \times 21.5 \times 15 \times \sin X$

$\quad\quad 90 = 161.25 \sin X$

$\quad \sin X = \dfrac{90}{161.25}$

$\quad\quad\quad X = 33.9°$

 EXERCISE 21B

1 Find the area of each triangle.

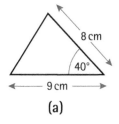 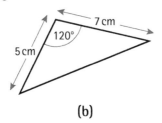

(a)   (b)

2 The area of a triangle RST is 64 cm². If all three angles of the triangle are acute and $RS = 13$ cm, $ST = 15$ cm, calculate the angle S.

3 $PQRS$ is a parallelogram with $PQ = 12$ cm, $QR = 7$ cm and angle $Q = 64°$. Work out the area of $PQRS$. Give your answer to 3 s.f.

Draw a sketch first.

4 A triangular field ABC has an area of 8320 m². If two sides of the field are 120 m and 410 m long what is the angle between them?

5 A tetrahedron is constructed from four equilateral triangles of side length 12 cm. What is the total surface area of the tetrahedron?

21.4 Segment of a circle

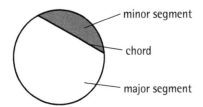

minor segment

chord

major segment

This diagram shows a circle with a chord, cutting the circle into two **segments**. The smaller portion is called the minor segment and the larger one is the major segment.

The chord divides a sector into a triangle and a segment.
This leads to a method for finding the area of a segment.

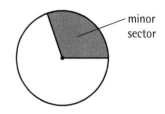

minor sector

Area of segment = area of sector − area of triangle

$$= \frac{\theta}{360} \times \pi r^2 - \frac{1}{2}r^2 \sin \theta$$

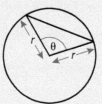

Area of sector $= \frac{\theta}{360} \times \pi r^2$

(See Chapter 5)

Area of triangle $= \frac{1}{2}ab \sin C$

So the area of a triangle formed by the radii of a circle $= \frac{1}{2}r^2 \sin \theta$.

EXAMPLE 6

(a) Find the arc length and area of the minor sector of this circle.

(b) Find the area of the minor segment cut off by the chord of this circle.

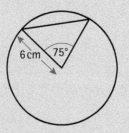

6 cm   75°

(a) Arc length $= \frac{75}{360} \times 2 \times \pi \times 6$

$= 7.85$ cm (3 s.f.)

Sector area $= \frac{75}{360} \times \pi \times 6^2$

$= 23.5619...$

$= 23.6$ cm^2 (3 s.f.)

(b) Area of segment = area of sector − area of triangle

$= 23.5619... - \frac{1}{2} \times 6^2 \times \sin 75^\circ$

$= 23.5619... - 17.3866...$

$= 6.1752...$

$= 6.18$ cm^2 (3 s.f.)

Use the non-rounded version of the sector area and only round to 3 s.f. at the end.

EXERCISE 21C

1 Find the area of the shaded segments.

(a)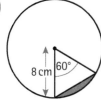

(b)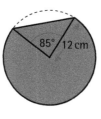

(c)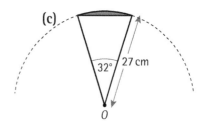

2 The following diagrams all show segments of a circle centre O.
   Calculate the shaded area.

(a)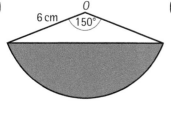

(b)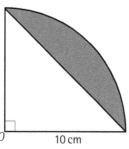

(c)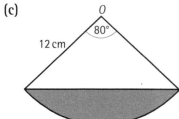

(d)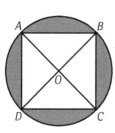

$AOB = 90°$

radius of circle centre O is 4 cm

3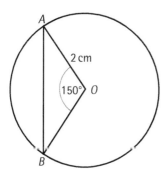

Triangle *AOB* has been drawn in a circle which has centre *O*, radius
2 cm. Angle *AOB* = 150°.

Calculate the area of

(a) sector *AOB*,   (b) triangle *AOB*,   (c) the minor segment.

4 The diagram shows the circular cross-section of a road tunnel through a mountain.

The road surface AB is 3.5m above the bottom of the tunnel. The radius of the circle is 4.5m.

Calculate the

(a) height of the tunnel CM,

(b) sector angle AOB,

(c) area of sector OAB,

(d) area of triangle OAB,

(e) the area of the minor segment.

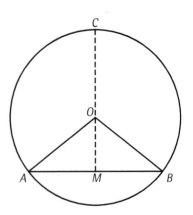

5 An Australian sound board is made out of a rectangular piece of wood 30 cm by 4 cm. It consists of a rectangle with a segment of a circle at each end.

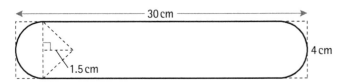

Use Pythagoras to find the radius first.

(a) Find the area of the board.

(b) Find the perimeter.

21.5 The sine rule

This is a very useful trigonometric rule that allows you to work out lengths or angles in triangles.

In the triangle ABC, h is the perpendicular from B to the line AC and meets the line at the point M.

From triangle ABM, $\sin A = \dfrac{h}{c}$ or $h = c \sin A$.

From triangle BCM, $\sin C = \dfrac{h}{a}$ or $h = a \sin C$.

So $\qquad c \sin A = a \sin C$

or $\qquad \dfrac{c}{\sin C} = \dfrac{a}{\sin A}$

This result is called the **sine rule**.

It can easily be shown that both of these are equal to $\dfrac{b}{\sin B}$.

The full version of the sine rule is then written as

$$\frac{a}{\sin A} = \frac{b}{\sin B} = \frac{c}{\sin C}$$

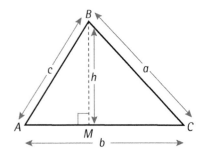

Use the sine rule when the problem has two sides and two angles.

EXAMPLE 7

In triangle PQR calculate the angle R correct to 1 d.p.

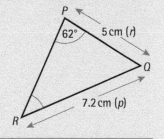

The sine rule can be inverted and this is useful when you want to work out an angle.

It makes it easier to rearrange the formula so that the unknown quantity is the numerator.

Using the sine rule

$$\frac{7.2}{\sin 62} = \frac{5}{\sin R}$$

$$\frac{\sin 62}{7.2} = \frac{\sin R}{5}$$

$$\sin R = 5 \times \frac{\sin 62°}{7.2}$$

$$= \frac{5 \times 0.8829}{7.2}$$

$$\sin R = 0.6131\ldots$$

$$R = 37.8182\ldots$$

$$R = 37.8° \text{ (correct to 1 d.p.)}$$

EXERCISE 21D

1 In triangle *ABC*, find the length *c* to 3 significant figures.

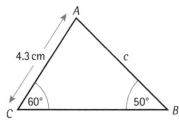

2 In the triangle *PQR*, angle $R = 120°$. Find angle *Q* to 1 d.p.

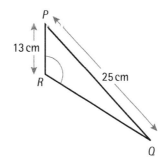

3 Find the length of each side marked with a letter.

(a)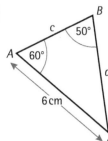

(b)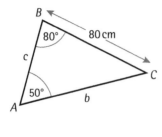

4 In a triangle *XYZ*, *XY* = 11 cm, *YZ* = 7.5 cm and the angle at *X* = 28°. Work out the two possible values for the angle at *Y*.

5 Nab End is due north of Midwich. Jim sets off from Midwich (*M*) and walks 8 km on a bearing 047° to reach Park Hill (*P*). He then walks to Nab End (*N*) on a bearing of 310°.

(a) Sketch the triangle *MNP*.

(b) Find angle *MNP*.

(c) Use the sine rule to find the distance from Park Hill to Nab End.

6 Triangle *RST* has angle *TRS* = 31°, side *RS* = 8 cm and side *ST* = 5 cm.

(a) Sketch two possible triangles that fit the description above.

(b) Find the two possible angles for ∠*STR*.

Remember, $\sin(180 - x) = \sin x$

7 Calculate the value of angle *ACB*.

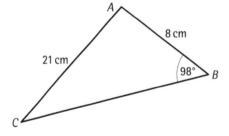

8 In triangle *ABC*, *BC* = 10 cm, *AB* = 8 cm and angle *ACB* = 48°. Find the two possible values of angle *BAC*.

9 In triangle *ABC*, *AB* = *x*, *AC* = 2*x* and angle *ACB* = 30°. Calculate angle *ABC*.

10 In triangle *ABC*, *AB* = 8 cm, angle *BD* = 40° and angle *ADB* = 80°.

Calculate

(a) the length of *AD*,

(b) angle *ADC*.

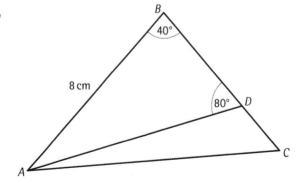

21.6 The cosine rule

This is another useful trigonometric formula that can be used on any triangle.

Consider the triangle ABC with h the perpendicular from B to the line AC, meeting the line at the point M.

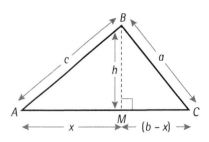

Using Pythagoras' theorem in triangle BCM gives

$$a^2 = h^2 + (b - x)^2$$
$$a^2 = h^2 + b^2 - 2bx + x^2$$
$$a^2 = h^2 + x^2 + b^2 - 2bx$$

If you now apply Pythagoras' theorem in triangle ABM you obtain

$$c^2 = h^2 + x^2$$

Substituting $h^2 + x^2 = c^2$ in the expression for a^2 gives

$$a^2 = c^2 + b^2 - 2bx$$

Now for triangle ABM we know that $\cos A = \dfrac{x}{c}$ and $x = c \cos A$

> Use the cosine rule when the problem has 3 sides and 1 angle.

Substituting for x we obtain the expression

$$a^2 = b^2 + c^2 - 2bc \cos A$$

> a is the side opposite angle A.

EXAMPLE 8

In triangle PQR, $PQ = 15$ cm, $QR = 5$ cm and $PR = 12$ cm. Calculate the angle at Q.

Using the cosine rule as normal

$$12^2 = 15^2 + 5^2 - 2 \times 5 \times 15 \cos A$$

$$144 = 225 + 25 - 150 \cos A$$

$$144 = 250 - 150 \cos A$$

$$150 \cos A = 106$$

$$= \frac{106}{150}$$

$$\cos Q = 0.7066$$

$$Q = 45.0°$$

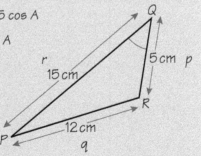

> Begin with a quick sketch.

> 12 is the side opposite the angle required.

> Do NOT subtract 150 from 250.

EXAMPLE 9

A yacht sets sail from port P and travels due East for 24 km towards a lighthouse L before turning on a bearing of 155°. The yacht travels a further 40 km towards a marker buoy B, before returning directly to port. How long is the journey from the buoy to port?   *continued* ▼

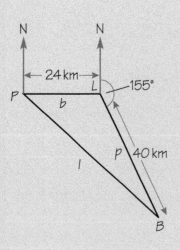

Begin with a sketch, marking on the diagram all the lengths and angles given.

Let $p = 40$ km, $b = 24$ km and
angle $PLB = (360° - 90° - 155°) = 115°$.
Let the distance required be l.

Using the cosine rule

$$l^2 = 24^2 + 40^2 - (2 \times 24 \times 40) \cos 115°$$

$$l^2 = 2176 - (-811.42)$$

$$l^2 = 2987.42$$

$$l = 54.7 \text{ km (3 s.f.)}$$

Remember for obtuse angles the cosine of an angle is negative, e.g. $\cos 120° = -\cos 60° = -0.5°$.

Take care when working this out on your calculator. Marks are often lost here.

Take the square root to find l.

EXERCISE 21E

1 In the triangle ABC shown below $BC = 9$ cm, $AB = 7$ cm and angle $B = 65°$. Work out the length of AC.

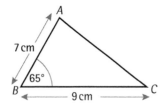

2 A triangular piece of land with corners at FGH is being fenced off as shown opposite. Only two sides have been completely fenced with $FG = 50$ m, $GH = 80$m and the angle at G is 115°.
Work out how much more fencing is needed to complete the job.

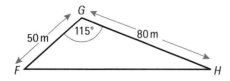

3 In the triangle shown, find angle C to 3 s.f.

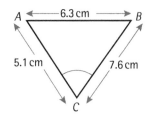

4 In triangle ABC, $AB = 14$ cm, $BC = 25$ cm and $AC = 15$ cm. Find the size of the angle at A (to 1 d.p.).

5

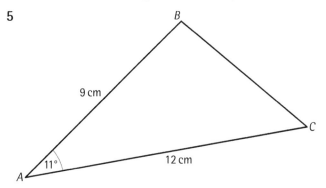

Calculate

(a) the length of side BC,

(b) the area of triangle ABC.

6 In triangle ABC, $AB = 2x$, $AC = x$, $BC = 14$ cm and angle $BAC = 120°$.
Calculate the value of x.

7 In triangle ABC, $AB = 13$ cm, $BC = 21$ cm and $AC = 20$ cm.

(a) Show that $\cos ABC = \dfrac{5}{13}$.

(b) Calculate the area of triangle ABC.

8 The sides of a triangle are of length 7 cm, 8 cm and 13 cm.

(a) Show that the largest angle in the triangle is 120°.

(b) Calculate the area of the triangle.

9 In triangle ABC, $AB = 8$ cm, $AC = 6$ cm and angle $BAC = 120°$.
Calculate

(a) the area of the triangle,

(b) the length of side BC.

10 Triangle ABC has vertices $A(6, 5)$, $B(9, 9)$ and $C(12, 5)$.
Calcualte

(a) the lengths of the sides of the triangle,

(b) angle ABC.

1

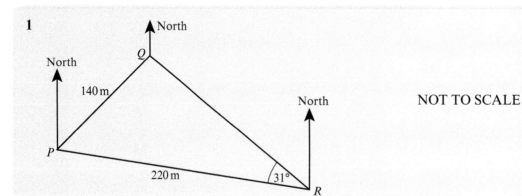

Theresa swims from P to Q, then from Q to R and finally returns from R to P.
$PQ = 140$ m, $RP = 220$ m and angle $PRQ = 31°$.
(a) Angle PQR is **obtuse**.
Calculate its size, to the nearest degree. [4]
(b) The bearing of Q from P is 060°.
Calculate the bearing of R from Q. [1]

(CIE Paper 2, Nov 2000)

2

A boat B is 1200 metres from a lighthouse L and 750 metres from a rock R. Angle LBR = 110°.
(a) Calculate
 (i) the length LR, correct to the nearest metre, [4]
 (ii) angle BLR, correct to the nearest degree. [4]
(b) The bearing of B from L is 053°. Calculate
 (i) the bearing of L from B, [2]
 (ii) the bearing of B from R. [2]

(CIE Paper 4, Jun 2001)

3

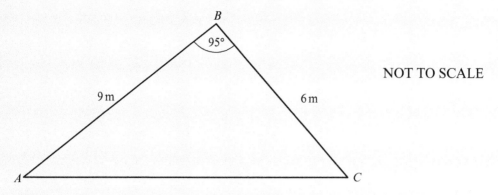

NOT TO SCALE

The triangular area ABC is part of Henri's garden.
$AB = 9$m, $BC = 6$m and angle $ABC = 95°$.
Henri puts a fence along AC and plants vegetables in the triangular area ABC.
Calculate

(a) the length of the fence AC. [3]

(b) the area for vegetables. [2]

(CIE Paper 2, Jun 2002)

4

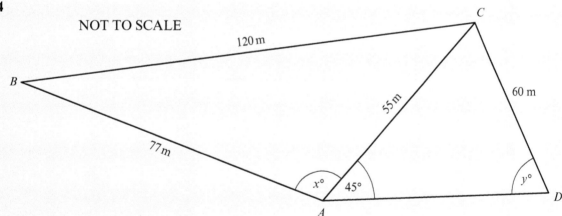

NOT TO SCALE

In quadrilateral $ABCD$, $AB = 77$ m, $BC = 120$ m, $CD = 60$ m and diagonal $AC = 55$ m.
Angle $CAD = 45°$, angle $BAC = x°$ and angle $ADC = y°$.

(a) Calculate the value of x. [4]

(b) Calculate the value of y. [4]

(CIE Paper 4, Jun 2003)

Chapter 22

Further algebraic methods

This chapter will show you how to

✔ simplify, add, subtract, multiply and divide algebraic fractions and use them to solve equations

✔ change of subject of a formula where the variable appears on both sides of the equation

22.1 Simplifying algebraic fractions

You will need to know
* how to factorise ... common factor, quadratic, difference of two perfect squares

Algebraic fractions have letters, or combinations of letters and numbers, in their numerator and denominator.

$\dfrac{4}{a} \quad \dfrac{b}{2} \quad \dfrac{2pq}{r} \quad \dfrac{x+6}{x} \quad \dfrac{4}{x-5} \quad \dfrac{18x^3}{3x} \quad \dfrac{2x-6}{10x}$ are all algebraic fractions.

Algebraic fractions can sometimes be simplified. Look for a common factor of the numerator and the denominator.

$\dfrac{x+6}{x}$ is an algebraic fraction that cannot be simplified.

> You cannot cancel the x terms ... **never cancel across a + or a − sign.**

$\dfrac{18x^3}{3x}$ can be simplified. $\dfrac{18x^3}{3x} = \dfrac{18 \times x \times x \times x}{3 \times x} = 6x^2$

> You can see that there are common factors of 3 and x.

$\dfrac{2x-6}{10x}$ can be simplified. $\dfrac{2x-6}{10x} = \dfrac{2(x-3)}{10x} = \dfrac{x-3}{5x}$

> Factorise then divide top and bottom by 2.

To simplify algebraic fractions

(1) factorise
(2) divide by the HCF (or cancel common factors).

> Remember to factorise first.

EXAMPLE 1

Simplify the following, where possible.

(a) $\dfrac{2x}{x + 3}$ (b) $\dfrac{3ab}{6a^2}$ (c) $\dfrac{4x - 16}{8}$

(d) $\dfrac{x^2 + 3x - 4}{x + 4}$ (e) $\dfrac{m^2 - 25}{m^2 - 3m - 10}$

(a) $\dfrac{2x}{x + 3}$ cannot be simplified

(b) $\dfrac{3ab}{6a^2} = \dfrac{3 \times a \times b}{6 \times a \times a} = \dfrac{b}{2a}$

(c) $\dfrac{4x - 16}{8} = \dfrac{4(x - 4)}{8} = \dfrac{x - 4}{2}$

(d) $\dfrac{x^2 + 3x - 4}{x + 4} = \dfrac{(x + 4)(x - 1)}{(x + 4)} = x - 1$

(e) $\dfrac{m^2 - 25}{m^2 - 3m - 10} = \dfrac{(m + 5)(m - 5)}{(m - 5)(m + 2)} = \dfrac{m + 5}{m + 2}$

> Always look for a common factor first.
> Then look for other forms of factorising such as quadratics and the difference of two perfect squares.
> All of these are present in these examples.

> Remember that you can only cancel whole brackets.

EXERCISE 22A

Simplify the following expressions, where possible.

1 $\dfrac{3x + 6}{9}$ 2 $\dfrac{4x + 5}{2}$ 3 $\dfrac{4x}{2x - 10}$

4 $\dfrac{4a^2}{6ab}$ 5 $\dfrac{3a + 2b}{a}$ 6 $\dfrac{10 - 5f}{2f}$

7 $\dfrac{ab + 2a}{a^2}$ 8 $\dfrac{p + 4}{3p + 6}$ 9 $\dfrac{5 - p}{5 + p}$

10 $\dfrac{x + 2}{x^2 - x - 6}$ 11 $\dfrac{x^2 + 7x + 6}{x + 1}$ 12 $\dfrac{y^2 - y - 20}{y^2 + y - 12}$

13 $\dfrac{x^2 - 36}{x^2 + 8x + 12}$ 14 $\dfrac{m^2 - 1}{5m^2 - 2m - 3}$ 15 $\dfrac{2x^2 - 5x - 12}{3x^2 - 7x - 20}$

22.2 Multiplying and dividing algebraic fractions

To multiply numerical fractions you multiply the numerators and multiply the denominators, simplifying if possible.

To divide numerical fractions you invert the second fraction and multiply, simplifying if possible.

The rules are exactly the same for algebraic fractions, but always remember to look for any factors before you simplify.

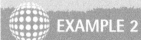

EXAMPLE 2

Work out the following, simplifying your answers.

(a) $\dfrac{2pq}{r} \times \dfrac{pr^2}{3q^2}$ (b) $\dfrac{4}{a} \div \dfrac{b}{2}$

(c) $\dfrac{2x + 6}{x^2 + 4x} \div \dfrac{x^2 + 2x - 3}{x^2 - 16}$

(a) $\dfrac{2pq}{r} \times \dfrac{pr^2}{3q^2} = \dfrac{2 \times p \times \cancel{q}}{\cancel{r}} \times \dfrac{p \times \cancel{r} \times r}{3 \times \cancel{q} \times q} = \dfrac{2pq}{r} \times \dfrac{2p^2r}{3q}$

(b) $\dfrac{4}{a} \div \dfrac{b}{2} = \dfrac{4}{a} \times \dfrac{2}{b} = \dfrac{8}{ab}$

(c) $\dfrac{2x + 6}{x^2 + 4x} \div \dfrac{x^2 + 2x - 3}{x^2 - 16} = \dfrac{2x + 6}{x^2 + 4x} \times \dfrac{x^2 - 16}{x^2 + 2x - 3}$

$= \dfrac{2\cancel{(x + 3)}}{x(x + 4)} \times \dfrac{\cancel{(x + 4)}(x - 4)}{\cancel{(x + 3)}(x - 1)}$

$= \dfrac{2(x - 4)}{x(x - 1)}$

In (c), invert the second fraction and change ÷ to ×.

Then factorise and cancel any common factors.

EXERCISE 22B

Work out the following, simplifying your answers.

1 $\dfrac{a}{4} \times \dfrac{a}{3}$ 2 $\dfrac{b}{2} \div \dfrac{a}{5}$ 3 $\dfrac{pq}{r} \times \dfrac{r^2}{p}$ 4 $\dfrac{x}{y^2} \div \dfrac{x}{yz}$

5 $\dfrac{y}{3} \times \dfrac{y + 2}{2}$ 6 $\dfrac{x + 1}{4} \times \dfrac{1}{3x + 3}$

7 $\dfrac{10a^3}{3b} \div \dfrac{5a}{6b^2}$ 8 $\dfrac{x^2 + 5x}{x^2 + 2x} \times \dfrac{x + 2}{4}$

9 $\dfrac{2x - 3}{14} \div \dfrac{4x - 6}{7}$ 10 $\dfrac{m^2 - 9}{4} \times \dfrac{8}{m + 3}$

11 $\dfrac{a^2 - 2a}{a^2 - 1} \div \dfrac{3a - 6}{a^2 + 4a + 3}$ 12 $\dfrac{y^2 - 16}{y^2 - y} \div \dfrac{y^2 - 9y + 20}{2y - 2}$

22.3 Addition and subtraction of algebraic fractions

When adding or subtracting algebraic fractions, the rules are the same as for numerical fractions. But *before you find the LCM* you must *factorise* the numerators and/or denominators if possible.

EXAMPLE 3

Work out **(a)** $\dfrac{2}{5} + \dfrac{3}{7}$ **(b)** $\dfrac{2}{a} + \dfrac{3}{b}$ **(c)** $\dfrac{x+4}{5} + \dfrac{x-6}{4}$

(a) $\dfrac{2}{5} + \dfrac{3}{7}$

$= \dfrac{14}{35} + \dfrac{15}{35}$

$= \dfrac{29}{35}$

(c) $\dfrac{x+4}{5} + \dfrac{x-6}{4}$

$= \dfrac{4(x+4)}{20} + \dfrac{5(x-6)}{20}$

$= \dfrac{4(x+4) + 5(x-6)}{20}$

$= \dfrac{4x + 16 + 5x - 30}{20} = \dfrac{9x - 14}{20}$

(b) $\dfrac{2}{a} + \dfrac{3}{b}$

$= \dfrac{2b}{ab} + \dfrac{3a}{ab}$

$= \dfrac{2b + 3a}{ab}$

> Look at a numerical example and an algebraic example side by side ... you will see the similar approach.

> Just as $5 \times 7 = 35$ is the LCM of 5 and 7 then $a \times b = ab$ is the LCM of a and b.
>
> Notice the equivalent fractions $\dfrac{2}{a} = \dfrac{2b}{ab}$ and $\dfrac{3}{b} = \dfrac{3a}{ab}$.

> The LCM of 4 and 5 is 20. Notice the equivalent fractions on the first line of the solution.

EXAMPLE 4

Simplify **(a)** $\dfrac{5}{2x} + \dfrac{3}{8y}$ **(b)** $\dfrac{4}{x+1} - \dfrac{3}{x-5}$

(a) $\dfrac{5}{2x} + \dfrac{3}{8y}$

$= \dfrac{20y}{8xy} + \dfrac{3x}{8xy}$

$= \dfrac{20y + 3x}{8xy}$

> Notice that in (a) the LCM of $2x$ and $8y$ is $8xy$.
>
> You do not need to use $2x \times 8y = 16xy$ although it is not wrong to do so ... you will need to simplify later if you do.

(b) $\dfrac{4}{x+1} - \dfrac{3}{x-5}$

$= \dfrac{4(x-5)}{(x+1)(x-5)} - \dfrac{3(x+5)}{(x+1)(x-5)}$

$= \dfrac{4(x-5) - 3(x+1)}{(x+1)(x-5)}$

$= \dfrac{4x - 20 - 3x - 3}{(x+1)(x-5)}$

$= \dfrac{x - 23}{(x+1)(x-5)}$

> When the denominator has more than one term, put brackets round the expression. It helps you to spot the LCM and get the correct equivalent fractions.

> Take care with the signs when you expand the brackets in the numerator.

Simplify each of the following.

1 $\dfrac{2x}{3} + \dfrac{x}{5}$ 　　　　2 $\dfrac{3}{a} + \dfrac{4}{b}$

3 $\dfrac{5}{x} - \dfrac{3}{2y}$ 　　　　4 $\dfrac{3}{4x} - \dfrac{2}{3x^2}$

5 $\dfrac{6}{5x} + \dfrac{3}{2xy}$ 　　　6 $\dfrac{x-1}{3} + \dfrac{x+5}{4}$

7 $\dfrac{2x-1}{5} + \dfrac{x+2}{4}$ 　　8 $\dfrac{x+6}{2} - \dfrac{x+1}{3}$

9 $\dfrac{y-3}{5} - \dfrac{y-2}{3}$ 　　10 $\dfrac{2m+3}{5} - \dfrac{3m-4}{2}$

11 $\dfrac{2}{x+3} + \dfrac{5}{x-1}$ 　　12 $\dfrac{3}{x+4} - \dfrac{1}{x+3}$

22.4 Equations involving algebraic fractions

You can use algebraic fractions to solve quite complicated equations.

The equation in the next example can be solved in two ways.

EXAMPLE 5

Solve the equation $\dfrac{3x+1}{2} - \dfrac{x+4}{3} = 5$

Method A

$$\dfrac{3x+1}{2} - \dfrac{x+4}{3} = 5$$

$$\dfrac{3(3x+1) - 2(x+4)}{6} = 5$$

$$\dfrac{9x+3-2x-8}{6} = 5$$

$$\dfrac{7x-5}{6} = 5$$

$$7x - 5 = 30$$

$$7x = 35$$

$$x = 5$$

continued ▼

Method B

$$\frac{3x + 1}{2} - \frac{x + 4}{3} = 5$$

The LCM of the terms in the denominator is 6

Multiply all terms by 6

$$\frac{6(3x + 1)}{2} - \frac{6(x + 4)}{3} = 5 \times 6$$

$$3(3x + 1) - 2(x + 4) = 30$$

$$9x + 3 - 2x - 8 = 30$$

$$7x - 5 = 30$$

$$7x = 35$$

$$x = 5$$

Mutiplying all terms by the LCM of the denominators (in this case 6) will give you an equation with no fractions in it.

 EXAMPLE 6

Solve the equation $\qquad \dfrac{4}{2x - 1} - \dfrac{1}{x + 1} = 1$

Method A

$$\frac{4}{2x - 1} - \frac{1}{x + 1} = 1$$

$$\frac{4(x + 1) - 1(2x - 1)}{(2x - 1)(x + 1)} = 1$$

$$\frac{4x + 4 - 2x - 1}{(2x - 1)(x + 1)} = 1$$

$$\frac{2x + 5}{(2x - 1)(x + 1)} = 1$$

$$2x + 5 = (2x - 1)(x + 1)$$

$$2x + 5 = 2x^2 + x - 1$$

$$0 = 2x^2 - x - 6$$

$$0 = (2x + 3)(x - 2)$$

Either $\quad 2x + 3 = 0 \quad$ giving $x = -1.5$
or $\qquad x - 2 = 0 \quad$ giving $x = 2$

Notice the equivalent fractions. Take care with the signs when expanding the numerator.

Multiply both sides by $(2x - 1)(x + 1)$ then expand and rearrange to get a quadratic equation.

These questions often have two solutions.

continued ▼

Method B

$$\frac{4}{2x-1} - \frac{1}{x+1} = 1$$

The LCM of the terms in the denominator is $(2x-1)(x+1)$

Multiply all terms by $(2x-1)(x+1)$

$$\frac{4(2x-1)(x+1)}{(2x-1)} - \frac{(2x-1)(x+1)}{(x+1)} = (2x-1)(x+1)$$

$$4(x+1) - (2x-1) = (2x-1)(x+1)$$

$$4x + 4 - 2x + 1 = 2x^2 + x - 1$$

$$0 = 2x^2 - x - 6$$

$$0 = (2x+3)(x-2)$$

Either $2x+3 = 0$ giving $x = -1.5$
or $x - 2 = 0$ giving $x = 2$

> Multiply throughout by the LCM of the terms in the denominator i.e. by $(2x-1)(x+1)$.
>
> Then simplify each term, expand and rearrange to get a quadratic equation.
>
> This is a standard method with which you need to be familiar.

EXERCISE 22D

The methods of solution are quite similar to each other and you can use either ... just choose the one you prefer.

Solve each of these equations.

1 $\dfrac{x+1}{2} + \dfrac{x-4}{3} = 5$

2 $\dfrac{x+5}{4} + \dfrac{x-1}{2} = 3$

3 $\dfrac{x-2}{3} - \dfrac{x+1}{4} = 1$

4 $\dfrac{2x-3}{3} + \dfrac{3x+1}{4} = 12$

5 $\dfrac{5x+1}{4} - \dfrac{x-4}{6} = 2$

6 $\dfrac{2x-5}{2} - \dfrac{4x-1}{3} = 0.5$

7 $\dfrac{3}{x+1} + \dfrac{2}{2x-3} = 1$

8 $\dfrac{9}{x-2} + \dfrac{5}{x+2} = 2$

9 $\dfrac{7}{x-3} - \dfrac{6}{x-1} = 2$

10 $\dfrac{9}{2x-7} + \dfrac{6}{x-1} = 3$

11 $\dfrac{11}{4x-5} - \dfrac{8}{x+1} = 1$

12 $\dfrac{7}{2x-1} + \dfrac{11}{x+1} = 6$

22.5 Changing the subject of a formula

In this section you will see how to change the subject of a formula when the subject appears more than once and on both sides of the formula.

You use the same methods as for solving equations. You will see that a pattern emerges for the order in which you do the operations.

> You learned how to change the subject of a formula in Chapter 8. In all of the questions the subject only appeared once.

EXAMPLE 7

(a) Solve the equation $2(2m + 1) = 7(m - 1)$.

(b) Make m the subject of the formula $a(bm + c) = d(m - e)$.

(a) $2(2m + 1) = 7(m - 1)$ (b) $a(bm + c) = d(m - e)$

      $4m + 2 = 7m - 7$ $abm + ac = dm - de$

        $2 + 7 = 7m - 4m$ $ac + de = dm - abm$

          $9 = 3m$ $ac + de = m(d - ab)$

          $\dfrac{9}{3} = m$ $\dfrac{ac + de}{d - ab} = m$

          $3 = m$

Expand.
Rearrange.
Factorise.
Divide through by $(d - ab)$.

 EXAMPLE 8

(a) Solve the equation $5 = \dfrac{y + 3}{y - 4}$.

(b) Make y the subject of the formula $t = \dfrac{hy + 3}{ky - 4}$.

(a) $5 = \dfrac{y + 3}{y - 4}$ (b) $t = \dfrac{hy + 3}{ky - 4}$

   $5(y - 4) = y + 3$ $t(ky - 4) = hy + 3$

   $5y - 20 = y + 3$ $tky - 4t = hy + 3$

     $5y - y = 3 + 20$ $tky - hy = 3 + 4t$

        $4y = 23$ $y(tk - h) = 3 + 4t$

         $y = \dfrac{23}{4}$ $y = \dfrac{3 + 4t}{tk - h}$

         $y = 5.75$

Multiply through by $(ky - 4)$.
Expand.
Rearrange.
Factorise.
Divide through by $(tk - h)$.

EXAMPLE 9

(a) Solve the equation $\sqrt{\dfrac{2a}{a-1}} = 3$.

(b) Make a the subject of the formula $\sqrt{\dfrac{2a}{a-x}} = 3x$.

(a) $\sqrt{\dfrac{2a}{a-1}} = 3$

(b) $\sqrt{\dfrac{2a}{a-x}} = 3x$ — Square both sides.

$\dfrac{2a}{a-1} = 9$

$\dfrac{2a}{a-x} = 9x^2$ — Multiply through by $(a-x)$.

$2a = 9(a-1)$

$2a = 9x^2(a-x)$

$2a = 9a - 9$

$2a = 9x^2a - 9x^3$ — Expand.

$9 = 9a - 2a$

$9x^3 = 9x^2a - 2a$ — Rearrange.

$9 = 7a$

$9x^3 = a(9x^2 - 2)$ — Factorise.

$\dfrac{9}{7} = a$

$\dfrac{9x^3}{(9x^2 - 2)} = a$ — Divide through by $(9x^2 - 2)$.

In this section each example also includes a traditional equation so that you can see the similarity in the method.

 EXERCISE 22E

You can see the pattern of the order in which you do the operations. The order is always the same.

Make y the subject of each of these formulae.

1 $my + b = d - my$

2 $py + 3 = 7 + qy$

3 $ay - x = w + by$

4 $w(y + a) = k(y + b)$

5 $h(ay - c) = m(y + d)$

6 $\dfrac{h-y}{h+y} = k$

7 $\dfrac{y+3}{y-2} = \dfrac{d}{e}$

8 $\sqrt{\dfrac{2y+a}{y}} = m$

9 $\sqrt{\dfrac{3y}{m-y}} = 2w$

10 $T = 2k\sqrt{\dfrac{y}{g}}$

11 $ky^2 + 2e = f - hy^2$

12 $m(2y^2 + a) = h(w - 3y^2)$

EXAMINATION QUESTIONS

1 **(a)** Write $\dfrac{1}{x-3} - \dfrac{1}{x}$ as a single fraction in its simplest form. [2]

(b) Use your answer to part(a) to make y the subject of
$$\frac{1}{y} = \frac{1}{x-3} - \frac{1}{x}$$
[2]

(CIE Paper 2, Jun 2000)

---

2 Write $2x - \dfrac{10x}{5-x}$ as a single fraction. [2]

(CIE Paper 2, Nov 2002)

---

3 Work out as a single fraction
$$\frac{2}{x-3} - \frac{1}{x+4}.$$
[3]

(CIE Paper 2, Jun 2003)

---

4 **(a)** Write $\dfrac{3}{x} - \dfrac{2}{x+1}$ as a single fraction in its simplest form. [3]

(b) Solve the equation
$$\frac{3}{x} - \frac{2}{x+1} = 0.$$
[1]

(CIE Paper 2, Nov 2003)

---

5 Simplify $\dfrac{x+2}{x} - \dfrac{x}{x+2}.$

Write your answer as a fraction in its simplest form. [3]

(CIE Paper 2, Jun 2005)

Chapter 23

Functions

This chapter will show you how to

✔ understand and use function notation

23.1 Function notation and mappings

You are familiar with writing equations to represent x–y relationships and the graphs of these relationships.

For example, $y = 3x^2 - 4$

There are other notations that can be used to relate x and y.

Two alternatives for the expression $y = 3x^2 - 4$ are:

$$f : x \rightarrow 3x^2 - 4 \quad \text{and} \quad f(x) = 3x^2 - 4$$

$f : x \rightarrow 3x^2 - 4$ is known as a **mapping** because it maps numbers on the x-axis onto corresponding numbers on the y-axis.

$f(x) = 3x^2 - 4$ is called **function** notation. $f(x)$ is read as 'f of x' and means a function of x. You can think of $f(x)$ in terms of a series of function boxes.

For the function $f(x) = 3x^2 - 4$, they will look like this.

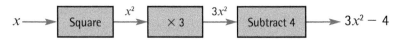

As you follow the instruction in each of the boxes in turn, in the correct order, you turn a value of x into a value of $f(x)$, or y.

> A mapping simply turns an x-value into a y-value. It is just like calculating y from an equation or from a table of values before you plot a graph.

> $y = 3x^2 - 4$, $f : x \rightarrow 3x^2 - 4$ and $f(x) = 3x^2 - 4$ are equivalent expressions. You can use whichever one you prefer but you need to be prepared to meet any of them in an exam.

EXAMPLE 1

$f(x) = 8 - x^2$. Find the value of $f(0)$, $f(2)$ and $f(-3)$.

___

$f(0) = 8 - 0^2 = 8 - 0 = 8$

$f(2) = 8 - 2^2 = 8 - 4 = 4$

$f(-3) = 8 - (-3)^2 = 8 - 9 = -1$

> Simply replace x by the number given and calculate the value of the expression.

If you think of functions as mappings then you will have a diagram like this.

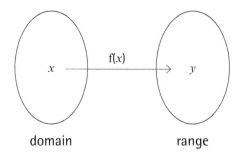

If you know what f(x) is then the diagram becomes more detailed.

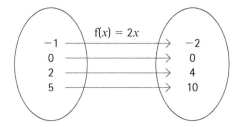

Not all mappings are functions.

A function is a mapping where every element in the domain maps to **only** one element in the range.

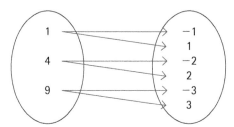

This is not a function.

You will also find letters other than f used.

EXAMPLE 2

$g(x) = 2 - x$ and $h(x) = x^2 + 2x - 5$.

Find the value of $g(-5)$, $g(8)$, $h(0)$ and $h(6)$.

$g(x) = 2 - x$

$g(-5) = 2 - (-5) = 7$

$g(8) = 2 - 8 = -6$

$h(x) = x^2 + 2x - 5$

$h(0) = 0^2 + 2 \times 0 - 5 = -5$

Substitute the numbers for x.

Problems can also be set in this notation.

 EXAMPLE 3

$p : x \rightarrow 2x - 5$. Find the value of x for which $p(x) = 16$

$p(x) = 2x - 5$ and $p(x) = 16$ so

$2x - 5 = 16$

$2x = 21$

$x = 10.5$

You now have an equation to solve in the usual way.

EXERCISE 23A

1 $f(x) = x^2 + 3$. Find the value of
   (a) $f(0)$ (b) $f(3)$ (c) $f(-3)$.

2 $g(x) = 4 - x$. Find the value of
   (a) $g(-8)$ (b) $g(4)$ (c) $g(0)$.

3 $h(x) = 2x^2 - 3x + 1$. Find the value of
   (a) $h(0)$ (b) $h(2)$ (c) $h(-1)$.

4 $p(x) = \dfrac{x - 5}{4}$. Find the value of
   (a) $p(9)$ (b) $p(5)$ (c) $p(5\frac{1}{2})$.

5 $q(x) = (4x - 3)^2$. Find the value of
   (a) $q(\frac{1}{4})$ (b) $q(\frac{1}{2})$ (c) $q(9.5)$.

6 $f(x) = x - 3$. Find the value of x when $f(x) = 5$.

7 $g(x) = x^2 - 9$. Find the value of x when $g(x) = 16$.

8 $h(x) = 2x^3$. Find the value of x when $h(x) = 54$.

9 $p(x) = x^2 - 5x + 6$. Find the values of x when $p(x) = 0$.

10 $q(x) = \frac{1}{2}x$. Find the value of x when $q(x) = \frac{1}{8}$.

Inverse functions

The inverse function is written $f^{-1}(x)$.

The inverse function does the opposite operation to the function.

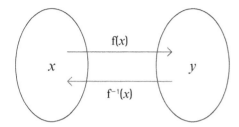

The inverse only exists if **one** element of the domain maps to only **one** element of the range.

Here are some examples of functions and their inverses.

Function	Inverse function
$f(x) = x + 3$	$f^{-1}(x) = x - 3$
$f(x) = x - 5$	$f^{-1}(x) = x + 5$
$f(x) = 2x$	$f^{-1}(x) = \dfrac{x}{2}$
$f(x) = \dfrac{x}{3}$	$f^{-1}(x) = 3x$

More complicated fuctions need a different technique.

There are two main methods for doing this.

EXAMPLE 4

Find $f^{-1}(x)$ if $f(x) = \dfrac{2x - 3}{5}$

Using mappings.

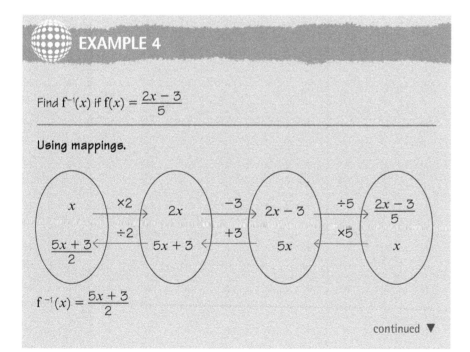

$f^{-1}(x) = \dfrac{5x + 3}{2}$

Build up the function.

Find each inverse and apply it.

continued ▼

Using algebra

$$y = \frac{2x - 3}{5}$$

$$5y = 2x - 3$$

$$5y + 3 = 2x$$

$$\frac{5y + 3}{2} = x$$

$$\frac{5x + 3}{2} = y$$

$$f^{-1}(x) = \frac{5x + 3}{2}$$

Rearrange to make x the subject.

Interchange x and y.

Either of these methods will be acceptable in the examination.

EXERCISE 23B

1 $f(x) = x - 6$.   Write down $f^{-1}(x)$.

2 $g(x) = x + 1$.   Write down $g^{-1}(x)$.

3 $h(x) = 2x$.   Write down $h^{-1}(x)$.

4 $p(x) = \frac{1}{2}x$.   Write down $p^{-1}(x)$.

For the following functions find their inverse.
You may use either method.

5 $f(x) = 2x - 5$

6 $g(x) = \frac{x + 5}{2}$

7 $h(x) = \frac{3x - 2}{4}$

8 $p(x) = 3(2x + 7)$

9 $q(x) = (2x + 5)^3$

10 $r(x) = \frac{(2x^3 - 8)}{7}$

Composite functions

Functions may be combined together.

The order is very important

The composite function $fg(x)$ means $f(g(x))$.

This is NOT $f(x) \times g(x)$.

EXAMPLE 5

$f : x = 2x$ and $g : x = x - 5$. Find $fg(x)$ and $gf(x)$

These are not the same.

$fg(x)$

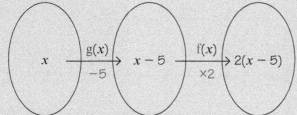

$$fg(x) = 2(x - 5)$$

$g(x)$ first and then $f(x)$.

$g\, f(x)$

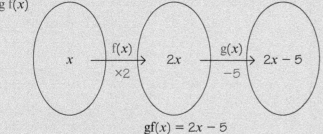

$$gf(x) = 2x - 5$$

This may also be numerical as in Example 7.

$f(x)$ first and then $g(x)$.

EXAMPLE 6

$p(x) = 2x - 3$ and $q(x) = 3x + 1$.

Find (a) $pq(2)$　　(b) $qp(1)$　　(c) $ppp(4)$

In this type of example no diagrams are necessary.

(a)　$q(2) = 3 \times 2 + 1 = 7$ and $p(7) = 2 \times 7 - 3 = 11$
　　so $pq(2) = p(7) = 11$

$pq(2)$ means put 2 into $q(x)$ and the result into $p(x)$.

(b)　$p(1) = 2 \times 1 - 3 = -1$ and $q(-1) = 3 \times -1 + 1 = -2$
　　so $qp(1) = q(-1) = -2$

$qp(1)$ means put 1 into $p(x)$ and the result into $q(x)$.

(c)　$p(4) = 5$　　　$p(5) = 7$　　　$p(7) = 11$
　　so $ppp(4) = pp(5) = p(7) = 11$

EXERCISE 23C

1　$f(x) = 4 - x$　　　$g(x) = x^2 + 1$　　　$h(x) = 5(x - 2)$. Find
　(a) $f(9)$　　　　　　(b) $g(4)$　　　　　　(c) $h(0)$
　(d) $gf(2)$　　　　　(e) $gh(3)$　　　　　(f) $hh(5)$.

2 $p(x) = \dfrac{x + 2}{3}$ $q(x) = x^3$ $r(x) = \dfrac{1}{x}$. Find

   (a) $p(-5)$ (b) $q(-4)$ (c) $r(4)$

   (d) $qp(4)$ (e) $rq(2)$ (f) $rr(8)$.

3 $f : x = 4x - 1$ $g : x = \dfrac{x + 1}{4}$ $h : x = \tfrac{1}{2}x$. Find

   (a) $f(2)$ (b) $g(7)$ (c) $h(12)$

   (d) $gf(5)$ (e) $gh(6)$ (f) $hh(1)$.

4 $f : x = x + 8$ $g : x = 4x$ $h : x = \dfrac{x}{2}$. Find

   (a) $fg(x)$ (b) $gf(x)$ (c) $fgh(x)$

   (d) $ff(x)$ (e) $gg(x)$ (f) $hh(x)$.

5 $f(x) = 5x + 2$ $g(x) = \dfrac{x - 2}{5}$ $h(x) = x^2$. Find

   (a) $gf(x)$ (b) $fg(x)$ (c) $fh(x)$

   (d) $hf(x)$ (e) $hh(x)$ (f) $ff(x)$.

6 $f(x) = 2x - 11$ $g(x) = 2(x - 4)$. Find

   (a) $f(3)$ (b) $g(2)$ (c) $fg(4)$ (d) $gg(8)$

   (e) $fg(x)$ (f) $ff(x)$ (g) $f^{-1}(x)$ (h) $f^{-1}(2)$

   (i) the value of x for which $f(x) = 2g(x)$.

EXAMINATION QUESTIONS

1 $f(x) = 3 + \sqrt{2x}$, for $x > 0$. Find $f^{-1}(x)$. [3]

(CIE Paper 2, Jun 2000)

---

2 $f : x \to 3 - 2x$ and $g : x \to \dfrac{x + 1}{4}$, for all values of x.
  (a) Find $f\left(-\frac{3}{4}\right)$. [1]
  (b) Find the inverse function, $g^{-1}(x)$. [2]
  (c) Find the composite function $fg(x)$, giving your answer as a single fraction. [2]

(CIE Paper 2, Nov 2000)

---

3 $f(x) = \dfrac{x + 1}{3x}$ for $x > 0$ $g(x) = 3 - 3x$ for any value of x.

  (a) Find $f\left(\frac{3}{4}\right)$, giving your answer as a fraction. [1]
  (b) Find $gf\left(\frac{3}{4}\right)$, giving your answer as a fraction. [1]
  (c) Find $g^{-1}(18)$. [2]

(CIE Paper 2, Jun 2001)

---

4 $f(x) = x^{\frac{1}{3}}$ and $g(x) = 2x^2 - 5$ for all values of x.
  (a) Find
      (i) $g(4)$, [1]
      (ii) $fg(4)$. [1]
  (b) Find an expression for $gf(x)$ in terms of x. [1]
  (c) Find $f^{-1}(x)$. [1]

(CIE Paper 2, Jun 2002)

---

5 $f : x \to 1 - 2x$ and $g : x \to \dfrac{x}{2}$.

  (a) Find $fg(7)$. [2]
  (b) (i) Solve $f(x) = g(x)$. [2]
      (ii) The graphs of $y = f(x)$ and $y = g(x)$ meet at M.
         Find the co-ordinates of M. [1]

(CIE Paper 2, Nov 2003)

6 $f(x) = \dfrac{x+1}{2}$ and $g(x) = 2x + 1$.

(a) Find the value of gf(9). [1]
(b) Find gf(x), giving your answer in its simplest form. [2]
(c) Solve the equation of $g^{-1}(x) = 1$. [2]

(CIE Paper 2, Jun 2004)

---

7 $f(x) = x^2 - 4x + 3$ and $g(x) = 2x - 1$.
(a) Solve f $(x) = 0$. [2]
(b) Find $g^{-1}(x)$. [2]
(c) Solve f(x) = g(x), giving your answer correct to 2 decimal places. [5]
(d) Find the value of gf(-2). [2]
(e) Find fg(x). Simplify your answer. [2]

(CIE Paper 4, Jun 2005)

Chapter 24

Vectors

This chapter will show you how to
- ✔ define a vector quantity
- ✔ use the correct notation for vectors
- ✔ add and subtract vectors
- ✔ recognise displacement vectors and position vectors
- ✔ solve problems using vector geometry

24.1 Definition and representation of a vector

A **vector** quantity is one which has magnitude (size) and direction.

Examples   Displacement (16 km on a bearing of 065°)
Velocity (110 km/h due east)
Acceleration (5 m/s² along the x-axis)
Force (150 N acting vertically upwards)

> Displacement is distance in a particular direction.

Quantities that have magnitude but no direction are called **scalar** quantities.

> Velocity and speed are measured in the same units.
> Velocity is speed in a particular direction.

Examples   Mass of car (1470 kg)
Length of room (3.6 m)
Speed of train (125 mph)

A vector can be represented by a **directed line segment** which is simply a line with an arrow on it

Length of line = magnitude of vector.

Direction of arrow = direction of vector.

24.2 Vector notation

You will recall using vectors in Chapter 13 (Transformations). They were column vectors of the form $\begin{pmatrix} 3 \\ -2 \end{pmatrix}$ where the numbers were the components in the x and y directions.

There are other ways of writing vectors and you need to be familiar with all of them.

The vector shown is written as $\overrightarrow{AB}$ which shows you that it is a displacement from A to B.

If lower case letters are used, it will be in **bold** print in a textbook, but since you cannot write in bold print you should <u>underline</u> the letter when you write it.

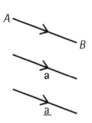

Both the capital letter notation and the bold lower case notation will be used in the rest of this chapter.

24.3 Multiplication by a scalar

Vectors are equal if they have the same magnitude and direction.

So, for example,

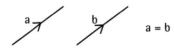

$a = b$

Vectors can be multiplied by scalars (numbers).

These examples show you some of the outcomes.

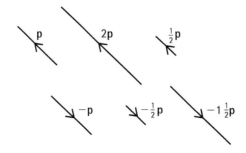

All of these vectors are parallel since they are written **in terms of p only**, but they have different lengths and the negative ones point in the opposite direction.

EXAMPLE 1

$$a = \begin{pmatrix} 3 \\ -1 \end{pmatrix}, \quad b = \begin{pmatrix} -4 \\ 2 \end{pmatrix}, \quad c = \begin{pmatrix} 0 \\ 4 \end{pmatrix}.$$

(a) Draw these vectors on a square grid

    a   b   c   −a   2b $\frac{1}{2}$c   −1$\frac{1}{2}$b   −2c

(b) What is the column vector notation for **(i)** 2a **(ii)** $\frac{1}{2}$b **(iii)** −c?

(a)

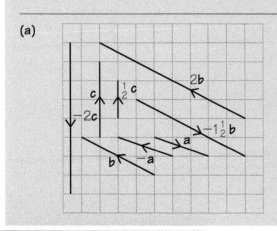

$a = \begin{pmatrix} 3 \\ -1 \end{pmatrix}$ which is 3 squares right and 1 square down.

$b = \begin{pmatrix} -4 \\ 2 \end{pmatrix}$ which is 4 squares left and 2 squares up.

$c = \begin{pmatrix} 0 \\ 4 \end{pmatrix}$ which is 4 squares up.

continued ▼

(b) **(i)** $2a = 2\begin{pmatrix} 3 \\ -1 \end{pmatrix} = \begin{pmatrix} 6 \\ -2 \end{pmatrix}$

  (ii) $\frac{1}{2}a = \frac{1}{2}\begin{pmatrix} -4 \\ 2 \end{pmatrix} = \begin{pmatrix} -2 \\ 1 \end{pmatrix}$

  (iii) $-c = -\begin{pmatrix} 0 \\ 4 \end{pmatrix} = \begin{pmatrix} 0 \\ -4 \end{pmatrix}$

EXERCISE 24A

1 Write these vectors in column vector form.

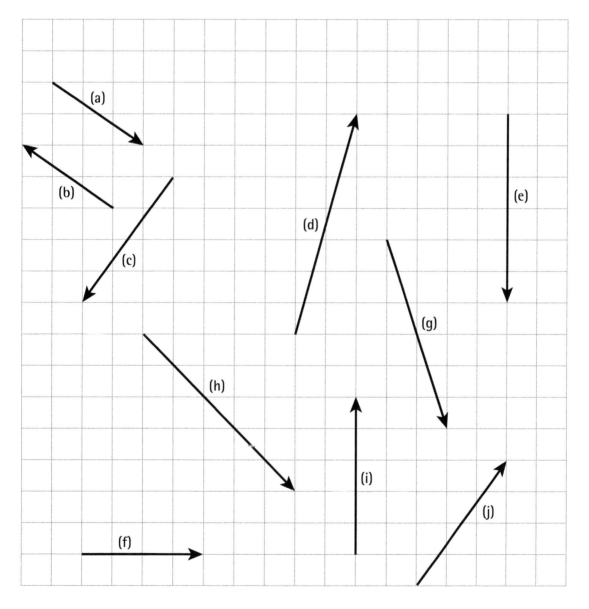

2 $a = \begin{pmatrix} 1 \\ 3 \end{pmatrix}$ $b = \begin{pmatrix} 4 \\ 2 \end{pmatrix}$ $c = \begin{pmatrix} 5 \\ 5 \end{pmatrix}$

Write as column vectors

(a) 2a   (b) 3b   (c) $\frac{1}{2}b$ (d) 3a

(e) –b   (f) 4c   (g) $-1\frac{1}{2}b$ (h) $-4c$

3 $p = \begin{pmatrix} 2 \\ -4 \end{pmatrix}$ $q = \begin{pmatrix} 1 \\ -3 \end{pmatrix}$ $r = \begin{pmatrix} -3 \\ -2 \end{pmatrix}$

Draw the following vectors on a square grid.

See Example 1 for help.

(a) p   (b) q   (c) r   (d) $\frac{1}{2}p$ (e) –p

(f) 2q   (g) –r   (h) 3q   (i) $-1\frac{1}{2}p$ (j) –2q

24.4 Adding and subtracting vectors

Look at this diagram showing three **displacement vectors**.

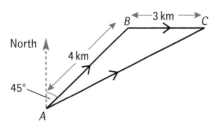

Displacement vectors are 'free' vectors as opposed to 'position' vectors.

You will see the difference between the two in the next section.

They represent a journey from A to B of 4 km on a bearing of 045, followed by a journey from B to C of 3 km due east.

You can see that you can go directly from A to C, the final destination is the same.

This can be expressed in vector notation as $\overrightarrow{AB} + \overrightarrow{BC} = \overrightarrow{AC}$ and forms the basis of vector addition.

The vector $\overrightarrow{AC}$ is called the **resultant** of vectors $\overrightarrow{AB}$ and $\overrightarrow{BC}$ because going from A to C is the same result as going from A to B then from B to C.

Look at this parallelogram *PQRS*.

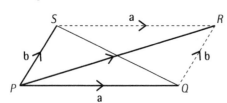

Notice that the order of the letters is important.

$\overrightarrow{SR} = a$ so $\overrightarrow{RS} = -a$

$\overrightarrow{QR} = b$ so $\overrightarrow{RQ} = -b$

$\overrightarrow{PQ} = a$ and $\overrightarrow{PS} = b$

A parallelogram has opposite sides that are equal and parallel, so this means that $\overrightarrow{SR} = a$ and $\overrightarrow{QR} = b$.

Using vector addition,

$$\overrightarrow{PR} = \overrightarrow{PQ} + \overrightarrow{QR}$$
$$= a + b$$

and $\quad \overrightarrow{SQ} = \overrightarrow{SR} + \overrightarrow{RQ}$
$$= a + -b$$
$$= a - b$$

and $\quad \overrightarrow{QS} = \overrightarrow{QR} + \overrightarrow{RS}$
$$= b + -a$$
$$= b - a$$

Notice the 'nose to tail' order of the capital letters.
PQ followed by QR is the same as PR.

This is always true for vector addition.

Notice that the diagonals of the parallelogram are represented by the vectors $a + b$ and either $a - b$ or $b - a$ depending on the direction.

 EXAMPLE 2

$$a = \begin{pmatrix} 3 \\ -2 \end{pmatrix} \quad b = \begin{pmatrix} -4 \\ 5 \end{pmatrix} \quad c = \begin{pmatrix} 0 \\ 6 \end{pmatrix}$$

Write these as column vectors.

(a) $a + b$ (b) $b - a$ (c) $2b + 3c$ (d) $c - 2a$

(a) $a + b \quad = \begin{pmatrix} 3 \\ -2 \end{pmatrix} + \begin{pmatrix} -4 \\ 5 \end{pmatrix} = \begin{pmatrix} -1 \\ 3 \end{pmatrix}$

(b) $b - a \quad = \begin{pmatrix} -4 \\ 5 \end{pmatrix} - \begin{pmatrix} 3 \\ -2 \end{pmatrix} = \begin{pmatrix} -7 \\ 7 \end{pmatrix}$

(c) $2b + 3c = \begin{pmatrix} -8 \\ 10 \end{pmatrix} + \begin{pmatrix} 0 \\ 18 \end{pmatrix} = \begin{pmatrix} -8 \\ 28 \end{pmatrix}$

(d) $c - 2a \quad = \begin{pmatrix} 0 \\ 6 \end{pmatrix} - \begin{pmatrix} 6 \\ -4 \end{pmatrix} = \begin{pmatrix} -6 \\ 10 \end{pmatrix}$

EXAMPLE 3

$$a = \begin{pmatrix} 2 \\ -1 \end{pmatrix} \quad b = \begin{pmatrix} 4 \\ 3 \end{pmatrix}$$

On a square grid draw diagrams to illustrate the vectors
$a + b \quad b - a \quad 2a - b$

continued ▼

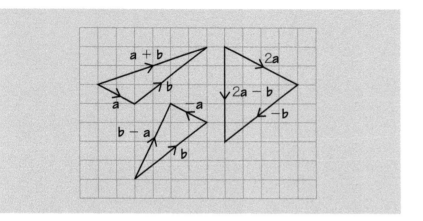

1 $p = \begin{pmatrix} 4 \\ 2 \end{pmatrix}$ $q = \begin{pmatrix} 2 \\ -6 \end{pmatrix}$ $r = \begin{pmatrix} -1 \\ 6 \end{pmatrix}$

Write as column vectors.

(a) p + q   (b) q + r   (d) p + r

(d) p − q   (e) 2p + q   (f) p + 3q

(g) $\frac{1}{2}$p + q   (h) 2p − q   (i) p − 4q

(j) $\frac{1}{2}$p + $\frac{1}{2}$q   (k) 5p − 3r   (l) p + q + r

2 $u = \begin{pmatrix} -2 \\ 1 \end{pmatrix}$ $v = \begin{pmatrix} 3 \\ 4 \end{pmatrix}$ $w = \begin{pmatrix} -4 \\ 0 \end{pmatrix}$

On squared paper draw diagrams to show these vectors.

See Example 3.

(a) u + v   (b) v − u   (c) w − 2u

(d) 2v + w   (e) u + v + w   (f) v + w − u

(g) u + v − w   (h) u − v − w   (i) v + w − 3u

24.5 Position vectors

You will need to know
- Pythagoras' theorem
- how to use the tangent ratio to calculate an angle

Look at these vectors drawn on the *x*–*y* plane.

They are all equal but only one of them starts at the origin.

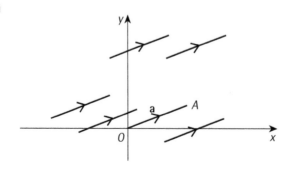

A vector that starts at the origin is known as a **position vector**.

So the vector labelled $\overrightarrow{OA}$, or **a**, is the position vector of A.

The other vectors are displacement vectors or **free vectors** because they are not connected to the origin.

You can see that if A is at (4, 3) then $\overrightarrow{OA} = \begin{pmatrix} 4 \\ 3 \end{pmatrix}$ so the coordinates of the point are the same as the components of the position vector.

This enables you to calculate the magnitude of the vector and its direction.

Using Pythagoras' theorem,

$$OA^2 = 4^2 + 3^2$$
$$= 25$$

so $\quad |OA| = \sqrt{25}$

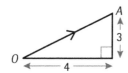

$|OA|$ is called the **modulus** of $\overrightarrow{OA}$ and is the notation used to represent the magnitude of a vector.

Alternatively, you can write $|\mathbf{a}| = 5$

To find the direction of a vector, use trigonometry.

If θ is the angle between OA and the x-axis,

$\tan \theta = \frac{3}{4}$

$\quad \theta = \tan^{-1}(0.75)$

$\quad \theta = 36.9°$ (1 d.p.)

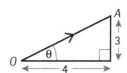

> You can use the same methods to calculate the magnitude (length) and direction of any vector.

EXAMPLE 5

The diagram shows a grid of congruent parallelograms.

The origin is labelled O and the position vectors of points A and B are given by $\overrightarrow{OA} = \mathbf{a}$ and $\overrightarrow{OB} = \mathbf{b}$.

Write, in terms of **a** and **b**,

(a) $\overrightarrow{OP}$ (b) $\overrightarrow{OV}$

(c) $\overrightarrow{OR}$ (d) $\overrightarrow{OG}$

(e) $\overrightarrow{AB}$ (f) $\overrightarrow{NE}$

(g) $\overrightarrow{FB}$ (h) $\overrightarrow{UG}$

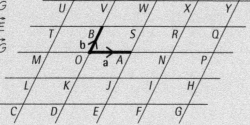

continued ▼

(a) $\overrightarrow{OP} = 3\mathbf{a}$

(b) $\overrightarrow{OV} = 2\mathbf{b}$

(c) $\overrightarrow{OR} = \overrightarrow{ON} + \overrightarrow{NR}$
$\qquad = 2\mathbf{a} + \mathbf{b}$

(d) $\overrightarrow{OG} = \overrightarrow{OP} + \overrightarrow{PG}$
$\qquad = 3\mathbf{a} - 2\mathbf{b}$

(e) $\overrightarrow{AB} = \overrightarrow{AO} + \overrightarrow{OB}$
$\qquad = -\mathbf{a} + \mathbf{b}$

(f) $\overrightarrow{NE} = \overrightarrow{NA} + \overrightarrow{AE}$
$\qquad = -\mathbf{a} - 2\mathbf{b}$

(g) $\overrightarrow{FB} = \overrightarrow{FD} + \overrightarrow{DB}$
$\qquad = -2\mathbf{a} + 3\mathbf{b}$

(h) $\overrightarrow{UG} = \overrightarrow{UY} + \overrightarrow{YG}$
$\qquad = 4\mathbf{a} - 4\mathbf{b}$

> $\overrightarrow{OP}, \overrightarrow{OV}, \overrightarrow{OR}, \overrightarrow{OG}$, are all position vectors because they start at the origin O.
>
> The others are free vectors.

> There are alternative solutions. For example,
>
> **(g)** $\overrightarrow{FB} = \overrightarrow{FR} + \overrightarrow{RB}$
> $\qquad = 3\mathbf{b} - 2\mathbf{a}$

⬤ EXAMPLE 5

Using the parallelogram grid for Example 4, answer the following.

(a) Write down the position vector equal to $3\mathbf{a} - \mathbf{b}$.

(b) Write down three other vectors equal to $3\mathbf{a} - \mathbf{b}$.

(c) Write down a vector parallel to $\overrightarrow{CP}$.

(d) Write down three vectors that are half the size of CP and in the opposite direction.

(e) Write down all the vectors that are equal to $3(\mathbf{a} + \mathbf{b})$.

(f) Write down, in terms of $\mathbf{a}$ and $\mathbf{b}$, the vectors
$\overrightarrow{CK} \quad \overrightarrow{CA} \quad \overrightarrow{CR} \quad \overrightarrow{CY}$

What is the connection between these answers and the positions of C, K, A, R and Y on the grid?

(a) $\overrightarrow{OH}$

(b) $\overrightarrow{VQ} \quad \overrightarrow{TN} \quad \overrightarrow{MI}$

(c) $\overrightarrow{CP} = 2\mathbf{b} + 4\mathbf{a}$
A parallel vector is $\overrightarrow{LQ}$

(d) New vector $= -\mathbf{b} - 2\mathbf{a}$
$\overrightarrow{QA} \quad \overrightarrow{PJ} \quad \overrightarrow{HE}$

(e) $\overrightarrow{CR} \quad \overrightarrow{LX} \quad \overrightarrow{DQ} \quad \overrightarrow{KY}$

(f) $\overrightarrow{CK} = \mathbf{a} + \mathbf{b}$
$\overrightarrow{CA} = 2\mathbf{a} + 2\mathbf{b}$
$\overrightarrow{CR} = 3\mathbf{a} + 3\mathbf{b}$
$\overrightarrow{CY} = 4\mathbf{a} + 4\mathbf{b}$
C, K, A, R and Y are all points on a straight line.

> You can choose *any* vectors from the grid that involve 3 steps in the same direction as $\mathbf{a}$ and one in the opposite direction to $\mathbf{b}$.

> Again, there is more than one choice. An alternative is $\overrightarrow{MY}$.

> Multiply by $-\frac{1}{2}$. There are many examples of $-\mathbf{b} - 2\mathbf{a}$ that you could choose here.

EXERCISE 24C

1. Draw a separate diagram for each of these position vectors. Find the magnitude and direction (the angle made with the positive *x*-axis) of each position vector.

   (a) $\begin{pmatrix} 0 \\ 4 \end{pmatrix}$ (b) $\begin{pmatrix} 3 \\ 5 \end{pmatrix}$ (c) $\begin{pmatrix} 6 \\ -2 \end{pmatrix}$ (d) $\begin{pmatrix} -4 \\ 6 \end{pmatrix}$ (e) $\begin{pmatrix} -3 \\ -7 \end{pmatrix}$

   > When measuring angles from the positive *x*-axis, those angles measured anticlockwise from 0° to 180° are positive and those measured clockwise from 0° to 180° are negative.

2. The diagram shows a grid of congruent parallelograms. The origin is labelled O and the position vectors of points A and B are given by $\overrightarrow{OA} = \mathbf{a}$ and $\overrightarrow{OB} = \mathbf{b}$.

   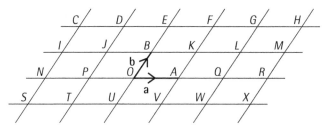

   Write, in terms of **a** and **b**,

   (a) $\overrightarrow{OR}$ (b) $\overrightarrow{OU}$ (c) $\overrightarrow{OC}$ (d) $\overrightarrow{OX}$ (e) $\overrightarrow{GP}$
   (f) $\overrightarrow{IW}$ (g) $\overrightarrow{HR}$ (h) $\overrightarrow{MJ}$ (i) $\overrightarrow{UF}$ (j) $\overrightarrow{ET}$

3. Use the parallelogram grid for question 2 to answer the following.

   (a) Write down the position vector equal to $3\mathbf{a} + \mathbf{b}$.
   (b) Write down three other vectors equal to $3\mathbf{a} + \mathbf{b}$.
   (c) Write down three vectors parallel to $\overrightarrow{ND}$.
   (d) Write down three vectors that are half the size of $\overrightarrow{TM}$ and in the opposite direction.
   (e) Write down the vectors $\overrightarrow{DI}$, $\overrightarrow{FP}$ and $\overrightarrow{HU}$.
       Explain the connection between these vectors.

4. Here is another grid of congruent parallelograms.

   The origin is labelled O and the position vectors of points A and B are given by $\overrightarrow{OA} = \mathbf{a}$ and $\overrightarrow{OB} = \mathbf{b}$.
   On a copy of the grid, mark the points C to L where

   (a) $\overrightarrow{OC} = -\mathbf{a} + 2\mathbf{b}$ (b) $\overrightarrow{OD} = 3\mathbf{a} + \mathbf{b}$
   (c) $\overrightarrow{OE} = -\mathbf{a} - \mathbf{b}$ (d) $\overrightarrow{OF} = \mathbf{a} - 3\mathbf{b}$
   (e) $\overrightarrow{OG} = 2\mathbf{a} - 2\mathbf{b}$ (f) $\overrightarrow{OH} = 3\mathbf{b}$
   (g) $\overrightarrow{OI} = \mathbf{a} + \frac{3}{2}\mathbf{b}$ (h) $\overrightarrow{OJ} = -\frac{3}{2}\mathbf{a} - 2\mathbf{b}$
   (i) $\overrightarrow{OK} = 2\mathbf{a} + \frac{1}{2}\mathbf{b}$ (j) $\overrightarrow{OL} = \frac{5}{2}\mathbf{a} - \frac{3}{2}\mathbf{b}$

   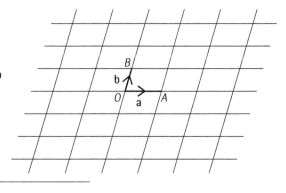

24.6 Vector geometry

The rules for the addition and subtraction of vectors and the multiplication of a vector by a scalar are the key elements of questions on vector geometry.

Showing that lines are parallel or that points are **collinear** (lie on a straight line) are typical examples.

Examples 6, 7 and 8 are typical of the questions you can expect on the extended level IGCSE papers.

 EXAMPLE 6

$OABC$ is a quadrilateral with $\overrightarrow{OA} = \mathbf{a}$, $\overrightarrow{OB} = \mathbf{b}$ and $\overrightarrow{OC} = \mathbf{c}$.

M is the mid-point of AB and P is the point on BC such that $BP : PC = 3 : 1$.

Find expressions for these vectors, giving your answers in their simplest form.

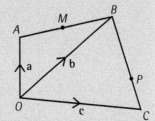

(a) $\overrightarrow{AB}$ (b) $\overrightarrow{AM}$ (c) $\overrightarrow{OM}$ (d) $\overrightarrow{BC}$ (e) $\overrightarrow{BP}$ (f) $\overrightarrow{MP}$

(a) $\overrightarrow{AB} = \overrightarrow{AO} + \overrightarrow{OB} = -\mathbf{a} + \mathbf{b}$ or $\mathbf{b} - \mathbf{a}$

(b) $\overrightarrow{AM} = \frac{1}{2}\overrightarrow{AB} = \frac{1}{2}(\mathbf{b} - \mathbf{a}) = \frac{1}{2}\mathbf{b} - \frac{1}{2}\mathbf{a}$

(c) $\overrightarrow{OM} = \overrightarrow{OA} + \overrightarrow{AM} = \mathbf{a} + \frac{1}{2}\mathbf{b} - \frac{1}{2}\mathbf{a} = \frac{1}{2}\mathbf{a} + \frac{1}{2}\mathbf{b}$

(d) $\overrightarrow{BC} = \overrightarrow{BO} + \overrightarrow{OC} = -\mathbf{b} + \mathbf{c}$ or $\mathbf{c} - \mathbf{b}$

(e) $\overrightarrow{BP} = \frac{3}{4}\overrightarrow{BC} = \frac{3}{4}(\mathbf{c} - \mathbf{b}) = \frac{3}{4}\mathbf{c} - \frac{3}{4}\mathbf{b}$

(f) $\overrightarrow{MP} = \overrightarrow{MB} + \overrightarrow{BP} = (\frac{1}{2}\mathbf{b} - \frac{1}{2}\mathbf{a}) + (\frac{3}{4}\mathbf{c} - \frac{3}{4}\mathbf{b})$

$\qquad = \frac{1}{2}\mathbf{b} - \frac{3}{4}\mathbf{b} - \frac{1}{2}\mathbf{a} + \frac{3}{4}\mathbf{c}$

$\qquad = \frac{3}{4}\mathbf{c} - \frac{1}{4}\mathbf{b} - \frac{1}{2}\mathbf{a}$

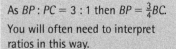

As $BP : PC = 3 : 1$ then $BP = \frac{3}{4}BC$. You will often need to interpret ratios in this way.

Since M is the mid-point of AB then $\overrightarrow{MB} = \overrightarrow{AM}$.

 EXAMPLE 7

In triangle ABC points P and Q are the mid-points of sides AB and AC respectively.

$\overrightarrow{AP} = \mathbf{x}$ and $\overrightarrow{AQ} = \mathbf{y}$.

Show that PQ is parallel to BC and half its length.

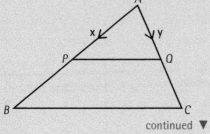

continued ▼

$$\vec{PQ} = \vec{PA} + \vec{AQ} = -\mathbf{x} + \mathbf{y} = \mathbf{y} - \mathbf{x}$$

$$\vec{AB} = 2\mathbf{x} \quad \text{and} \quad \vec{AC} = 2\mathbf{y}$$

So $\quad \vec{BC} = \vec{BA} + \vec{AC} = -2\mathbf{x} + 2\mathbf{y} = 2\mathbf{y} - 2\mathbf{x}$

So $\quad \vec{BC} = 2(\mathbf{y} - \mathbf{x}) = 2\vec{PQ}$

... which means that BC is twice the length of PQ and that BC and PQ have the same direction or ... PQ is parallel to BC and half its length.

> This is the most important point in the final statement of the proved result.

Remember that when vectors are equal they are equal in two ways ... their lengths are equal and they have the same direction.

 EXAMPLE 8

The diagram shows a trapezium $OABC$ in which OC is parallel to AB and $OC = \frac{2}{3}AB$. $\vec{OA} = \mathbf{a}$ and $\vec{OB} = \mathbf{b}$.

P is the point on AB such that $AP : PB = 1 : 2$ and M is the mid-point of OB.

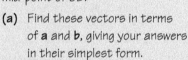

(a) Find these vectors in terms of $\mathbf{a}$ and $\mathbf{b}$, giving your answers in their simplest form.

    (i) $\vec{AB}$ **(ii)** $\vec{AP}$ **(iii)** $\vec{PM}$ **(iv)** $\vec{MC}$

(b) What do your answers to $\vec{PM}$ and $\vec{MC}$ tell you about the relationship between points P, M and C?

(a) (i) $\quad \vec{AB} = \vec{AO} + \vec{OB} = -\mathbf{a} + \mathbf{b} = \mathbf{b} - \mathbf{a}$

   (ii) $\quad \vec{AP} = \frac{1}{3}\vec{AB} = \frac{1}{3}(\mathbf{b} - \mathbf{a})$ or $\frac{1}{3}\mathbf{b} - \frac{1}{3}\mathbf{a}$

> As $AP : PB = 1 : 2$ then $AP = \frac{1}{3}AB$.

   (iii) $\vec{PM} = \vec{PA} + \vec{AO} + \vec{OM}$

$$= (-\tfrac{1}{3}\mathbf{b} + \tfrac{1}{3}\mathbf{a}) + (-\mathbf{a}) + (\tfrac{1}{2}\mathbf{b})$$

$$= -\tfrac{1}{3}\mathbf{b} + \tfrac{1}{2}\mathbf{b} + \tfrac{1}{3}\mathbf{a} - \mathbf{a}$$

$$= \tfrac{1}{6}\mathbf{b} - \tfrac{2}{3}\mathbf{a}$$

   (iv) $\vec{MC} = \vec{MO} + \vec{OC} = \vec{MO} + \frac{2}{3}\vec{AB}$

$$= -\tfrac{1}{2}\mathbf{b} + \tfrac{2}{3}(\mathbf{b} - \mathbf{a})$$

$$= -\tfrac{1}{2}\mathbf{b} + \tfrac{2}{3}\mathbf{b} - \tfrac{2}{3}\mathbf{a}$$

$$= \tfrac{1}{6}\mathbf{b} - \tfrac{2}{3}\mathbf{a}$$

(b) You can see from parts **(a)(iii)** and **(iv)** that $\vec{PM} = \vec{MC}$

So PM and MC are equal in length and have the same direction

... but M is a point in common to both of these line segments so if the directions are the same points P, M and C must all be part of the same straight line.

So P, M and C are collinear and M is the mid-point of PC.

> Remember that when vectors are equal they are equal in two ways ... their lengths are equal and they have the same direction.
>
> When you have a common point and vectors are equal (or where one is a multiple of the other) then you can deduce that the points lie in a straight line.

Diagrams in this exercise are not drawn accurately.

1 OPQ is a triangle.
   A, B and C are the mid-points of OP, OQ and PQ respectively.
   $\overrightarrow{OA}$ = a and $\overrightarrow{OB}$ = b

   Find these vectors in terms of a and b, simplifying your answers

   (a) $\overrightarrow{OP}$ (b) $\overrightarrow{OQ}$ (c) $\overrightarrow{PQ}$ (d) $\overrightarrow{AB}$

   (e) $\overrightarrow{PC}$ (f) $\overrightarrow{OC}$ (g) $\overrightarrow{BP}$ (h) $\overrightarrow{QA}$

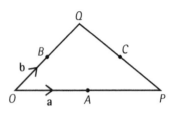

2 OFG is a triangle.
   A and C are the mid-points of OF and FG respectively.
   B lies on OG such that OB : BG = 1 : 2
   $\overrightarrow{OA}$ = a and $\overrightarrow{OB}$ = b

   Find these vectors in terms of a and b, simplifying
   your answers

   (a) $\overrightarrow{AF}$ (b) $\overrightarrow{AB}$ (c) $\overrightarrow{OG}$ (d) $\overrightarrow{FO}$

   (e) $\overrightarrow{FG}$ (f) $\overrightarrow{GA}$ (g) $\overrightarrow{BF}$ (h) $\overrightarrow{OC}$

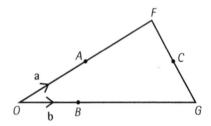

3 OAB is a triangle with $\overrightarrow{OA}$ = a and $\overrightarrow{OB}$ = b
   M is the mid-point of OB and P is the point on AB such
   that AP : PB = 2 : 1

   Find expressions for these vectors in terms of a and b, simplifying
   your answers

   (a) $\overrightarrow{OM}$ (b) $\overrightarrow{AB}$ (c) $\overrightarrow{AP}$ (d) $\overrightarrow{OP}$

   (e) $\overrightarrow{BA}$ (f) $\overrightarrow{MA}$ (g) $\overrightarrow{MP}$

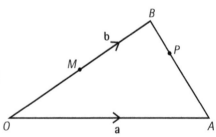

4 OAB is a triangle.
   M is the mid-point of OB, N is the mid-point of AB.
   P and Q are points of trisection of OA.
   $\overrightarrow{OP}$ = p and $\overrightarrow{OM}$ = m

   (a) Find expressions for these vectors in terms
       of p and m, simplifying your answers.

       (i) $\overrightarrow{OA}$ (ii) $\overrightarrow{OB}$ (iii) $\overrightarrow{BA}$

       (iv) $\overrightarrow{MN}$ (v) $\overrightarrow{PQ}$ (vi) $\overrightarrow{MP}$

       (vii) $\overrightarrow{MQ}$ (viii) $\overrightarrow{NQ}$ (ix) $\overrightarrow{PN}$

   (b) What kind of quadrilateral is PQNM?
       Explain your answer.

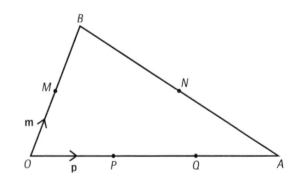

5 ABCDEF is a regular hexagon with centre O.
   $\overrightarrow{AB}$ = b and $\overrightarrow{AC}$ = c

   Find these vectors in terms of b and c,
   simplifying your answers

   (a) $\overrightarrow{BC}$ (b) $\overrightarrow{AO}$ (c) $\overrightarrow{AD}$

   (d) $\overrightarrow{EC}$ (e) $\overrightarrow{AF}$ (f) $\overrightarrow{AE}$

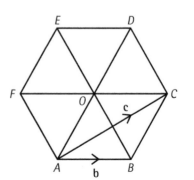

6 *OPQR* is a trapezium with *PQ* parallel to *OR*.
$\vec{OP} = -2a + 3b$ and $\vec{OQ} = 4a + 5b$

(a) Find $\vec{PQ}$ in terms of **a** and **b**, simplifying your answer.

(b) $\vec{QR} = 5a + kb$ (where *k* is a number to be determined).

Find $\vec{OR}$ in terms of **a** and **b** and *k* and hence work out the value of *k*.

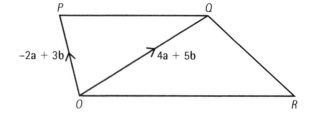

7 In the diagram $\vec{OP} = 2a$, $\vec{PA} = a$, $\vec{OB} = 3b$ and $\vec{BR} = b$
Q lies on *AB* such that $AQ : QB = 2 : 1$

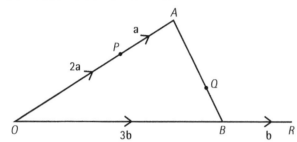

(a) Find expressions for these vectors in terms of **a** and **b**, simplifying your answers.

(i) $\vec{AB}$ (ii) $\vec{AQ}$ (iii) $\vec{QB}$ (iv) $\vec{PQ}$ (v) $\vec{QR}$ (vi) $\vec{PR}$

(b) Explain clearly the relationship between points *P*, *Q* and *R*.

8 *OATB* is a quadrilateral.
P, Q, R and *S* are the mid-points of *OA, AT, TB* and *OB* respectively.
$\vec{OA} = a$, $\vec{OB} = b$ and $\vec{OT} = t$

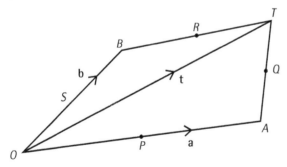

(a) Find, in terms of **a** and **b**, simplifying your answers.

(i) $\vec{AT}$ (ii) $\vec{QT}$ (iii) $\vec{TB}$ (iv) $\vec{TR}$ (v) $\vec{PS}$ (vi) $\vec{QR}$

(b) Explain why your answers for vectors *PS* and *QR* show that *PQRS* is a parallelogram.

9 The diagram shows a quadrilateral *OAGB*.
$\vec{OA} = \mathbf{a}$, $\vec{OB} = 2\mathbf{b}$ and $\vec{OG} = 3\mathbf{a} + 2\mathbf{b}$

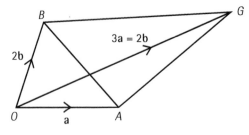

(a) Find expressions for these vectors in terms of **a** and **b**, simplifying your answers.

   (i) $\vec{AG}$ (ii) $\vec{BG}$

(b) What kind of quadrilateral is *OAGB*?
    Give a reason for your answer.

(c) Point *P* lies on *AB* such that $AP : PB = 1 : 3$
    Find expressions for these vectors in terms of **a** and **b**, simplifying your answers.

   (i) $\vec{AB}$ (ii) $\vec{AP}$ (iii) $\vec{OP}$

(d) Describe, as fully as possible, the position of *P*.

10 The diagram shows a triangle *OAB*
  M is the mid-point of *OA*.
  P lies on *BM* and $BP = \frac{3}{4}BM$
  $\vec{OA} = 2\mathbf{a}$ and $\vec{OB} = 2\mathbf{b}$

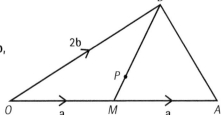

(a) Find expressions for these vectors in terms of **a** and **b**, simplifying your answers.

   (i) $\vec{BM}$ (ii) $\vec{BP}$ (iii) $\vec{OP}$

(b) *N* lies on *OB* such that $ON = \frac{2}{5}OB$
    Q lies on *AN* such that $AQ = \frac{5}{8}AN$
    Find expressions for these vectors in terms of **a** and **b**, simplifying your answers.

   (i) $\vec{ON}$ (ii) $\vec{AN}$ (iii) $\vec{AQ}$ (iv) $\vec{OQ}$

(c) What can you deduce about points *P* and *Q*?

EXAMINATION QUESTIONS

1

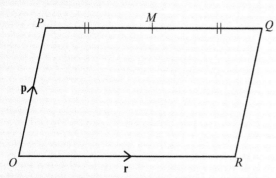

NOT TO
SCALE

(a) $OPQR$ is a parallelogram and M is the mid-point of PQ.
Vector $\overrightarrow{OP} = \mathbf{p}$ and vector $\overrightarrow{OR} = \mathbf{r}$.
Write in terms of $\mathbf{p}$ and $\mathbf{r}$.
(i) $\overrightarrow{QM}$, [1]
(ii) $\overrightarrow{RM}$. [1]

(b) The position of R is 3 units due east of O, so that the column vector $\overrightarrow{OR} = \begin{pmatrix} 3 \\ 0 \end{pmatrix}$.

The position of S is 3 units south of O.
Write down the column vector $\overrightarrow{OS}$. [1]

(CIE Paper 2, Jun 2000)

2

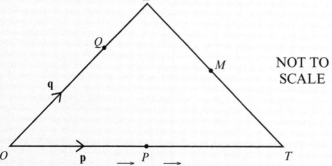

NOT TO
SCALE

The position vectors $\overrightarrow{OP}$ and $\overrightarrow{OQ}$ are $\mathbf{p}$ and $\mathbf{q}$.
OP is extended to T so that OP = PT.
OQ is extended to L so that $OQ : QL = 2 : 1$.

(a) Find, in terms of $\mathbf{p}$ and/or $\mathbf{q}$.
(i) $\overrightarrow{OL}$, [1]
(ii) $\overrightarrow{LT}$. [1]
(b) M is the mid-point of LT.
Find $\overrightarrow{OM}$ in terms of $\mathbf{p}$ and $\mathbf{q}$.
Give your answer in its simplest form. [2]

(CIE Paper 2, Nov 2000)

3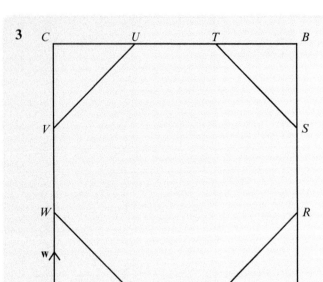

NOT TO SCALE

Each side of the square *OABC* is divided into 3 equal parts to form the octagon *PQRSTUVW*.

$\overrightarrow{OP} = \mathbf{p}$ and $\overrightarrow{OW} = \mathbf{w}$.

(a) Find the following vectors in terms of **p** and **w**.
Write your answers in their simplest form.

(i) $\overrightarrow{WP}$,   [1]

(ii) $\overrightarrow{OB}$,   [1]

(iii) $\overrightarrow{RV}$.   [1]

(b) Find $|\overrightarrow{OB}|$ when $|\mathbf{p}| = |\mathbf{w}| = 5$.   [2]

(CIE Paper 2, Jun 2001)

4

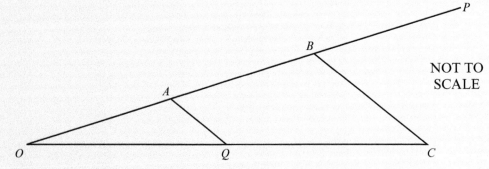

NOT TO SCALE

Q is the mid-point of *OC* and *OABP* is a straight line with *OA* = *AB* = *BP*.

$\overrightarrow{OP} = 6\mathbf{p}$ and $\overrightarrow{OQ} = \mathbf{q}$.

Find in terms of **p** and/or **q**,

(a) $\overrightarrow{OB}$,   [1]

(b) $\overrightarrow{BC}$,   [1]

(c) $\overrightarrow{AQ}$.   [1]

(d) Use your answers to parts (b) and (c) to explain why *AQ* is parallel to *BC*.   [1]

(CIE Paper 2, Nov 2001)

5

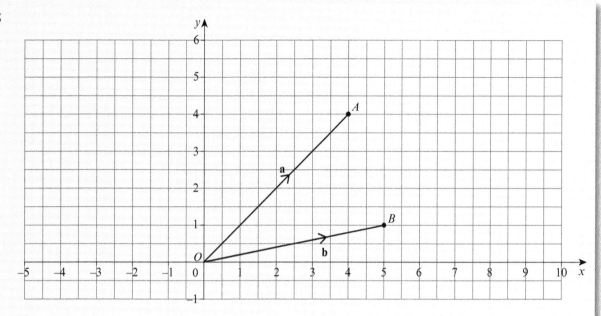

(a) Copy the diagram and draw the vector $\overrightarrow{OC}$ so that $\overrightarrow{OC} = \mathbf{a} - \mathbf{b}$. [1]

(b) Write the vector $\overrightarrow{AB}$ in terms of $\mathbf{a}$ and $\mathbf{b}$. [1]

(CIE Paper 2, Jun 2002)

---

6 $\mathbf{a} = \begin{pmatrix} 2 \\ -3 \end{pmatrix}$ and $\mathbf{b} = \begin{pmatrix} 5 \\ -1 \end{pmatrix}$. Find $3\mathbf{a} - 2\mathbf{b}$. [2]

(CIE Paper 2, Jun 2003)

7

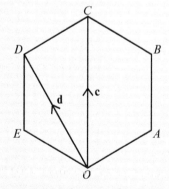

NOT TO
SCALE

$OABCDE$ is a regular hexagon.

With O as origin the position vector of C is $\mathbf{c}$ and the position vector of D is $\mathbf{d}$.

(a) Find, in terms of $\mathbf{c}$ and $\mathbf{d}$,

    (i) $\overrightarrow{DC}$, [1]

    (ii) $\overrightarrow{OE}$, [2]

    (iii) the position vector of B. [2]

(CIE Paper 4, Jun 2005)

Index

Page numbers in *italics* refer to hint boxes.

V

Y

Z